P9-DTY-530

HIGH POLYMERS

Vol. I: **Collected Papers of W. H. Carothers on High Polymeric Substances**
Edited by H. Mark and G. S. Whitby

Vol. II: **Physical Chemistry of High Polymeric Systems**
Second Edition. By H. Mark and A. V. Tobolsky

Vol. III: **Mechanism of Polymer Reactions**
By G. M. Burnett

Vol. V: **Cellulose and Cellulose Derivatives** (in three parts)
Second Edition. Edited by Emil Ott, H. M. Spurlin, and M. W. Grafflin

Vol. VI: **Mechanical Behavior of High Polymers**
By Turner Alfrey, Jr.

Vol. VII: **Phenoplasts: Their Structure, Properties, and Chemical Technology**
By T. S. Carswell

Vol. IX: **Emulsion Polymerization**
By F. A. Bovey, I. M. Kolthoff, A. I. Medalia, and E. J. Meehan

Vol. X: **Polymer Processes**
Edited by Calvin E. Schildknecht

Vol. XII: **Analytical Chemistry of Polymers** (in three parts)
Edited by Gordon M. Kline

Vol. XIII: **Polyethers** (in three parts)
Edited by Norman G. Gaylord

Vol. XIV: **Polyesters** (in two parts)
Edited by Norman G. Gaylord

Vol. XV: **Radiation Chemistry of Polymeric Systems**
By Adolphe Chapiro

Vol. XVI: **Polyurethanes: Chemistry and Technology** (in two parts)
By J. H. Saunders and K. C. Frisch

Vol. XVII: **Configurational Statistics of Polymeric Chains**
By M. V. Volkenstein. Translated by Serge N. Timasheff and Marina J. Timasheff

Vol. XVIII: **Copolymerization**
Edited by George E. Ham

Vol. XIX: **Chemical Reactions of Polymers**
Edited by E. M. Fettes

Vol. XX: **Crystalline Olefin Polymers** (in two parts)
Edited by R. A. V. Raff and K. W. Doak

Vol. XXI: **Macromolecules in Solution**
By Herbert Morawetz

Vol. XXII: **Conformations of Macromolecules**
By T. M. Birshtein and O. B. Ptitsyn. Translated by Serge N. Timasheff and Marina J. Timasheff

Vol. XXIII: **Polymer Chemistry of Synthetic Elastomers** (in two parts)
Edited by Joseph P. Kennedy and Erik G. M. Törnqvist

HIGH POLYMERS

A SERIES OF MONOGRAPHS ON THE CHEMISTRY, PHYSICS, AND TECHNOLOGY OF HIGH POLYMERIC SUBSTANCES

VOLUME XVI

Part I

POLYURETHANES

CHEMISTRY AND TECHNOLOGY

Part I. Chemistry

J. H. SAUNDERS

Director of Research
Mobay Chemical Company
Pittsburgh, Pennsylvania

and

K. C. FRISCH

Director of Polymer Research
Wyandotte Chemicals Corporation
Wyandotte, Michigan

INTERSCIENCE PUBLISHERS

a division of John Wiley & Sons, New York • London • Sydney

5 6 7 8 9 10
Library of Congress Catalog Card Number 62-18932

PRINTED IN THE UNITED STATES OF AMERICA

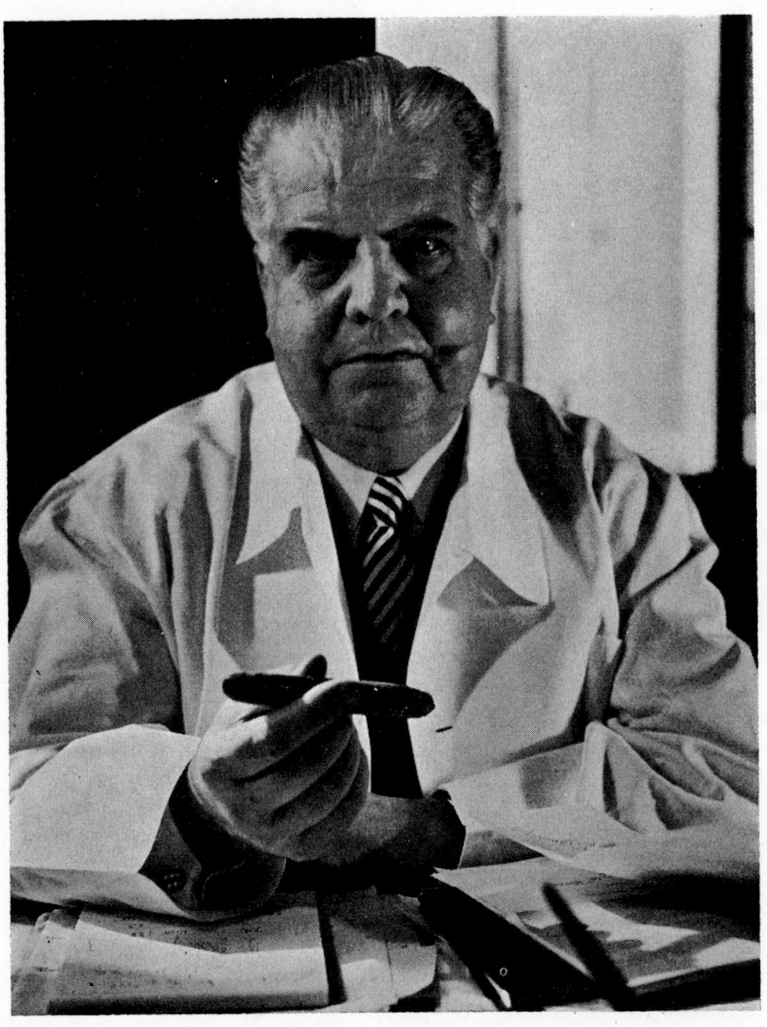

Professor Otto Bayer, pioneer in the discovery, exploration, and development of the polyurethanes. Professor Bayer is the Director of the Main Scientific Laboratory, Farbenfabriken Bayer, Leverkusen, Germany.

PREFACE

Unlike many other great discoveries in chemistry, polyurethanes were not the outgrowth of an accidental discovery, but were the result of painstaking and systematic efforts to develop new polymers that could rival in properties those of the commercially eminently successful nylon fibers. This search did not stop with the development of polyurethane fibers but branched into a broad new concept of polymer chemistry that can be characterized as the polyaddition principle. It is a tribute to the genius of Professor Otto Bayer and his co-workers that they clearly recognized the great versatility of this new polymerization procedure and started to explore the many branches of polyurethane chemistry. To bring together the many ramifications of polyurethane chemistry in one place is the object of this volume on "Polyurethanes."

In Part I, an effort is made to group systematically the chapters dealing with the basic chemistry of polyurethanes and of the raw materials going into the make-up of these polymers. This part concludes with a chapter on the relationship between structure and physical properties of polyurethanes. The Appendices to Part I contain a series of tables with information on suppliers of raw materials, lists of trade names and abbreviations, additional tables of properties, and other statistics of interest to scientists.

Part II will be concerned mainly with the various aspects of the technology of polyurethanes, particularly as it applies to the preparation, properties, and applications of the most important end uses of these polymers. Although urethane foams have drawn most of the attention in recent years, having undergone a spectacular growth especially in the flexible foam field, other polyurethane areas are finding increasing attention. It is difficult to determine at this stage which of these fields will reach commercial importance approaching that of foams; however, elastomers and coatings have been singled out for more extensive treatment. The appendix to Part II will be a complete index of United States patents, with a very short description and key symbol denoting the special field of application of each. This index should prove helpful to those wishing to screen the patent literature for new and patentable items, as well as to those wishing to accumulate information regarding a special field of interest.

The spectacular growth of polyurethane technology in recent years, particularly in the field of flexible foams, has aroused widespread interest in promoting more comprehensive understanding and obtaining information about this relatively new class of polymers. A great deal of the earlier literature on polyurethanes is contained, unfortunately, in either patents or more inaccessible foreign journals, and documents such as P. B. Reports issued after World War II. In the development of the polyurethane industry in this country the suppliers of raw materials have done much to make available reviews and translations of earlier work, and have contributed many reports of their own original research. This information has contributed greatly to the development of the industry. However, it must be recognized that a great share of the growth of polyurethanes has come from the research laboratories of the consumer industries, small and large alike, that worked out and perfected the formulations and processes, making possible the large-scale acceptance of these products by the public.

Through the efforts of organizations in this country such as the Cellular Plastics Division of the Society of Plastics Industry and the American Society of Testing Materials, suppliers and consumers of polyurethane raw materials worked jointly in drawing up specifications for the raw materials as well as suitable test methods for end products in order to set up and maintain high standards of performance. This created a favorable climate for free interchange of technical information and helped substantially in the advancement of the art.

A major objective set by the authors of this volume is the systematic and critical presentation of available information on the various aspects of the chemistry and technology relating to polyurethanes. Although this information is treated in a fairly comprehensive manner, it is impractical to present every detail. It is hoped that all or nearly all of the most singificant information—judged from today's knowledge—is included. Sufficient reference to the original literature is given that the discussions presented herein should be adequate guides to the sources of those details that could not be included. It is hoped that Part I covers the literature adequately through 1960; some selected references and papers through approximately June 1, 1961, are also included.

Ultimately, the aim of the authors is to offer a better understanding of the basic and applied aspects of polyurethanes, with the hope that these works may serve both as a reference work and a starting point for future research. While it is realized that a certain amount of information presented in the series may be superseded by more recent developments, the basic facts uncovered in these investigations should be of interest to research workers in those fields for many years, and may give them helpful clues for future work.

It is only logical to assume, and rightly so, that a great number of people have assisted the authors, either by encouraging them in their undertaking or by contributing to the text of the book or otherwise helping them in the preparation of the manuscript. However, while it would not be feasible to list all who so generously have contributed their council or time, it is with pleasure that the authors acknowledge their indebtedness to Dr. John T. Patton of Wyandotte Chemicals Corp. for his contribution to the section of "Polyethers" in Chapter II on "Raw Materials"; to Dr. R. G. Arnold of Du Pont for reviewing Chapter IV, "The Kinetics and Catalysis of Isocyanate Reactions"; and to Mrs. Lorraine Demkovich and Mr. Charles Crookshanks of Mobay Chemical Co. for outstanding effort in preparing the manuscript for this volume.

The authors also thank the following companies for providing data describing their commercial products: Atlas Powder Co., Baker Castor Oil Co., Carwin Chemical Co., The Dow Chemical Co., E. I. du Pont de Nemours and Co., Inc., Jefferson Chemical Co., Mobay Chemical Co., National Aniline Division of Allied Chemical Corp., Olin-Mathieson Chemical Corp., Ott Chemical Co., Pittsburgh Plate Glass Co., Spencer Kellog and Sons, Inc., Union Carbide Chemicals Corp., Witco Chemical Co., and Wyandotte Chemicals Corp.

Special appreciation is extended to the colleagues of the authors in their respective research departments and at Farbenfabriken Bayer who have by conversation and council helped them in developing their knowledge of polyurethanes. In addition to the outstanding contributions in this respect that have been made by Professor Otto Bayer and his co-workers in Leverkusen, special thanks are extended to Dr. Erwin Weinbrenner, Dr. H. H. Wollthan, Dr. A. M. Gemassmer, and Dr. E. E. Hardy, who have been or are associated with the Mobay Chemical Company, and to Dr. E. Denton and Dr. H. C. Vogt of Wyandotte Chemicals Corp.

Finally, the authors wish to express their sincere appreciation to Mr. J. D. Mahoney, President of the Mobay Chemical Company, Mr. Robert B. Semple, President and Dr. J. William Zabor, Director of the Research Division of Wyandotte Chemicals Corp., without whose authorization and encouragement this undertaking would have been impossible.

October 15, 1961

J. H. SAUNDERS
K. C. FRISCH

CONTENTS

Frontispiece v
Preface vii
List of Abbreviations xv
I. Introduction 1
II. Raw Materials 17
I. Introduction 17
II. Isocyanates 17
1. Preparation of Isocyanates 17
2. Molecular Structure and Spectra 28
3. Analytical Methods for Isocyanates and Urethanes 29
4. Handling Precautions 30
III. Polyethers 32
1. General 32
2. Preparation 33
3. Reactions of Polyether Polyols 42
4. Properties 43
IV. Polyesters 44
1. General 44
2. Preparation 45
3. Reactions 47
V. Castor Oil and Derivatives 48
1. Origin and Manufacture 48
2. Composition and Properties 50
3. Reactions of Castor Oil and of Ricinoleic Acid 51
4. Uses 54

III. The Reactions of Isocyanates and Isocyanate Derivatives 63
I. Introduction 63
II. Reactions of Isocyanates 64
1. Reactions with Compounds Containing the N—H Group 65
2. Reactions with Compounds Containing the O—H Group 73
3. Reactions with Compounds Containing the C—H Group 84
4. Reactions with Compounds Containing the S—H Group 86

5. Reaction with Miscellaneous Active Hydrogen Compounds 86
6. Reactions with Unsaturated Compounds 88
7. Dimerization 91
8. Trimerization 94
9. Miscellaneous Reactions 97
10. Reactions of "Inorganic" Isocyanates 100
11. Charts of Reactions 103

III. Reactions of Isocyanate Derivatives 103
1. Reactions of Urethanes 103
2. Reactions of Substituted Ureas 111
3. Reactions of Isocyanate Dimers 113
4. Reactions of Isocyanate Trimers 116
5. Reactions of Carbodiimides 116
6. "Splitting" of "Blocked" Isocyanates 118

IV. The Kinetics and Catalysis of the Isocyanate Reactions 129

I. Introduction 129
II. General Considerations 129
III. Reactions with Alcohols 134
1. Reactions of Monoisocyanates 134
2. Reactions of Diisocyanates 150
3. Catalysis of the Isocyanate-Hydroxyl Reaction 161

IV. Reactions with Amines 173
V. Reactions with Water 180
VI. Reactions with Carboxylic Acids 186
VII. Reactions with Phenols 189
VIII. Reactions with Ureas 190
IX. Reactions with Urethanes 194
X. Reactions with Thiols 198
XI. Summary of Relative Rates of Reactions with Active Hydrogen Compounds 204
XII. Summary of Catalytic Effects 208
XIII. Catalysis in the Control of Polymer Formation 211

V. Formation of Urethane Foams 219

I. Introduction 219
II. The Chemistry of Foam Formation and Cure 220
1. Reactions of Isocyanates 220
2. Function of the Isocyanate in Foaming 223
3. Role of Catalysts in Foam Systems 227
4. The Final Cure of Urethane Foams 232

III. Colloid Chemistry of Foam Formation 235
1. Bubble Nucleation 237
2. Bubble Stability 241
3. Urethane Foam Systems 245

IV. Viscoelastic Changes in Foaming 249
1. Effect on Cell Structure, Voids and Foam Collapse 249
2. Relations between Cell Structure and Properties 255
3. Structural Factors Affecting Stress Relaxation and Creep in Flexible Foams 259

VI. The Relationships between Polymer Structure and Properties in Urethanes 261
I. Introduction 261
II. General Considerations 262
1. Molecular Weight 262
1. Intermolecular Forces 262
3. Stiffness of Chain Units 263
4. Crystallization 263
5. Ease of Rotation of Chain Segments 264
6. Cross Linking 264
7. Theory of Rubber Elasticity 267
III. The Influence of Component Group Structures in Urethanes 269
IV. Urethane Elastomers 273
1. Polyester-Urethane Elastomers 276
2. Polyether-Urethane Elastomers 293
V. Urethane Foams 314
1. Polyether-Urethane Foams 316
2. Polyester-Urethane Foams 323
VI. Urethane Coatings 323
VII. Other Urethane Polymer Applications 326
VIII. Flow, Creep, and Stress Relaxation in Urethane Polymers. 327
1. Factors Related to Primary Chemical Bonds. 328
2. Factors Related to Secondary Bonds 329
3. Compression Set 331
4. Softening of Urethane Polymers during Flexing 335
IX. Summary of Structure-Property Relations in Urethanes. . 337
X. Conclusions 343

Appendix A. Commercially Available Isocyanates 347
Appendix B. Commercially Available Polyethers 349
Appendix C. Commercially Available Polyesters 351
Appendix D. Trade Names and Generic Names 352
Index 355

LIST OF ABBREVIATIONS

The following abbreviations of isocyanate names are used in the text:

TDI: Tolylene diisocyanate (isomer positions being 2,4 except as designated in text)

MDI: 4,4′-Diphenylmethane diisocyanate

HDI: 1,6-Hexamethylene diisocyanate

NDI: 1,5-Naphthalene diisocyanate

DADI: 3,3′Dimethoxy-4,4′-biphenyl diisocyanate ("dianisidine diisocyanate")

TODI: 3,3′-Dimethyl-4,4′-biphenyl diisocyanate ("tolidine diisocyanate")

PDI: Phenylene diisocyanate (isomer positions designated in text)

XDI: 4,4′-Biphenyl diisocyanate ("xenylene diisocyanate")

Polyethers of the poly(1,2-oxypropylene) types will often be designated "PPG," of the poly(oxyethylenetype) "PEG."

Reports issued following World War II by the "Office of Production Board" and later by the Department of Commerce are given the familiar abbreviation "P. B. Report."

I. INTRODUCTION

The polyurethanes are among the most recent additions to the many commercially important classes of polymers. The term "polyurethane" is more one of convenience than of accuracy, since these polymers are not derived by polymerizing a monomeric urethane molecule, nor are they usually polymers containing primarily urethane groups. The polyurethanes include those polymers which contain a significant number of urethane groups, regardless of what the rest of the molecule may be. Usually these polymers are obtained by the combination of a polyisocyanate with reactants which have at least some hydroxyl groups, e.g., polyethers, castor oil, and simple glycols. Other reactive groups may also be present, such as amino and carboxyl. Thus a typical "polyurethane" may contain, in addition to urethane groups, aliphatic and aromatic hydrocarbon, ester, ether, amide, and urea groups. These polymers are also sometimes called simply "urethanes," and sometimes "isocyanate polymers."

Urethanes can be considered esters of the unstable carbamic acid, or amide esters of carbonic acid:

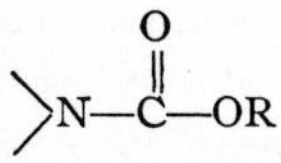

$$\rangle N{-}\overset{\overset{\displaystyle O}{\|}}{C}{-}OR$$

and the urethane group has the characteristic configuration:

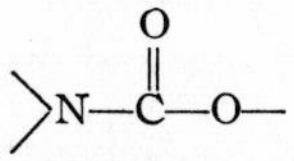

$$\rangle N{-}\overset{\overset{\displaystyle O}{\|}}{C}{-}O{-}$$

Thus a polyurethane has a significant number of these urethane groups, although not necessarily repeating in a regular order.

It is not surprising that some confusion in nomenclature has arisen. One not familiar with this field might assume that the essential monomer is ethyl carbamate ($H_2NCOOC_2H_5$), which has been known for many years by the simple term "urethane." It is readily apparent, however, that this compound is not a precursor of the polyurethanes, and that polyurethanes cannot be depolymerized or hydrolyzed to give this compound. Thus there is no basis for assuming that any toxicity characteristics associated with ethyl carbamate ("urethane") in any way apply to the polyurethanes.

Polyurethanes can be formed by a variety of methods, although the most widely used production method is the reaction of di- or polyfunctional hydroxyl compounds, e.g., hydroxyl-terminated polyesters or polyethers, with di- or polyfunctional isocyanates. The general structure of a linear polyurethane derived from a dihydroxy compound, HOROH, and a diisocyanate, OCNR′NCO, can be represented by the following general formula:

$$(-R-O-\overset{\overset{\displaystyle O}{\|}}{C}-NH-R'-NH-\overset{\overset{\displaystyle O}{\|}}{C}-O-)_n$$

The functionality of the hydroxyl-containing component as well as of the isocyanate can be increased to three or more to form branched or cross-linked polymers. Other structural changes can be made at will, also. For example the nature of R may be changed drastically, such as in molecular weight and type (polyether, polyester, simple glycol), and mixtures of these polyhydroxy compounds can be used. Similarly, the nature of the R′ may be altered, as in the change from naphthalene diisocyanate to hexamethylene diisocyanate. For these reasons the polyurethanes are almost unique in that cross linking, chain flexibility, and intermolecular forces can be varied widely and almost independently. It is to be expected, then, that the polyurethanes include fibers, soft and hard elastomers, flexible and rigid foams, coatings for many purposes, and highly cross linked plastics.

While the chemistry and technology of polyurethanes are of relatively recent origin, the chemistry of organic isocyanates dates back over a hundred years. Wurtz (48), in 1849, was the first to synthesize aliphatic isocyanates by reacting organic sulfates with cyanates:

$$R_2SO_4 + 2KCNO \rightarrow 2RNCO + K_2SO_4$$

The structure of the isocyanates obtained by Wurtz was later confirmed by Gautier (14), who oxidized aliphatic isocyanides with mercuric oxide to the corresponding isocyanates:

$$R-N{=}C + HgO \rightarrow R-N{=}C{=}O + Hg$$

Wurtz (48) also observed several of the simple reactions of isocyanates, reactions which are of commercial importance today. He found that ethyl isocyanate reacted with ethyl alcohol to form ethyl carbamate:

$$C_2H_5N{=}C{=}O + C_2H_5OH \rightarrow C_2H_5{-}NH{-}\overset{\overset{\displaystyle O}{\|}}{C}{-}OC_2H_5$$

Addition of a secondary amine to ethyl isocyanate yielded the corresponding substituted urea:

$$C_2H_5N{=}C{=}O + HN\begin{matrix} \diagup R \\ \diagdown R' \end{matrix} \rightarrow C_2H_5{-}NH{-}\overset{\overset{\displaystyle O}{\|}}{C}{-}N\begin{matrix} \diagup R \\ \diagdown R' \end{matrix}$$

The first aromatic isocyanate, phenyl isocyanate, was prepared by Hofmann (23), by pyrolysis of symmetrical diphenyl oxamide:

$$(C_6H_5{-}NH{-}\overset{\overset{\displaystyle O}{\|}}{C}{-})_2 \rightarrow 2C_6H_5NCO + H_2$$

Of the many methods developed for the synthesis of organic isocyanates, only that of Hentschel (18) is still commercially in use today. It is based on the treatment of amines or their salts with phosgene:

$$RNH_2 + COCl_2 \rightarrow RNHCOCl + HCl$$
$$RNHCOCl \rightarrow RNCO + HCl$$

In the years following the research of Wurtz and Hentschel many isocyanates were prepared and their simple reactions were characterized. It was not until approximately 1937, however, that the use of diisocyanates for polymer synthesis was explored. Carother's successful studies with super polyamides prompted the German I. G. Farbenindustrie to investigate similar materials, which would not be covered by Du Pont patents.

In 1937, Professor Otto Bayer and co-workers (4,6) discovered the diisocyanate addition polymerization that resulted in the preparation of many different types of polyurethanes and polyureas. Initial work consisted in the reaction of diisocyanates with diamines, yielding polyureas which were, however, infusible and strongly hydrophilic, hence less interesting for plastic or fiber applications:

$$H_2N(CH_2)_6NH_2 + O{=}C{=}N{-}(CH_2)_6{-}N{=}C{=}O \rightarrow$$
$$\left[{-}NH{-}(CH_2)_6{-}NH{-}\overset{\overset{\displaystyle O}{\|}}{C}{-}NH{-}(CH_2)_6{-}NH{-}\overset{\overset{\displaystyle O}{\|}}{C}{-}\right]_n$$

However the reaction of diisocyanates with glycols such as 1,4-butylene glycol, led to the formation of polyurethanes possessing properties that made them of interest in the production of plastics and fibers, especially of bristles:

$$HO(CH_2)_4OH + O{=}C{=}N{-}(CH_2)_6{-}N{=}C{=}O \rightarrow \left[{-}O{-}(CH_2)_4{-}O{-}\overset{\overset{\displaystyle O}{\|}}{C}{-}NH{-}(CH_2)_6{-}NH{-}\overset{\overset{\displaystyle O}{\|}}{C}{-} \right]_n$$

These polyurethanes found commercial use under the trade name of Igamid U for plastics and Perlon U for synthetic fibers and bristles. However, Perlon U reached only a limited sales volume in Germany and did not find acceptance in the United States.

About the same time as polyurethane developments started in Germany, work on isocyanates began in the United States, foremost by Du Pont investigators. An early Du Pont patent (36) disclosed the use of diisocyanates, e.g., hexamethylene diisocyanate, to effect more rapid drying of alkyd resins, but the first U. S. patent dealing with the reaction of diisocyanates and dihydroxy compounds was issued to Lieser (24) of Germany. Tetra- and octamethylene diisocyanates were reacted with glycols, e.g., 1,6-hexanediol, as well as with polyhydroxy compounds such as certain cellulose derivatives.

A short time later the reaction between glycols and diisocyanates was described more broadly in a patent issued to Catlin (8). The principal applications for the resulting polymers were fibers and flexible sheets.

A patent of very broad coverage by Hanford and Holmes (15) described the reactions of polyfunctional compounds, containing active hydrogen atoms, with polyisocyanates. This patent was issued at the same time as Catlin's patent (8).

The preparation of linear polyurethanes from glycols and diisocyanates as previously reported in Germany by Rinke *et al.* eventually led to the issue of a U. S. patent (35). This patent was applied for as early as 1938 but did not issue until 1950.

Additional methods for the preparation of linear polyurethanes other than by the diisocyanate-dihydroxy reaction were investigated in Germany. The most promising alternate route was described by Hoff and Wicker (22). It consisted in the reaction of glycol bis(chloroformates) with diamines:

$$\text{Cl—}\overset{\text{O}}{\overset{\|}{\text{C}}}\text{—O—R—O—}\overset{\text{O}}{\overset{\|}{\text{C}}}\text{—Cl} + \text{H}_2\text{N—R'—NH}_2 \rightarrow \left[\text{—}\underset{\text{O}}{\underset{\|}{\text{C}}}\text{—O—R—O—}\underset{\text{O}}{\underset{\|}{\text{C}}}\text{—NH—R'—NH—}\right]_n$$

The development of polyurethanes in fields other than plastics and fibers was actively pursued in Germany during the years of World War II. In 1940, Schlack (42) reacted polyesters containing terminal hydroxyl groups with diisocyanates, e.g., 1,6-hexamethylene diisocyanate, leading to chain extension, with an appreciable increase in viscosity. However, the resulting products had very low softening temperatures. A very active research program in the laboratories of Farbenfabriken Bayer, a branch of the former I. G. Farbenindustrie, soon showed promising uses in rigid foams, adhesives, and coatings (4). These applications reached moderate commercial importance in Germany, but were not recognized in the United States until after the war. In the period 1945–1947, scientific teams studying German developments issued a number of PB Reports describing the uses of polyurethanes. These reports and independent evaluations intrigued the United States industry, particularly that portion cooperating with the U. S. Air Force. With Du Pont and Monsanto supplying 2,4-tolylene diisocyanate in pilot plant quantities, Goodyear Aircraft Corporation (31) and Lockheed Aircraft Corporation (43) in 1946–1948 developed techniques for rigid foam production that were similar to the Bayer systems.

Interest in isocyanates and polyurethanes grew slowly in the United States, spurred by the Bayer development of polyurethane elastomers (5) and flexible foams (21), which were disclosed in 1950 and 1952, respectively. Prior to 1952, the polyurethanes were characterized by good properties and high prices. It was not until the advent of flexible urethane foams, with their high strength at very low densities, that large scale commercial use of polyurethanes seemed assured.

In the period 1952–1954, chemists and engineers at the Bayer laboratories developed their diisocyanate-polyester flexible foam system to a degree suitable for commercial production, including the necessary continuous machinery. To introduce this system and other polyurethane technology to the United States, Bayer and Monsanto formed the jointly owned Mobay Chemical Company in 1954. At about the same time National Aniline entered the field as a third major producer of isocyanates, along with Mobay and Du Pont.

The flexible foam industry was started largely on Bayer know-how and utilizing machinery imported from Germany. Other Bayer developments in the coatings, elastomer, and adhesives fields were introduced that also utilized polyesters as the principal resin component. As the polyurethane industry matured it became apparent that the original polyester-based systems, with their outstanding properties, were commercially suitable for some applications but too expensive for many others.

In order to reach much broader markets, American companies soon developed the uses of cheaper resins, such as polyethers derived from propylene oxide, and castor oil, to partially replace the more expensive polyesters in the urethane systems. For technical and economic reasons the use of these polyethers new exceeds that of all other resins.

The commercial entry in 1957 of urethane grade polyether polyols derived from propylene oxide brought about a major change in polyurethane technology and market potential. The use of these polyethers provided a greater range of foam properties then did the polyesters, and at a significantly lower price. Du Pont had previously offered a poly(oxytetramethylene) glycol, Teracol 30 (3), in pilot plant quantities, but because of a relatively high cost did not go into full scale commercial production of this product. Block copolymers of poly(oxypropylene)-poly(oxyethylene)glycols (Pluronic polyols) and similar block copolymers based on ethylenediamine (Tetronic polyols) were introduced by Wyandotte Chemicals Corporation. Urethane grade poly(oxypropylene) glycols became commercially available from Dow, Union Carbide, and Wyandotte. An extensive series of polyether diols, triols, and polyols of higher functionality are now being offered by these polyether suppliers. In addition to the above, other companies have announced their intention of manufacturing polyethers.

Flexible urethane foam, with a much more favorable strength-to-density ratio than foamed rubber, brought the polyurethane industry to a truly commercial stage. Production of this foam was approximately 100,000,000 pounds in 1960 (44). With this volume of production, diisocyanates and suitable resins were available at low enough prices to justify renewed interest in the many other applications of the polyurethanes. Other major uses which are growing at significant rates include elastomers, coatings, and adhesives.

With this very brief history of the over-all polyurethane story, it may now be desirable to look in more detail at the development of each of the principal areas of application.

One of the earliest commercial applications of isocyanates was in the adhesive field. During World War II the Germans succeeded in bonding Buna S rubber to metals, using 4,4′,4′′-triphenylmethane triisocyanate (4). The successful applications of this bonding agent for tank caterpillar treads ushered in an extensive investigation of di- and triisocyanates for adhesive uses in general. Polyurethane adhesives, developed by Bayer and co-workers (4), prepared from combinations of polyesters and diisocyanates, became commercially known as Polystal.

By varying the nature of the polyester and the isocyanate component, a wide range of properties was obtained. In addition, triphenylmethane triisocyanate (Desmodur R) was used as an adhesive to bond rubber to fibers as well as to metal. A third type of adhesive consisted of polymers containing an active hydrogen atom, e.g., polyvinyl alcohol, and which were modified with diisocyanates.

Some of the earlier U. S. patent literature on diisocyanates disclosed their use as adhesives, particularly to bond elastomers to fibers and metals. During the early phases of World War II, methylene bis(4-phenyl isocyanate) was used in the bonding of rubber and neoprene to synthetic fibers, and the resulting products were employed as life rafts and inflatable vests (13).

Prior to the formation of Mobay, Monsanto investigators prepared polyurethane adhesives from simple polyols, castor oils and polyether polyols, and diisocyanates. Various methods for applying these adhesives, including low and high temperature and "carrier" bonding, were described (17).

The field of polyurethane coatings was also among the earliest to be investigated, leading to many commercial applications, particularly in Germany and more recently in the United States. In Germany, Bayer and co-workers (4) developed polyester-diisocyanate coatings (Desmodur-Desmophen combinations), which were found to be eminently suitable for substrates such as wood, rubber, leather, fabrics, paper, and metals. By varying the type and the degree of branching of the polyester and of the diisocyanate, as well as the NCO/OH ratio, a wide variety of properties was obtained, ranging from very flexible to hard and brittle films. Some of the other outstanding characteristics of these coatings included high gloss, good adhesion to many substrates, excellent water, oil, and solvent resistance, high abrasion resistance, excellent electrical properties, and good weather resistance.

During World War II, polyurethane coatings were employed for the impregnation of paper, which subsequently was used in the manufacture of mustard gas-resistant garments (4). Other applications were high gloss finishes on airplanes and anticorrosion paints in chemical plants. Pigmented coatings were particularly recommended for the protection of metal, wood, and masonry.

It was soon recognized that monomeric diisocyanates, because of their irritant characteristics, presented some difficulties during their application. To eliminate this problem it was found preferable to use certain adducts of tolylene diisocyanate and polyols such as trimethylolpropane or hexanetriol (4). Preparation of these adducts can be schematically represented as follows:

$$RC(OH)_3 + 3OCN—R'—NCO \rightarrow RC(O—\overset{\overset{\displaystyle O}{\|}}{C}—NH—R'—NCO)_3$$

These adducts have good stability and provide controlled activity of the isocyanate groups.

In two-component coatings the principal reaction is the formation of urethane groups by the reaction of the hydroxyl groups of the polyesters with the isocyanate groups, as previously described. However, depending upon the NCO/OH ratio and the relative humidity, the excess isocyanate groups react with atmospheric moisture to form urea groups, as well.

A type of one-component urethane coating utilizes "blocked" isocyanates (4). Certain "blocking" agents such as phenols, certain aromatic amines, and other materials, react with isocyanates to form adducts, e.g.:

$$\underset{\text{Adduct of trimethylolpropane and a diisocyanate}}{C_2H_5C(CH_2—O—CO—NH—R—NCO)_3} + \underset{\text{Phenol}}{C_6H_5—OH} \rightleftharpoons \underset{\text{"Blocked" adduct}}{C_2H_5—C(CH_2—O—CO—NH—R—NH—COOC_6H_5)_3}$$

Heating coatings containing the blocked adducts to approximately 150°C. causes reaction with a polyol to occur as if the free isocyanate were regenerated. One-component coatings, consisting of blocked isocyanates and polyols, have found commercial use as wire enamels.

Literature on these types of one- and two-component urethane coatings has been available in this country for several years (26).

Bayer also reported another kind of urethane coating, referred to as "urethane oils" (4). These coatings were made by the reaction of diisocyanates with the alcoholysis products of a drying oil, e.g., mono- or diglycerides from linseed oil. Since these products did not contain free isocyanate groups, they were stable on storage and could readily be pigmented. Drying of these coatings takes place through the double bond of the fatty acid part of the molecule. The properties of these coatings were found to be superior to alkyd resins with regard to drying speed, hardness, and water resistance. Such systems constitute the largest volume of urethane coatings used in the United States in 1960 (45).

Urethane coatings based on castor oil-diisocyanate adducts have been reported by several investigators (2,25,32,46,47). These coatings have found commercial acceptance for concrete floors, in maintenance and protective coatings, and other applications requiring good chemical, weather, and abrasion resistance.

Recently, one- and two-component polyether urethane coatings were described (10,27,30,34). By ordered addition of the polyol and isocyanate components, isocyanate- or hydroxyl-terminated intermediates were obtained that allowed considerable variation in the coating formulation and their resulting properties. Recommended uses for polyether-based coatings include wood and leather finishes, concrete coatings, and metal finishes for corrosion protection.

Simultaneously with initial adhesives and coatings research, early polyurethane foam development in Germany took place primarily in the field of rigid foams. The German urethane foams, commercially known as Moltoprens, were made from tolylene diisocyanate (approximately 65/35 mixtures of 2,4- and 2,6-tolylene diisocyanates, known as Desmodur T) and hydroxyl-terminated polyesters (Desmophens) (4,11). Initially, the reaction between the diisocyanates and some carboxylic groups in the polyesters was utilized for the gas evolution, which can be schematically represented as follows:

$$\text{RNCO} + \text{R'COOH} \rightarrow \text{RNHCOR'} + \text{CO}_2$$

The small amount of water present in polyesters also contributed to the carbon dioxide evolution:

$$2\text{RNCO} + \text{H}_2\text{O} \rightarrow \text{RNHCONHR} + \text{CO}_2$$

The foams were produced by mixing the diisocyanate with the polyester until the resulting exothermic reaction (formation of polyurethane) set off the gas evolution. At first polyesters of relatively high acid number (approximately 30 or more) were used in the manufacture of Moltopren. Later the tendency was to employ polyesters of low acid number and to control the foaming reaction by the addition of a measured amount of water instead of adjusting the acid number of the polyester (21).

Moltopren was used in filling aircraft parts, to improve the buoyancy of boats and ships, and for insulation.

The rigid foam applications in the German aircraft industry led the U. S. Air Force to place research contracts with Goodyear Aircraft Corp. as well as with other organizations. Work begun at Goodyear Aircraft Corp. in 1946 led to the development of low density foam core materials, which could be used for the construction of radomes. The materials used in the manufacture of the core consisted of an alkyd resin, made from glycerol, phthalic anhydride, and adipic acid, and tolylene diisocyanate (31). Lockheed Aircraft Corp., in 1947–1948, independently developed a technique for foamed-in-place rigid polyurethane foam (Lockfoam) and was granted a series of patents (43).

The commercial success of polyurethanes in postwar Germany, notable in the field of foams, brought about a considerable spur of activity on the part of American industry. In 1950, Du Pont and Monsanto started semicommercial production of diisocyanates, primarily aromatic ones. Du Pont, in 1953, announced a polyurethane foam and also provided information on its method of preparation via the prepolymer route. Bayer began to introduce its know-how into the United States slowly in 1953, and then with Monsanto formed Mobay in 1954. Through this means a considerable amount of German technology on polyurethanes was disseminated in the U. S. and German foam machines were imported which helped to speed up the commercial production of flexible foam. Du Pont, Mobay, and, to a lesser extent, Lockheed Aircraft Corp., extended licenses to foam manufacturers and provided technical assistance.

The urethane foam industry developed along lines indicated previously, first with diisocyanate-polyester combinations, more recently with diisocyanate-polyether combinations being used in the largest volume. The polyester systems employed a "one-shot" technique in which polyester, diisocyanate, water, catalysts, and foam stabilizers were all mixed in one step, and permitted to foam. The first commercial use of polyethers employed a "prepolymer" process, wherein the polyether and diisocyanate were first reacted to form a "prepolymer" that was subsequently mixed with catalyst, water, and stabilizers to produce foam. By the end of 1958, a "one-shot" process for polyether-urethane foam, but with different catalysts and stabilizers than are used for polyester foams, was developed. This newer technology, and especially the very low foam densities available from it, marked a further economic improvement. Both foam producers and raw material suppliers contributed heavily to these developments.

Synthetic elastomers comprise a fourth major application of polyurethanes. Whereas Schlack (42) and Christ and Hanford (9) in the United States noticed the formation of elastic urethane products, they did not pursue the subject further. To Pinten (33) goes the credit of preparing the first highly elastic isocyanate rubbers ("I rubbers"). These elastomers were prepared from diisocyanates and a polyester obtained by condensing a glycol, 4% of which was replaced with a trifunctional alcohol, with adipic acid. The "I rubbers" of Pinten had high tensile strength and abrasion resistance but poor tear resistance, and exhibited changes in elongation and hardening on exposure to low temperatures.

Bayer and co-workers (5) reported extensive investigations on polyurethane elastomers, leading to the development of Vulcollan rubbers. The first step consisted in the reaction of linear hydroxyl-terminated polyesters, made from glycols and dibasic acids, with a diisocyanate to form a prepolymer:

$$4R(NCO)_2 + 3HO\text{———}OH \rightarrow$$

$$OCNR\left[NH\overset{O}{\overset{\|}{C}}O\text{———}O\overset{O}{\overset{\|}{C}}NHR\right]_3NCO$$

Prepolymer

The glycols used in the manufacture of the linear polyesters were varied, although ethylene and propylene glycols or mixtures of the two were preferred; adipic acid was the standard acid. Aromatic diisocyanates, particularly 1,5-naphthalene diisocyanate, were found to be especially suited for urethane rubbers.

The prepolymer was then chain extended with a controlled amount of water, forming urea groups and leaving about 2–5% of unreacted isocyanate groups:

$$\underset{\text{Prepolymer}}{\text{OCN}\text{———}\text{NCO}} + H_2O \rightarrow \underset{\text{Chain extended polymer}}{\text{OCN}\text{———}\text{NH}\overset{\overset{\text{O}}{\|}}{\text{C}}\text{NH}\text{———}\text{NCO}} + CO_2$$

The cross linking of the chain extended polymer then took place at elevated temperatures (125–150°C.) through the reaction of the excess isocyanate groups with the active hydrogen on either the urea or the urethane groups in the polymer chain. Since the urea group reacts much faster than the urethane group, this is the favored curing reaction:

$$2\ \underset{\text{Chain extended polymer}}{\text{OCN}\text{———}\text{NH}\overset{\overset{\text{O}}{\|}}{\text{C}}\text{NH}\text{———}\text{NCO}} \rightarrow$$

$$\begin{array}{l}
\text{——}\overset{\text{H}}{\text{OCN}}\text{———}\text{N}\overset{\overset{\text{O}}{\|}}{\text{C}}\text{NH}\text{——}\overset{\text{H}}{\text{NCO}}\text{——} \\
\qquad\qquad\qquad\ \ | \\
\qquad\qquad\qquad\ \text{C=O} \\
\qquad\qquad\qquad\ \ | \\
\qquad\qquad\qquad\ \text{HN}\text{———}\text{NH}\overset{\overset{\text{O}}{\|}}{\text{C}}\text{NH}\text{———}\overset{\text{H}}{\text{NCO}}\text{——}
\end{array}$$

Cross-linked polymer

Several methods were used in the preparation of Vulcollan, and it was soon recognized that other chain extenders such as glycols, diamines, or amino alcohols, could be used (29).

Polyurethane elastomers were also investigated in England and the United States. The English Vulcaprene A was developed through the work of Imperial Chemical Industries (16) whereby the polyester component was replaced with a polyesteramide. In the United States, Goodyear Tire and Rubber Co. brought out a polyurethane rubber, Chemigum SL (12). The latter was made by using a deficit of diisocyanate in the reaction with polyesters, thereby forming an uncured gum stock, which was storable and which could be cured with additional amounts of diisocyanate. Du Pont developed their own line of polyurethane rubbers (Adiprene), which were based on poly(oxytetramethylene) glycols rather than polyesters (19,37).

Fabrication methods for urethane elastomers underwent a significant development. While most of the early urethane rubbers were prepared on conventional rubber equipment, a liquid rubber casting technique described by Müller *et al.* (29) permitted the manufacture of many rubber goods at considerable savings in fabrication costs.

In addition to these major areas of applications, isocyanates have been used for a variety of purposes, including the waterproofing of textiles, tanning leather, modifying many polymers, and as chemical intermediates, particularly in the pharmaceutical field.

In recent years several companies have joined the ranks of the isocyanate suppliers. Carwin Chemical Company was one of the first, offering a variety of specialty isocyanates for elastomers, adhesives, coatings, specialty foams, and other uses. Recently Nopco Chemical Company announced plans for the large scale manufacture of tolylene diisocyanate in the near future. Ott Chemical Company is a recent supplier of aliphatic monoisocyanates.

The development of the urethane industry has been accompanied by the publication of many excellent reviews of the preparation of isocyanates (1,28,39,41), their reactions (1,28,38,39), and commercial applications (4,7,11,13,20,21,28,40).

References

1. Arnold, R. G., J. A. Nelson, and J. J. Verbanc, *Chem Revs.* **57,** 47 (1957).
2. Bailey, M. F., *S. P. E. Journal* **14,** 41 (1958).
3. Barringer, C. M., "Teracol 30–Polyalkylene Ether Glycol," *Bulletin* **HR-11,** E. I. du Pont de Nemours and Co., Inc., 1956.
4. Bayer, O., *Angew. Chem.* **A59,** 275 (1947).
5. Bayer, O., E. Müller, S. Petersen, H. F. Piepenbrink, and E. Windemuth, *Angew Chem.* **62,** 57 (1959) ; *Rubber Chem. and Technol.* **23,** 812 (1950).
6. Bayer, O., H. Rinke, W. Siefken, L. Orthner, and H. Schild, Ger. Pat. 728,981 (to I. G. Farbenindustrie), Nov. 12, 1942.
7. Beutel, A. C., and co-workers, Harvard University, *Polyurethanes, A Versatile Synthetic for a Dynamic Era,* Polyurethane Associates, Cambridge, Mass., 1956.
8. Catlin, W. E., U. S. Pat. 2,284,637 (to Du Pont), June 2, 1942.
9. Christ, E., and W. E. Hanford, U. S. Pat. 2,333,639 (to Du Pont), June 6, 1940.
10. Damusis, A., J. M. McClellan, and K. C. Frisch, *Ind. Eng. Chem.* **51,** 1386 (1959) ; *Off. Digest* **32,** 251 (1960).
11. DeBell, J. M., W. C. Goggin, and W. E. Gloor, *German Plastics Practice,* DeBell and Richardson, Cambridge, Mass., 1946.
12. Dinsmore, R. P., "The New Goodyear Rubber, Chemigum SL," Address before the Washington Rubber Group, Washington, D. C., March 18, 1953.
13. Dombrow. B. A.. *Polyurethanes,* Reinhold Publishing Corp., New York, 1957.

14. Gautier, A., *Ann.* **149,** 313 (1869).
15. Hanford, W. E., and D. F. Holmes, U. S. Pat. 2,284,896 (to Du Pont), June 2, 1942.
16. Harper, D. A., W. F. Smith, and H. G. White, *Rubber Chem. and Technol.* **23,** 608 (1950).
17. Heiss, H. L., J. H. Saunders, M. R. Morris, B. R. Davis, and E. E. Hardy, *Ind. Eng. Chem.* **46,** 1498 (1954).
18. Hentschel, W., *Ber.* **17,** 1284 (1884).
19. Hill, F. B., C. A. Young, J. A. Nelson, and R. G. Arnold, *Ind. Eng. Chem.* **48,** 927 (1956).
20. Höchtlen, A., *Kunststoffe* **40,** 221 (1950).
21. Höchtlen, A., *Kunststoffe* **42,** 303 (1952).
22. Hoff, G. P., and D. B. Wicker, *Perlon U; Polyurethans at I. G. Farben,* Boringen, Augsburg, PB Report 1122, Sept. 12, 1945.
23. Hofmann, A. W., *Ann.* **74,** 9 (1850).
24. Lieser, T., U. S. Pat. 2,266,777, Dec. 23, 1941.
25. Metz, H. M., A. Ehrlich, M. K. Smith, and T. C. Patton, *Paint, Oil, Chem. Rev.* **121,** No. 8, 6 (1958).
26. Mobay Chemical Company bulletin, "Prepolymer Type Urethane Coatings," May 9, 1959.
27. Mobay Chemical Company bulletin, "Urethane Surface Coatings," 1955.
28. Müller, E., "Polyurethanes," in *Houben-Weyl, Methoden der organischen Chemie,* E. Müller, editor, Thieme-Verlag, Stuttgart, Vol. 14, in press.
29. Müller, E., O. Bayer, S. Peterson, H. F. Piepenbrink, F. Schmidt, and E. Weinbrenner, *Angew. Chem.* **64,** 523 (1952) ; *Rubber Chem. and Technol.* **26,** 493 (1953).
30. Owen Jr., G. E., R. J. Athey, and W. J. Remington, Elastomer Chemicals Dept., E. I. du Pont de Nemours and Co., *Paint Bulletin* **PB-4.**
31. Pace, H. A., and co-workers, *Final Report on Foaming in Place of Alkyd Resins for Sandwich Radomes,* PB Report 107,373, Feb. 29, 1952.
32. Patton, T. C., and H. M. Metz, *Off. Digest* **32,** 222 (1960).
33. Pinten, H., Ger. Pat. Appl. D-90,260 (Dynamit Nobel A.G.), March, 1942. See ref. 4.
34. Remington, W. J., and J. C. Lorenz, Elastomer Chemicals Dept., E. I. du Pont de Nemours and Co., *Paint Bulletins* **PB-2, PB-3.**
35. Rinke, H., H. Schild, and W. Siefken, U. S. Pat. 2,511,544 (Alien Property Custodian), June 13, 1950.
36. Rothrock, H. S., U. S. Pat. 2,282,827 (to Du Pont), May 12, 1942.
37. Rugg, J. S. and G. W. Scott, *Ind. Eng. Chem.* **48,** 930 (1956).
38. Saunders, J. H., *Rubber Chem. and Technol.* **32,** 337 (1959).
39. Saunders, J. H., and R. J. Slocombe, *Chem. Revs.* **43,** 203 (1948).
40. Saunders, J. H., and E. E. Hardy, in *Encyclopedia of Chemical Technology,* R. E. Kirk and D. F. Othmer, editors, Interscience, New York–London, First Supplement Volume, 1957, p. 888.
41. Siefken, W., "Isocyanate," in Ullmann's *Encyklopädie der technischen Chemie,* Urban und Schwarzenberg, Munich-Berlin, 3rd ed., Vol. 9, 1957; *Ann.* **562,** 75 (1949).

y Saunders and Slocombe (160) and by Arnold, Nelson, and c (10).

A. PHOSGENATION METHODS

reaction between primary amines and phosgene lends itself to the commercial preparation of isocyanates:

$$RNH_2 + COCl_2 \rightarrow \left[R{-}\overset{\overset{\textstyle H}{|}}{\underset{\underset{\textstyle H}{|}}{N}}{:} \rightarrow \overset{\overset{\textstyle Cl}{|}}{\underset{\underset{\textstyle Cl}{|}}{C}}{=}O \right] \rightarrow RNCO + 2HCl$$

t once apparent that a number of side reactions are possible, s the formation of amine hydrochlorides, carbamoyl chlorides, bstituted ureas:

$$RNH_2 + HCl \rightleftharpoons RNH_2{\cdot}HCl$$
$$RNCO + RNH_2 \rightarrow RNHCONHR$$
$$2RNH_2 + COCl_2 \rightarrow RNHCONHR + 2HCl$$
$$RNCO + HCl \rightleftharpoons RNHCOCl$$

reas and amine hydrochlorides may also react with phosgene more vigorous conditions than are required for the reaction the amine itself. In fact, the amine hydrochloride or other salts may be preferred in some cases, and an amine salt was n the earliest phosgenation experiments.

ntschel, in 1884, showed that an isocyanate could be obtained the reaction between phosgene and the salt of a primary amine This reaction was modified by Gattermann and Schmidt, who ted an almost quantitative yield of methyl isocyanate (77). They d molten methylamine hydrochloride with phosgene at 250°C. btained methylcarbamoyl chloride, which was decomposed by g with lime:

$$CH_3NH_2{\cdot}HCl + COCl_2 \rightarrow CH_3NHCOCl + 2HCl$$
$$2CH_3NHCOCl + 2CaO \rightarrow 2CH_3NCO + CaCl_2 + Ca(OH)_2$$

later years several modifications of this reaction were developed. boiling isocyanates can be prepared readily by a reaction be- a refluxing slurry of the amine hydrochloride in a suitable nt and phosgene. Solvents such as ethyl acetate, toluene, and hlorobenzene have been used to advantage. Yields are usually

42. Schlack, P., Ger. Pat. Appl. J-66,330, Jan. 17, 1940; Fr. Pat. 869,243 (to I. G. Farbenindustrie).
43. Simon, E., and F. W. Thomas (to Lockheed Aircraft Corp.), U. S. Pats. 2,577,279, Dec. 4, 1951; 2,577,280, Dec. 4, 1951; 2,577,281, Dec. 4, 1951; 2,591,884, April 8, 1952; 2,603,782, July 8, 1952; 2,634,244, April 7, 1953; 2,642,403, June 16, 1953.
44. Staff report, *Chem. Eng. News* **39,** No. 11, 62 (1961).
45. Terrill, R. L., paper presented at the Chemical Marketing and Economics symposium, American Chemical Society meeting, March 1961; see *Chem. Eng. News* **39,** No. 14, 39 (1961).
46. Toone, G. C., and G. S. Wooster, *Off. Digest* **32,** 230 (1960).
47. Wells, E. R., G. A. Hudson, J. H. Saunders, and E. E. Hardy, *Off. Digest* **31,** 1181 (1959).
48. Wurtz, A., *Ann.* **71,** 326 (1849).

II. RAW MAT

I. Introduct

The principal purpose of this discus
materials for urethane polymers is to
standing of the chemistry of these m
preparative procedures is not necessary
reader is referred to selected articles a
may be found if desired. The importa
containing resins, being relatively few
the appropriate sections of this chapter.
such a wide variety of reactions that
have been reserved for Chapters III anc

The properties and sources of comm
polyethers, and polyesters are given in
the end of the book.

II. Isocyanat

1. Preparation of Isc

A considerable variety of methods of
ported in the literature. The only me
portance, however, is that of phosgenati
economics of this process have been imp
ten years, primarily due to the increas
While phosgenation may be preferred in
requiring phosgene, such as the Curtius r
may be more suitable for certain laborato
lated mechanistically are the Hofmann an

The preparation of isocyanates has bee
notably by Siefken (173) and by Peters
These two reviews also gave experimen
laboratory procedures. Other reviews of

those
Verba

The
readil

It is
such
and s

The
unde
with
amin
used

He
from
(90)
repo
treat
and
heati

In
High
twee
solve
o-di

good; for example, *p*-nitrophenyl isocyanate has been prepared in 85–95% yield by this method (171). The use of the carbamate salt was found to be superior to the use of hydrochloride for the preparation of hexamethylene diisocyanate (52), probably because it is more soluble in the medium used than is the hydrochloride:

$$H_2N(CH_2)_6NH_2 + CO_2 \rightarrow \overset{+}{H_3}N(CH_2)_6NHCO\overset{-}{O} \xrightarrow[2COCl_2]{} OCN(CH_2)_6NCO + 4HCl + CO_2$$

The SO_2 salt has also been used with success (86).

Siefken has reported experimental laboratory details of the liquid-phase phosgenation of many amines and amine salts (173). He prepared a large variety of isocyanates and reported extensive tables of physical properties of many mono- and polyisocyanates. It was shown that many substituted amines could be converted to isocyanates in good yields. For example, olefinic, halogen, sulfone, ester, nitrile, and azo groups survive the phosgenation; carboxylic and sulfonic acid groups are converted to the corresponding acid chlorides; secondary amino groups are converted to the carbamoyl chlorides; aliphatic ether and thioether groups are usually broken, giving chlorinated derivatives, whereas aromatic ethers are not usually cleaved.

The lower molecular weight diisocyanates, such as ethylene and tetramethylene diisocyanate, have not been made successfully by this method, because of intramolecular urea formation:

$$\overset{+}{H_3}NCH_2CH_2NHCO\overset{-}{O} + COCl_2 \rightarrow \begin{array}{ccc} H_2C & — & CH_2 \\ | & & | \\ HN & & NH \\ & \diagdown\!\diagup & \\ & CO & \end{array}$$

Several materials have been reported to be catalysts for the phosgenation reactions, e.g., tertiary amines (118), metal halides (36), and boron trifluoride (3). However, Siefken (173) noted that these same types of materials may be undesirable because of their catalytic effect in polymerizing the isocyanates, as during distillation.

A large number of modifications of the phosgenation procedure has been reported as commercial production has become important, e.g., with operation under pressure (80,135), with an initial phosgenation at a very low temperature (162), and continuous operations (24, 99.176).

As commercially practiced, the method for diisocyanates usually involves two steps. In the first an amine solution is mixed with phosgene at a low or moderate temperature. The resulting slurry is then treated with more phosgene at a temperature such as 120–150°C. The product is purified by distillation:

$$R(NH_2)_2 + COCl_2 \rightarrow ClC(=O)NH—R—NH_2 \cdot HCl$$

$$ClC(=O)NH—R—NH_2 \cdot HCl + COCl_2 \xrightarrow[120–150°]{} R(NCO)_2 + 4HCl$$

Flow sheets outlining the stages in commercial production of several diisocyanates are given in Table I (186).

In addition to the liquid-phase procedures, the preparation of isocyanates by a vapor-phase reaction has been used (173,177). This reaction is very fast at about 300°, with good yields being obtained with contact times in the hot reactor as short as one quarter of a second (177). The attractive features of this process are limited primarily to monoisocyanates containing about five to twelve carbon atoms, and to carbamoyl chlorides containing up to about twelve carbon atoms. Higher boiling isocyanates usually give poorer yields, compared to a liquid-phase method. Isocyanates boiling below butyl isocyanate combine with by-product hydrogen chloride to a considerable extent at or near the boiling point of the isocyanate, thus making a treatment with a base necessary to liberate the isocyanate. For example, ethyl isocyanate boils at 60°C., but at this temperature will readily absorb hydrogen chloride to give ethylcarbamoyl chloride. Thus ethyl isocyanate itself cannot be isolated directly from the reaction mixture by simple condensation.

A gas-phase reaction between an amine and phosgene at 180–400°C., in the presence of a catalyst such as bleached clay impregnated with barium chloride, zinc chloride, or sodium bisulfate, was used in Germany. Yields as high as 80% were reported for isocyanates containing as many as seven carbon atoms per molecule (173). The method was not found to be satisfactory for isocyanates of very high boiling points or for diisocyanates.

Other work showed that isocyanates could be prepared very rapidly and in good yields, without a catalyst (177). The amine vapor and phosgene were mixed efficiently at about 275°C., and the products

TABLE I

Flowsheet of Commercial Diisocyanate Preparation

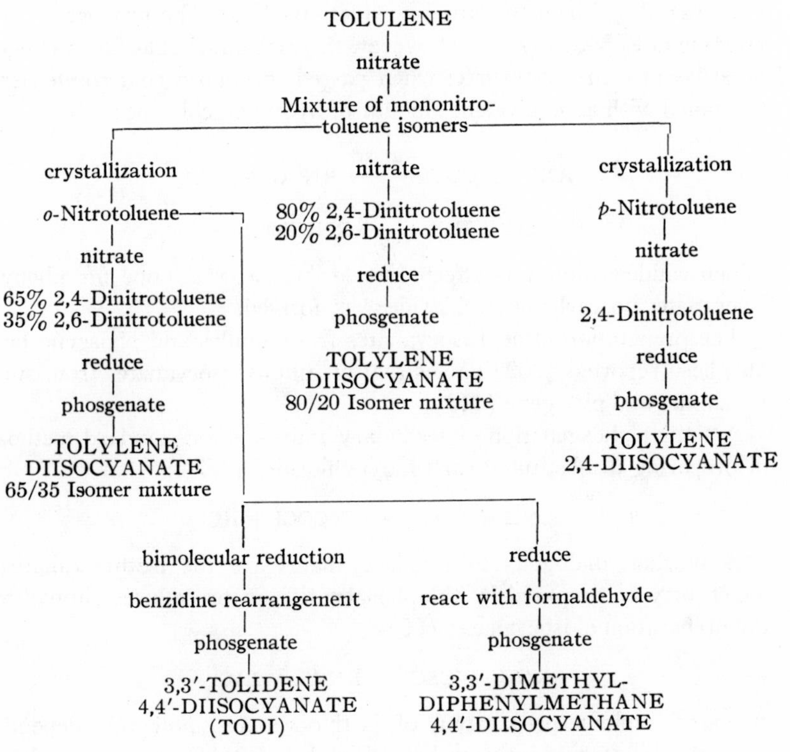

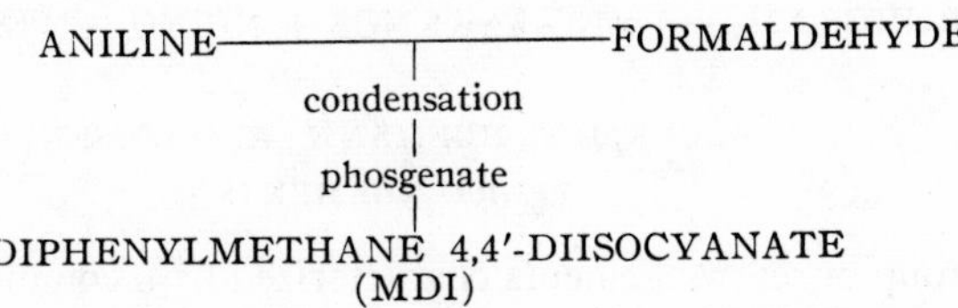

cooled. The carbamoyl chloride corresponding to the amine used was isolated. The higher boiling isocyanates were obtained by refluxing the carbamoyl chloride in benzene or toluene solution; the low boiling isocyanates were obtained by treating the carbamoyl chloride with a tertiary amine. Yields were 75–86% for the isocyanates of nine or fewer carbon atoms per molecule.

It was also shown that the isocyanate itself was the product of the reaction at 275°C. (177). However, the carbamoyl chloride was isolated because the isocyanate, when passed through a cold condenser, combined with an equivalent amount of hydrogen chloride:

$$RNH_2 + COCl_2 \xrightarrow{275°C.} RNCO + 2HCl$$

$$RNCO + HCl \xrightarrow{25°C.} RNHCOCl$$

When condensation was effected at 115°C., as was done for phenyl isocyanate, no carbamoyl chloride was formed.

The preparation of acyl isocyanates from amides and phosgene has also been reported (200) as has that of sulfonyl isocyanates from sulfonamides and phosgene (113).

A similar phosgenation of secondary amines is the standard method of preparing disubstituted carbamoyl chlorides (177):

$$R_2NH + COCl_2 \rightarrow R_2NCOCl + HCl$$

Somewhat analogous to the isocyanates are the isothiocyanates, which may be prepared by thiophosgenation in procedures similar to the preparation of isocyanates (65):

$$RNH_2 + CSCl_2 \rightarrow RNCS + 2HCl$$

A more common preparation of isothiocyanates, however, depends upon the reaction of a thiocarbamate with a suitable mercuric or lead salt (50):

$$RNH_2 + CS_2 + NH_4OH \rightarrow RNHCS_2NH_4 + H_2O$$

$$RNHCS_2NH_4 + Pb(NO_3)_2 \rightarrow RNCS + NH_4NO_3 + PbS + HNO_3$$

B. CURTIUS, HOFMANN, AND LOSSEN REARRANGEMENTS

A group of rearrangements characterized by a common intermediate has been used for the preparation of isocyanates in the laboratory. The Curtius rearrangement of acid azides, the Hofmann rearrangement of acid amides, and the Lossen rearrangement of hydroxamic acids all appear to involve a similar intermediate which rearranges to the isocyanate (Scheme I). The preparative method other than

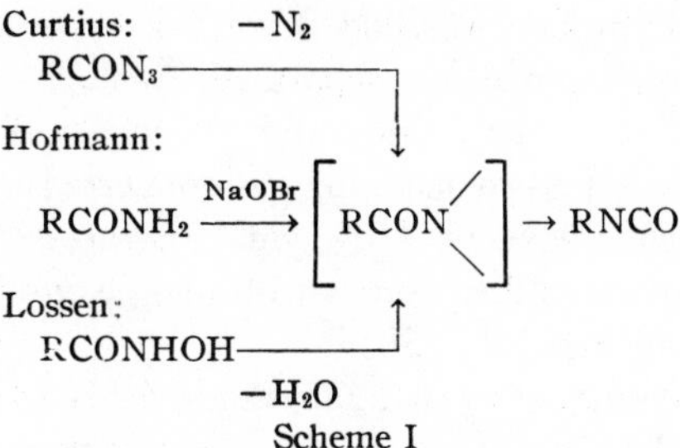

Scheme I

phosgenation which has been used most is the Curtius rearrangement of an acid azide in a neutral solvent:

$$RCON_3 \xrightarrow{-N_2} \left[RCON\langle\right] \rightarrow RNCO$$

The method was first developed to a considerable extent by Schroeter (165), who prepared several isocyanates by treating an acid chloride with sodium azide and warming the resulting product in benzene solution. Curtius later used the method for the preparation of substituted ethylene diisocyanates (47,48). However, he prepared the diazide by treating substituted succinic hydrazides with nitrous acid. Yields from the reaction are usually good, as in the case of undecyl isocyanate, which has been obtained in 81–86% yield (2). A survey of such preparations reported in the literature is given by Smith (180).

The Curtius reaction is useful primarily for the preparation of short chain aliphatic diisocyanates and unsaturated isocyanates. Recent patents and articles illustrate its use for isopropenyl isocyanate (43), vinyl isocyanate (103), and methylene diisocyanate (158).

The Hofmann rearrangement of amides is useful only for those isocyanates which do not react readily with water, since an aqueous medium is required:

$$RCONH_2 \xrightarrow{NaOBr} (RCONBr^-)Na^+$$

$$(RCONBr^-)Na^+ \rightarrow \left[RCON\langle\right] \rightarrow RNCO$$

Pyman (155) has given a discussion of the limitations and scope of this reaction as well as numerous examples. As an illustration, α-propylvaleramide was dissolved in chloroform, bromine was added, then dilute potassium hydroxide was added while keeping the temperature below 0°. The bromoamide was separated, washed, and then shaken with a small amount of 10% sodium hydroxide. The mixture became warm and the solid bromoamide was converted to an oil. Steam distillation reportedly gave an 80% yield of the isocyanate. More recent results are given in the papers of Montagne and Guilmart (134) and of Cagniant and Buu-Hoï (38).

The Lossen rearrangement of hydroxamic acids has not been used frequently. The chemistry of the hydroxamic acids and the nature of the Lossen rearrangement have been reviewed by Yale (209), and preparations of aliphatic diisocyanates by this method are described in recent patents (45,64). As an illustrative example, the disodium salt of sebacic dihydroxamic acid was suspended in benzene and thionyl chloride was added. The mixture was refluxed for two hours, washed with water, and the solvent was removed. The residue was distilled to give about 50–60% yield of octamethylene diisocyanate (64).

C. DOUBLE DECOMPOSITION REACTIONS

The reaction between organic halides or sulfates and salts of cyanic acid was the first method used for the preparation of isocyanates. Wurtz obtained the first alkyl isocyanates by this procedure in 1849 (208).

$$R_2SO_4 + KNCO \rightarrow RNCO$$

Slotta and Lorenz later prepared ethyl isocyanate in 95% yield, and expressed the opinion that the reaction between the alkyl sulfate and potassium cyanate was a relatively convenient laboratory procedure (179). In their experiment 50 g. of technical potassium cyanate was mixed with 10 g. of anhydrous sodium carbonate and heated; 80 g. of diethyl sulfate was added slowly, and the ethyl isocyanate distilled from the mixture. Methyl and propyl isocyanates were also prepared similarly.

Alkyl esters of aryl sulfonic acids (179) and of phosphoric acid (21) have also been used as alkylating agents.

In addition, acyl isocyanates may be prepared in this way, using acid chlorides (91):

$$RCOCl + AgNCO \rightarrow RCONCO$$

"Inorganic" isocyanates, i.e., those isocyanates with the NCO group attached to an element other than carbon, are usually prepared similarly (7,8,72):

$$R_xSiCl_y + yAgNCO \rightarrow R_xSi(NCO)_y$$

Other cyanates that have been used instead of silver cyanate include lead cyanate (108) and lithium cyanate (101). Other "inorganic" isocyanates that have been prepared similarly include isocyanate derivatives of phosphorus (101), germanium (7), and boron (82).

Analogous reactions of silver thiocyanates have been used to prepare alkyl silicon isothiocyanates (6,7).

Trimethylsilicon isocyanate has also been prepared by heating trimethyl chlorosilane and urea (81).

D. PREPARATION FROM ISOCYANATE DERIVATIVES

The addition of many active hydrogen compounds to isocyanates can be reversed under sufficiently vigorous conditions. Thus it is not surprising that isocyanates can be prepared from derivatives such as certain urethanes and ureas. In some special cases these preparations are useful.

Certain *N*-substituted carbamates may be decomposed to give the isocyanate from which the carbamate was derived. This is usually done by heating the carbamate at temperatures ranging from 135 to 500°C. (169), or by distilling the carbamate from phosphorus pentoxide (94,202):

$$RNH\overset{\overset{\displaystyle O}{\|}}{C}OR' \xrightarrow{P_2O_5} RNCO$$

Treatment of carbamates with phosgene at 200°C. has also been described (153), but in the aromatic series this method seems to be specific for *N*-phenylcarbamates (40):

$$C_6H_5NHCOOR \xrightarrow{COCl_2} C_6H_5NCO$$

Secondary and tertiary alkyl isocyanates have been obtained in 50–80% yields from the base-catalyzed dissociation of *N*-alkyl carbamates (28).

The decomposition of the urethane proceeds much more easily if the urethane is derived from a phenol rather than from an alcohol. The regeneration of isocyanates from *O*-phenylurethanes is discussed more fully in Chapter III. This difference in the ease of decomposition is illustrated by the following example (31):

$$Ar(NCO)_2 + 2HOCH_2CH_2NHCOOAr' \rightarrow Ar(NHCOOCH_2CH_2NHCOOAr')_2 \xrightarrow{\Delta} Ar(NHCOOCH_2CH_2NCO)_2 + Ar'OH$$

The reaction also may serve as a useful route to low boiling isocyanates, as in the case of the ethylurethane of pyrocatechol. Heating slowly to 250°C. while distilling out ethyl isocyanate (eq. 1) gives a good yield (173).

$$C_6H_4O_2CO + C_2H_5NH_2 \longrightarrow o\text{-}HOC_6H_4OC(=O)NHC_2H_5 \xrightarrow{\Delta} C_2H_5NCO + C_6H_4(OH)_2 \quad (1)$$

Thiourethanes dissociate similarly, e.g., as in the preparation of *p*-tolyl isocyanate by heating the thiourethane from that isocyanate and ethyl mercaptan (204).

The dissociation of substituted ureas may also be used as a source of isocyanates. This reaction provides a relatively simple laboratory preparation of low boiling alkyl isocyanates when *N*-alkyl-*N'*,*N'*-diarylurea is used. It was reported that methyl isocyanate was obtained in nearly quantitative yield by heating the *N*-diphenyl-*N'*-methylurea to 240–290° and distilling out the methyl isocyanate (173):

$$Ar_2NCOCl + CH_3NH_2 \rightarrow CH_3NHCONAr_2 \xrightarrow{\Delta} CH_3NCO + Ar_2NH$$

In most other cases special precautions are used to prevent recombination of the amine and isocyanate, such as treatment with phosgene or hydrogen chloride. A process used in Germany for the preparation of phenyl isocyanate consisted in the treatment of *sym*-diphenylurea with phosgene at 150°C., in a high boiling solvent such as chlorinated naphthalene. Yields of 70–80% were reported (173).

$$C_6H_5NHCONHC_6H_5 + COCl_2 \rightarrow 2C_6H_5NCO + 2HCl$$

Heating disubstituted ureas with hydrogen chloride at 350–370° has given 51–70% yields of the corresponding isocyanate and high yields of the amine hydrochloride (18,100). Monosubstituted ureas and HCl were also used to give low yields of isocyanates (18,178). It was further found that primary amines and cyanic acid or its precursors could be heated with HCl (18,159), and tertiary alkylamines with urea (27) to give isocyanates. All of these preparations apparently involve the dissociation of a substituted urea, with the acid serving to prevent recombination, for example:

$$RNH_2 + HNCO \rightleftharpoons RNHCONH_2$$

$$RNHCONH_2 + HCl \rightleftharpoons RNCO + NH_4Cl$$

Similarly, heating diphenylbiuret with HCl gave phenyl isocyanate (95).

A relatively high boiling isocyanate may be used instead of an acid to prevent recombination of amine and isocyanate, as in the following example (35):

$$(CH_3)_2NCONHCH_2CH_2CH_2OCH_3 + TDI \xrightarrow[20\text{ mm.}]{140°} CH_3OCH_2CH_2CH_2NCO$$

This type of reaction may be a good laboratory source of aliphatic isocyanates containing other groups that would also react with phosgene, even though yields may be low. The methoxyalkyl isocyanates, for example, are very difficult to obtain by phosgenation procedures because the alkyl ether group is replaced by chlorine during the phosgenation (173).

E. MISCELLANEOUS PREPARATIONS

A variety of other methods has been used for the synthesis of isocyanates, but these procedures are usually less practical than those described above. Some of the more interesting of these miscellaneous methods are indicated briefly.

Diazonium chlorides, when treated with potassium cyanate in the presence of copper, are converted to isocyanates (75,76):

$$ArN_2Cl + KNCO \xrightarrow{Cu} ArNCO + N_2 + KCl$$

Either isocyanides (78) or isothiocyanates (115) may be oxidized with mercuric oxide to give the isocyanate:

$$RNC + HgO \rightarrow RNCO$$

$$RNCS + HgO \rightarrow RNCO$$

Olefins will add iodoisocyanate almost quantitatively at —80°C. to give isocyanates (22). The reaction (eq. 2) may be used to characterize olefins, since crystalline ureas may easily be prepared.

$$\text{cyclohexene} + \text{INCO} \longrightarrow \text{2-iodocyclohexyl isocyanate (NCO, I)} \quad (2)$$

Formamides have been dehydrogenated by a sequence of halogenation and dehydrohalogenation (98):

$$\text{RNHCHO} + \text{BuOCl} \rightarrow \underset{\displaystyle\text{Cl}}{\text{RNCHO}} \xrightarrow{-\text{HCl}} \text{RNCO}$$

A number of other miscellaneous methods of limited value have reviewed previously (160).

2. *Molecular Structure and Spectra*

The structure of the isocyanate group in methyl isocyanate has been studied by electron diffraction methods by Eyster and co-workers (69). With the assumption of a linear N=C=O group, the bond angle between the C—N bond and the NCO group was calculated to be 125 ± 5°; the C—N bond length was 1.47 A., the C=N bond 1.19 A., and the C=O bond 1.18 A.

Dipole moments have been reported for several isocyanates, as indicated in Table II. These dipole moments and the Raman spectra support the assumption of a linear structure for the NCO group (44).

TABLE II
Dipole Moments of Isocyanates

Isocyanate	Ref.	Dipole moment, D
Ethyl	(44)	2.81
p-Tolyl	(102)	2.68
Phenyl	(44)	2.28
1-Naphthyl	(44)	2.30
2-Naphthyl	(44)	2.34
p-Chlorophenyl	(172)	0.84
2-Biphenylene	(102)	2.19
2,4-Tolylene diisocyanate	(102)	2.52

Ultraviolet absorption spectra (104,199,207), infrared (120), Raman spectra (49,109) and vibration spectrum in the 2–20 micron range (68) have been reported for a variety of isocyanates.

The electronegativity of the NCO group was found to be 3.52, compared to values of 3.72 for —OH, 3.58 for HCOO—, and 3.36 for the —NH_2 group (206).

3. *Analytical Methods for Isocyanates and Urethanes*

The most widely used analytical method for the —NCO group itself is the "amine equivalent" method, which depends upon reaction of the isocyanate with an amine. The isocyanate, or polymer containing isocyanate groups, is dissolved in a suitable solvent and permitted to react with an excess of a standard amine solution, such as 1*N* dibutylamine solution. The unreacted amine is then titrated with standard acid. The amine consumed by isocyanate can be readily calculated, hence the per cent NCO and the equivalent weight (174,188). This method is now a standard ASTM procedure (4).

Modifications of the amine equivalent method have been used for determination of NCO in rubber adhesives (205) and in polymers. Kubitz (114) found that traces of isocyanates in certain polyurethanes can be determined quantitatively by allowing the residual isocyanate to react with an excess of a solution of *n*-butylamine in tetrahydrofuran and determining the unreacted butylamine colorimetrically with malachite green. In a similar rapid qualitative test, a colored product is formed by treating a colorless amine derived from malachite green with isocyanate. The method will detect less than 0.5% of isocyanate.

Tolylene diisocyanate gives a characteristic color when treated with nitrite ion in an alcoholic solution in the presence of acetone (13). Hydroxamic acid may also be used for the detection of isocyanates (34).

An analytical method for tolylene diisocyanate vapor in air was reported by Zapp (211). Similar to the procedure of Bank (13), this method depends upon a quantitative development of a yellow-orange color when the isocyanate vapor is bubbled through a sodium nitrite solution in ethylene glycol monoethyl ether. A similar procedure was given by Pflueger (150).

An alternate air analysis method based on the hydrolysis of the diisocyanate to the diamine, followed by diazotization and coupling with

N-1-naphthylethylenediamine was described by Marcali (129). A photochemical method has also been used for the determination of hexamethylene diisocyanate in air (67).

The ratio of 2,4- and 2,6-isomers in tolylene diisocyanate has been determined by an infrared method (4,120), and, more simply, by dielectric constant measurements (189).

Resins containing isocyanate, urea, and urethane groups can be identified colorimetrically, using glacial acetic acid and *p*-dimethylaminobenzaldehyde (190). In addition, polyester-based urethanes can be distinguished from polyether-urethanes by treatment with hydroxylamine, potassium hydroxide, phenolphthalein, and ferric chloride. A violet color is obtained from polyester-urethanes, not from polyether-urethanes (16).

4. Handling Precautions

Isocyanates, like other chemicals, can be safely handled, stored, and used if their properties are fully understood and the necessary precautions are observed. From the viewpoint of safety for personnel, the most noteworthy feature of the isocyanates is the irritating character of their vapors. They are respiratory irritants and also irritate the eyes and skin if the contact is sufficient. Their oral toxicity, based on animal feeding experiments, is relatively mild.

The low molecular weight isocyanates, with their correspondingly high vapor pressure, are extreme lachrymators. Such compounds as methyl isocyanate and ethyl isocyanate are such powerful lachrymators that it is extremely unlikely that anyone could willingly tolerate a concentration of these compounds for a long enough time to suffer any lasting effects. As the molecular weight of the isocyanate is raised, however, the lachrymatory effects are reduced. Thus, phenyl isocyanate is a fairly strong lachrymator, tolylene diisocyanate is a mild lachrymator, and little, if any, effect on the eyes would normally be noted from diphenylmethane diisocyanate or octadecyl isocyanate.

Because of its commercial significance, tolylene diisocyanate has been studied most extensively regarding the necessity for safe handling. An excellent chemical safety data sheet on this compound has been published by the Manufacturing Chemists' Association (41). As recommended by Zapp (211), based on animal experiments, the safety data sheet recommends a maximum allowable concentration of 0.1

p.p.m. TDI vapor in air for extended exposure. A concentration which can be smelled may be in the range of 0.1 to 1.0 p.p.m., depending on individual sensitivity. Consequently, any concentration that can be smelled is too high for continuous exposure.

The safety data sheet describes tolylene diisocyanate as an irritating substance in either its liquid or its vapor form. On contact with the skin or eyes, it produces irritation and if not removed immediately may cause burns. Inhalation of the vapor may be injurious to the lungs. The vapor is capable of producing difficult and labored breathing in some individuals.

Sufficient ventilation is recommended to insure a concentration below 0.1 p.p.m. The ventilating system may often be designed to give excellent ventilation at any specific points at which the isocyanate is exposed to air, for example, at the mixhead of a foam machine. If the ventilation does not reduce the isocyanate concentration below the level at which it can be smelled, the personnel should use a respirator or a gas mask. An industrial canister type of gas mask approved by the U. S. Bureau of Mines and fitted with the proper canister for organic vapor will give protection against concentrations not exceeding 2% by volume when used in accordance with the manufacturer's instructions. For higher concentrations, air- or oxygen-supplied masks equipped with full face pieces should be used (41).

A powder has been developed that is convenient to use and effective in neutralizing isocyanate spillage (41). It is recommended that spills be covered with a thin layer of this powder, which will absorb and destroy the isocyanate within a few minutes. The product can then be swept away. The powder is made up as follows:

Sawdust	23.0 lb.	
Fuller's earth	38.5 lb.	
	61.5 lb.	carrier solids
Ethanol	19.2 lb.	
Triethanolamine	3.8 lb.	
Concentrated ammonia solution	3.8 lb.	
Water	11.5 lb.	
Dye (water solvent type)	0.2 lb.	
	38.5 lb.	active solution
Total	100.0 lb.	powder

Details of preparing this powder and additional information concerning the safe handling of isocyanates are given in the chemical safety data sheet (41).

Adequate care should be used in handling all isocyanates and isocyanate derivatives. The safety precautions necessary for tolylene diisocyanate may also be necessary with prepolymers prepared from tolylene diisocyanate if they contain several per cent or more of free, uncombined tolylene diisocyanate.

III. Polyethers

1. General

The commercial use of polyether polyols in the urethane field is a relatively recent development. The first report of experiments with polyethers as intermediates for polyurethanes utilized polyethers derived from ethylene oxide or propylene oxide (88). Though several of these were commercial materials, they were not designed for use as polymer intermediates and were not of the purity that was later established as standard "urethane grade." The first polyether designed specifically for use in preparing polyurethanes was a poly(oxytetramethylene) glycol derived from tetrahydrofuran (14). Today, most of the polyethers used for the manufacture of urethane foam products are derivatives of propylene oxide.

In the early stages of the commercial development of urethane products, particularly when flexible foams were made by prepolymer techniques, diols such as poly(oxypropylene) glycol and block copolymers of propylene oxide and ethylene oxide were the polyethers of major interest. These products, because of their use in elastomers and propellant applications, still represent an important segment of polyether sales. However, with the development of the "one-shot" technique for the manufacture of flexible foams, and with the growth of the rigid foam and the coatings applications, poly(oxyalkylene) derivatives of polyhydric alcohols have taken over the major portion of the polyether market. Poly(oxypropylene) ethers of glycerol, trimethylolpropane, 1,2,6-hexanetriol, and sorbitol are commercially available, as are the poly(oxypropylene)-poly(oxyethylene) block copolymers derived from some of these polyhydric initiators. Other poly(oxypropylene) polyethers are offered as commercial products but as yet the initiators have not been identified publicly by the manufacturers. Tetrahydrofuran-derived polyethers are used in significant quantities for elastomers.

In addition to the above neutral polyols, nitrogen-containing polyols such as the poly(oxyethylene)-poly(oxypropylene) block copolymers with ethylenediamine are used commercially. Generally the tertiary nitrogen present in these polyethers causes them to be more reactive in urethane systems than the neutral polyols.

2. *Preparation*

Poly(oxyalkylene) ethers are prepared by the polymerization of alkylene oxides with suitable initiators. The literature on the polymerization of these oxides is extensive. However, the only method of commercial significance for the manufacture of polyethers for use as polyurethane intermediates is the reaction of alkylene oxides with an initiator having active hydrogens in its structure. These reactions are carried out in the presence of either an acidic or basic catalyst.

A. POLY(OXYETHYLENE) GLYCOLS

Because of their hydrophilic character, poly(oxyethylene) glycols are rarely used for urethane applications. The physical form of these polyethers ranges from colorless liquids to wax-like solids. Poly(oxyethylene) glycols are water soluble and nonvolatile polyether diols containing terminal primary hydroxyl groups.

Commercially the poly(oxyethylene) glycols are produced by the reaction of ethylene oxide with water, ethylene glycol, or diethylene glycol in the presence of sodium hydroxide as a catalyst. A fuller discussion of poly(oxyethylene) glycols, their preparation, and their properties is given by Curme and Johnson (46).

B. POLY(OXYPROPYLENE) GLYCOLS

Propylene oxide was first prepared in 1861 by Oser (143) by the dehydrohalogenation of 1-chloro-2-propanol with potassium hydroxide. The polymerization of propylene oxide, however, was not reported until 1927, when Levene and Walti (117) reacted propylene oxide with propylene glycol to give dipropylene glycol and tripropylene glycol. These investigators also obtained dimethyldioxane and a mixture of various ethers when they heated propylene oxide in a sealed tube.

In 1944, Schlosser and Gray (164) reported the preparation of poly (oxypropylene) glycol by the polymerization of propylene oxide in the presence of water, with sodium hydroxide as the catalyst. The polymerization was carried out by heating the monomer in a closed system at about 100°C. until the pressure dropped to atmospheric.

The preparation of poly(oxypropylene) glycol by the reaction of propylene oxide with propylene glycol was described by Lundsted (124) in 1954. For example, 7.5 g. of anhydrous sodium hydroxide was dissolved in 57 g. of propylene glycol, under nitrogen, at 120°C. Sufficient propylene oxide was added to give a product having a molecular weight of 2380. The mixture was cooled under nitrogen, the catalyst was neutralized with sulfuric acid, and the product was filtered.

Dege, Harris, and MacKenzie (53) reported the synthesis of poly (oxypropylene) glycol of molecular weight 2000 by the base-catalyzed addition of propylene oxide to propylene glycol in batch and continuous reactors. In most preparations the catalyst was 0.1–0.5% potassium hydroxide. Reaction temperatures varied from 120 to 160°C. The use of dipropylene glycol as the initiator has also been described (116).

Besides reacting with an initiator to give poly(oxypropylene) glycols, propylene oxide polymerizes to give cyclic ethers (46) and linear polyethers or poly(oxypropylene) oxides. The latter are for the most part monofunctional by virtue of their high terminal unsaturation content and, therefore, are of little significance in polyurethane chemistry. Sokata and co-workers (181) and Ebert (66) summarized the literature concerning this type of propylene oxide polymerization.

Commercially, poly(oxypropylene) glycols are prepared by the base-catalyzed addition of propylene oxide to propylene glycol or dipropylene glycol as the initiator. The mechanism of the polymerization may be represented by equations (3) to (6). The polymerization

$$\mathrm{HO\overset{\overset{\large CH_3}{|}}{C}HCH_2OH} + \mathrm{B}^{\ominus} \rightleftharpoons \mathrm{HO\overset{\overset{\large CH_3}{|}}{C}HCH_2O}^{\ominus} + \mathrm{BH} \tag{3}$$

$$\mathrm{HO\overset{\overset{\large CH_3}{|}}{C}HCH_2O}^{\ominus} + \mathrm{CH_2\!\!-\!\!\overset{\overset{\large CH_3}{|}}{C}H}\ (\text{epoxide, bridged by O}) \rightarrow \mathrm{HO\overset{\overset{\large CH_3}{|}}{C}HCH_2OCH_2\overset{\overset{\large CH_3}{|}}{C}HO}^{\ominus} \tag{4}$$

$$\mathrm{HO\overset{\displaystyle CH_3}{\overset{|}{C}}HCH_2OCH_2\overset{\displaystyle CH_3}{\overset{|}{C}}HO^{\ominus} + xCH_2\!-\!\overset{\displaystyle CH_3}{\overset{|}{C}}H\ (\text{epoxide, O bridging}) \rightarrow HO\overset{\displaystyle CH_3}{\overset{|}{C}}HCH_2O(CH_2\overset{\displaystyle CH_3}{\overset{|}{C}}HO)_xCH_2\overset{\displaystyle CH_3}{\overset{|}{C}}HO^{\ominus}} \quad (5)$$

$$\mathrm{HO\overset{\displaystyle CH_3}{\overset{|}{C}}HCH_2O(CH_2\overset{\displaystyle CH_3}{\overset{|}{C}}HO)_xCH_2\overset{\displaystyle CH_3}{\overset{|}{C}}HO^{\ominus} + BH \rightarrow HO\overset{\displaystyle CH_3}{\overset{|}{C}}HCH_2O(CH_2\overset{\displaystyle CH_3}{\overset{|}{C}}HO)_xCH_2\overset{\displaystyle CH_3}{\overset{|}{C}}HOH + B^-} \quad (6)$$

proceeds by the attack of the anion, formed by action of the basic catalyst on the initiator, upon monomeric propylene oxide. The chain propagates by successive attacks on monomer by anions resulting from the oxirane ring opening. Chain termination results from the deactivation of the polymer anion by a proton.

While this mechanism shows the formation of only secondary hydroxyl groups, the propylene oxide ring can open to form derivatives containing either primary or secondary hydroxyl groups. However, the observation that the base-catalyzed opening of the propylene oxide ring yields predominantly secondary hydroxyl groups is well documented (15,42,79,85,105,149,156,170). Havlik and Hildebrandt (87) found that nuclear magnetic resonance measurements indicate a higher primary hydroxyl content in poly(oxypropylene) glycol than was previously reported.

The base-catalyzed polymerization of propylene oxide is accompanied by a competing reaction which gives rise to monohydroxy polyethers. Poly(oxypropylene) polyols prepared by this method contain both allyl and propenyl ethers of poly(oxypropylene) glycols (53,175,185).

Simons and Verbanc (175) demonstrated that the formation of these unsaturated ethers is dependent upon the presence of propylene oxide and is a consequence of the rearrangement of propylene oxide to allyl alcohol. The allyl alcohol subsequently reacts with propylene oxide to form the allyl ethers of poly(oxypropylene) glycol. These same workers also demonstrated that the propenyl ethers present in poly(oxypropylene) polyols result from rearrangement of the allyl ethers in the presence of the basic polymerization catalyst. The latter is an equilibrium reaction in which the propenyl ether is the favored species. Treatment of the polyol with aqueous acid hydrolyzes the propenyl ethers, converting the propenyl group to propionaldehyde and generating a terminal hydroxyl on the polymer moiety.

The amount of double bond formed during the base-catalyzed polymerization of propylene oxide is very dependent on temperature, increasing rapidly as the temperature increases. In addition, at constant polymerization temperature, the concentration of double bond increases with the molecular weight of the polyglycol produced. The rapid increase in the concentration of double bond as the molecular weight of the glycol increases suggests that the rate of polymerization is decreased relative to the rate of unsaturation formation (175).

Further indication that the rate of polymerization of propylene oxide decreases with increased molecular weight is found in the work of Morris and Persinger (136). These workers fractionated a poly(oxypropylene) glycol of number-average molecular weight 2000 by a liquid chromatographic technique and found a more narrow range of molecular species then predicted by calculations based on Flory's assumptions (71). This narrow distribution apparently is a consequence of the differences in the reaction rates between the low and high molecular weight homologs. The activity of the terminal hydroxyl group decreases as the molecular weight of the product increases, causing propylene oxide to add preferentially to the more reactive lower molecular weight species. Because of this difference in reactivity the formation of very high molecular weight species is suppressed, the low molecular weight species are depleted by reaction, and the resulting poly(oxypropylene) glycol has a much narrower molecular weight range than theoretically predicted.

Okawara (142) observed that the molecular weight of the polyglycol formed was also temperature dependent. In studying the base-catalyzed preparation of poly(oxypropylene) glycol he found that high molecular weight polyethers were obtained at lower reaction temperatures.

C. POLY(OXYPROPYLENE)-POLY(OXYETHYLENE) COPOLYMERS

Among the first polyethers offered for use in the manufacture of polyurethanes were block copolymers of ethylene oxide and propylene oxide (51,74,187). The preparation of this type of polyol was described by Lundsted (124) and Vaughn and Jackson (198). These block copolymers can be represented by the general formula:

$$HO(CH_2CH_2O)_a(CH_2\underset{\displaystyle |}{\overset{CH_3}{C}}HO)_b(CH_2CH_2O)_cH$$

In their preparation, propylene oxide is reacted with propylene glycol or water in the presence of a basic catalyst to form a poly(oxypropylene) homopolymer. This polymer is then reacted with ethylene oxide to form the block copolymer. The resulting polyether has a higher incidence of primary hydroxyl groups than does a poly(oxypropylene) ether of comparable molecular weight.

Similar compounds in which trimethylolpropane (124), glycerol (124,154), pentaerythritol (124), sorbitol (83), and sucrose (124) are used as the initiating compounds have been described. Polyethers of this type derived from trimethylolpropane, glycerol and other polyhydric alcohols are commercially available.

Random copolymers of ethylene oxide and propylene oxide have been prepared by Toussaint and Fife (196). These workers reacted mixtures of ethylene oxide and propylene oxide with aliphatic diols such as propylene glycol to give high molecular weight poly(oxyalkylene) diols. The preparation of these diols was carried out using sodium hydroxide or potassium hydroxide as the catalyst. After the polymerization was complete the catalyst was neutralized with sulfuric acid or carbon dioxide and the resultant salts were removed by filtration or by extraction with water. Horsley and Britton (96) described the preparation of trihydroxy poly(oxyalkylene) ethers by the reaction of mixtures of ethylene oxide and propylene oxide with glycerol.

Random copolymers of ethylene oxide and propylene oxide derived from polyglycerol, pentaerythritol, sorbitol, and mannitol have been disclosed by Todd and Fuchs (194). Block copolymers derived from mixtures of ethylene oxide and propylene oxide have been reported by Lundsted (122) and Patton (146).

D. POLY(OXYTETRAMETHYLENE) GLYCOLS

Poly(oxytetramethylene) glycols are prepared by the polymerization of tetrahydrofuran. In general the polymerization of this monomer is brought about by the use of Lewis acid catalysts such as BF_3, $SnCl_4$, $SbCl_5$, $SbCl_3$, PF_5, and SO_2Cl_2. Trialkyl oxonium salts such as

$(C_2H_5)_2O \cdot BF_3$ have also been used as catalysts for this polymerization (131). The polymerization has been pictured as proceeding as the consequence of the formation of an oxonium ion followed by rupture of the tetrahydrofuran ring to generate a carbonium ion. This ion reacts with a second tetrahydrofuran ring, which in turn is opened, and thus the polymerization is propagated. The chain reaction is terminated when reaction with an anion occurs. For use in polyurethane synthesis it is necessary that the polyether have terminal hydroxyl groups. The presence of these groups can be assured by carrying out the polymerization in the presence of regulators such as water or a diol, or by the use of catalysts which terminate the polymer with a hydroxyl or with an end group such as the chloro, acetoxy, or sulfate groups, which upon hydrolysis will be replaced by a hydroxyl group (eq. 7).

$$R^+ + \underset{O}{\square} \longrightarrow \left[\underset{\underset{R}{O}}{\square}\right]^+ \xrightarrow{n\,\underset{O}{\square}} R\left[O(CH_2)_4\right]_n \overset{+}{O}\square$$

$$\xrightarrow{HCl} R\left[O(CH_2)_4\right]_{n+1} Cl \xrightarrow{H_2O} H\left[O(CH_2)_4\right]_{n+1} OH \qquad (7)$$

Tetrahydrofuran has been copolymerized with alkylene oxides and with oxetanes to form polyethers. Meerwein and co-workers (131) investigated the polymerization of tetrahydrofuran with ethylene oxide, propylene oxide, butylene oxide and oxetane with catalysts such as metal halides, hetero poly acids, and boron trifluoride.

Similar preparations in the presence of acidic clays are disclosed in a patent issued to Bayer (33). Prior to 1945, I. G. Farbenindustrie manufactured polyethers by the copolymerization of tetrahydrofuran and ethylene oxide using thionyl chloride and ferric chloride as cocatalysts (29). More recently the boron trifluoride catalyzed copolymerization of tetrahydrofuran and ethylene oxide has been described (139). The copolymerization of tetrahydrofuran and alkylene oxides or oxetanes to give high molecular weight polymers is also the subject of a patent issued to Du Pont (32).

E. POLY(OXYBUTYLENE) GLYCOLS

Poly(oxybutylene) glycols are prepared by the base-catalyzed reaction of either 1,2- or 2,3-butylene oxide or mixtures of the isomeric oxides with an initiator molecule. Lundsted (121) described the sodium hydroxide catalyzed reaction of butylene oxides with propylene glycol and other initiators to give poly(oxybutylene) polyols. Spriggs (184) reacted butylene oxides with butylene glycol to form poly(oxybutylene) glycols. Both Lundsted and Spriggs prepared block copolymers of butylene oxide and ethylene oxide (121,184).

DeGroote and Pettingill (62) reported the preparation of copolymers of butylene oxide and ethylene oxide, and of butylene oxide, ethylene oxide, and propylene oxide in which mono-, di-, and tri-pentaerythritol and tetramethylolcyclohexane were used as initiators.

F. BASIC POLYETHERS

In addition to the neutral polyethers, certain nitrogen-containing polyethers are used in the manufacture of polyurethanes. Foremost among these are the tetrafunctional ethylene oxide-propylene oxide block copolymers initiated with ethylenediamine. The preparation of these polyethers is described by Lundsted *et al.* (124–127). In the manufacture of these polyethers aqueous ethylenediamine is reacted with propylene oxide to give the totally hydroxypropylated ethylenediamine (127). This compound is subsequently reacted with propylene oxide and then with ethylene oxide, using potassium hydroxide or sodium hydroxide as the catalyst.

Other nitrogen-containing polyethers derived from propylene oxide, from ethylene oxide and butylene oxide, and from ethylene oxide, propylene oxide, and butylene oxide have been described. Typical of the initiators used in preparing these polyethers are benzenesulfonamide (56,123), 2-aminoethylethanolamine (56), *N*-methyldiethanolamine (56), diethylenetriamine (56), and tris(hydroxymethyl)aminomethane (63).

G. POLY(OXYPROPYLENE) TRIOLS

Poly(oxypropylene) triols are currently the most important class of polyethers used in the manufacture of polyurethanes. These products are made by the base-catalyzed reaction of propylene oxide with low molecular weight triols such as trimethylolpropane, glycerol (124,154), and 1,2,6-hexanetriol (59).

A patent issued to Union Carbide Corp. (17) discloses the preparation of polyether triols from propylene oxide and hydroxyphenylalkanes such as 1,1,3-tris(4-hydroxyphenyl)propane by the reaction of the oxide with the triphenol compound in the presence of an alkaline catalyst and in an inert solvent. These products are described as being particularly useful in the preparation of cellular structures by reaction with diisocyanates.

In general, the preparation of polyether triols is quite similar to that of poly(oxypropylene) glycol with the same basic problems of propylene oxide polymerization being encountered in each case.

H. POLYETHERS OF HIGHER FUNCTIONALITY

Polyethers having four or more hydroxyl groups in their structure have found use in urethane applications, particularly in rigid foams. The oxyalkylation of sorbitol, mannitol, and dulcitol has been described by Griffin (83) and others (54). Pentaerythritol and polypentaerythritol have also been used as initiators for the preparation of polyethers (55,151), but reaction with these polyols proceeds with difficulty because of their high melting points. Water is not a suitable solvent for this reaction because alkylene oxides react with water to form polyglycols. Price described a process in which liquid propylene oxide appears to be the reaction medium (151). Sokol (182) carried out the oxyalkylation in a medium such as xylene, which is a solvent for the alkylene oxide and the resultant polyether but a nonsolvent for the pentaerythritol.

A two-step process for the preparation of poly(oxyalkylene) derivatives of pentaerythritol has been reported. This process involves the heating of the polyol with an alkylene carbonate to form liquid derivatives containing a few oxyalkylene groups and subsequently treating the intermediates with an alkylene oxide (133).

The preparation of poly(oxyalkylene) derivatives of many other polyols has been reported. Such derivatives have been made from sucrose (54,124), 2,2,6,6-tetrakis(hydroxymethyl) cyclohexanol (60, 61), glucose (158), sorbitan (54), mannitan (54), degraded starches and cellulose (54), diglycerol (54), monoglycerol and monohydroxyethyl ethers of sorbitan, mannitan, sorbitol, dulcitol, pentaerythritol, and the like (54).

In addition to polyether polyols, several low molecular weight hydroxyalkyl derivatives have been used as urethane intermediates. These include the totally hydroxypropylated ethylenediamines (127), diethylenetriamine (166), various primary aliphatic amines (25), sucrose, glycerol (5), and sorbitol, prepared by reacting the stoichiometric amount of propylene oxide with the active hydrogen compound. These polyols are primarily designed for use as chain extenders and cross-linking agents in rigid urethane foams.

I. MISCELLANEOUS POLYETHERS

Polyether polyols have been prepared from other than the C_2–C_4 epoxides. Homopolymers of styrene oxide and epichlorohydrin are available commercially. Copolymers of ethylene oxide or propylene oxide with styrene oxide have been reported by Britton and Petri (30). Benoit (19) prepared copolymers of propylene oxide and pentene oxides. Block copolymers of styrene oxide, cyclohexene oxide, or butadiene monoxide with ethylene oxide have also been described (121).

The preparation of polyethers by the polymerization of 1,4-epoxycyclohexane has been patented by Wilkins (203). Copolymers of 1,4-epoxycyclohexane with tetrahydrofuran, epichlorohydrin, or propylene oxide have also been prepared.

Methods other than the polymerization of alkylene oxides have been employed for the preparation of polyethers. These methods involve the catalytic dehydration of diols to give polyethers. Catalysts such as iodine, inorganic acids, and organic acids have been used for the dehydration of glycols such as hexamethylene glycol, decamethylene glycol, and mixtures of trimethylene and hexamethylene glycols (12).

Alkylene carbonates may also be used to bring about oxyalkylation, and are often more convenient to use in the laboratory than are alkylene oxides (39) because this reaction may be run in refluxing toluene without the extreme safety precautions required for handling ethylene oxide (eq. 8).

$$ROH + \underset{\underset{\underset{\displaystyle \overset{\|}{O}}{\displaystyle C}}{\displaystyle O\quad O}}{H_2C{-}CH_2} \xrightarrow{\text{base}} ROCH_2CH_2OH + CO_2 \qquad (8)$$

J. POLYTHIOETHERS

Polythioethers have been of limited interest as urethane intermediates. These products are usually prepared by the acid-catalyzed condensation of thiodiglycol with itself or with polyols at elevated temperatures (167). The reaction with a glycol provides a typical "polythioether."

$$R(OH)_2 + HOCH_2CH_2SCH_2CH_2OH \xrightarrow{\text{Acid}} H[OCH_2CH_2SCH_2CH_2OR]_nOH$$

Polythioether triols may be obtained by using a triol as an initiator and a glycol as a comonomer.

The polythioether glycols have not reached a stage of commercial interest in this country, largely because of the success of the polypropylene glycols and triols. The very great difficulty of eliminating all odor of sulfur-containing by-products is also a handicap.

3. *Reactions of Polyether Polyols*

Polyether polyols undergo the characteristic reactions of hydroxyl-containing compounds. The terminal hydroxyl groups can be esterified with organic acids (57,70). With dibasic acids polyesters are formed. Inorganic esters of poly(oxyalkylene) polyols such as the sulfates have been reported as being useful as surfactants (107).

The reaction of the hydroxyl groups of polyether polyols with polyisocyanates is a typical example of polyurethane formation.

The incorporation of the ether oxygen in the backbone of the aliphatic polymer chain lowers its oxidative and thermal stability. The oxidation of the polyethers proceeds through a hydroperoxide intermediate, as indicated by a study of diethylene glycol (119). The peroxide decomposes to form aldehydes, organic acids, and esters. Polyethers may be protected against oxidative degradation by stabilization with alkylated phenols (116), phenothiazine (145), or aromatic amines (193).

The thermal degradation of propylene oxide polymers has been investigated by St. Pierre and Price (185) and by Madorsky and Straus (128). The decomposition products identified in these studies were low molecular weight hydrocarbons, ketones, aldehydes, and ethers.

One of the early difficulties with the use of polyethers for polyurethane production was associated with the presence of residual alkaline catalyst in the polyether (89). Alkaline catalysts, such as potassium hydroxide, are strong catalysts for such isocyanate reactions as trimerization and allophanate and biuret formation. Even basic salts such as disodium phosphate may catalyze these reactions (89). One of the significant improvements in "urethane grade" polyethers is the removal of all but traces of alkaline catalyst, and neutralization of the remainder to provide a very slightly acidic polyether. Such an acidic impurity, in the concentration normally present, has essentially no effect on isocyanate reactions.

An additional improvement in commercial polyethers is the reduction in unsaturation. The significance of unsaturation can readily be appreciated if it is realized that a typical maximum level of 0.04 milliequivalent of unsaturation per gram of a 2000 molecular weight polyether glycol corresponds to a glycol composition of approximately 92% difunctional and 8% monofunctional components. This calculation is based on the assumption that all unsaturation is terminal. Since, as pointed out earlier, the per cent unsaturation increases as the polyether molecular weight increases, the problem of monofunctional content is relatively small at lower polyether molecular weights, but becomes more significant at glycol molecular weights above 2000 and triol molecular weights above about 4000.

4. Properties

The polyethers used in polyurethane applications are nonvolatile, viscous liquids. They range from water-white to brown in color. Solubility of the polyethers in water decreases as the molecular weight increases, with lower molecular weight polyethers being water soluble. The presence of oxyethylene structures in the polyethers tends to increase the water solubility of the polyethers.

Most of the polyethers are soluble in the common organic solvents such as alcohols, ketones, esters, hydrocarbons, and halogenated solvents.

The use of polyether glycols as chemical intermediates has shifted emphasis from the above purely physical properties to the chemical properties of the polyethers. Of importance are properties such as hydroxyl content, unsaturation, water content, acidity, carbonyl content, and molecular weight.

The physical properties of typical commercial polyether glycols are listed in Table III; those of typical triols (based on trimethylolpropane) in Table IV. Commercial polyether glycols and triols, and specifications recognized by the Society of Plastics Industry and

American Society for Testing Materials, are given in Appendix B at the end of the book. Analytical methods are also indicated.

TABLE III

Typical Physical Properties of Commercially Available Poly(oxypropylene) Glycols

Av. mol. wt.	Hydroxyl no.	Sp. gr. (20°/20°)	Total unsatn., meq./g.	Viscosity, cps., 100°C.	Flash pt.,[a] °C.
150	750	1.025	—	3	121
250	450	1.011	—	3.4	168
400	280	1.008	—	5	199
750	150	1.006	0.01	7.6	215
1000	112	1.005	0.01	11.5	227
1200	93	1.004	0.015	13.7	232
1850	61	1.003	0.03	—	232
2000	56	1.003	0.04	23.0	232
3000	37	1.002	0.09	48.0	232
4000	28	1.002	0.11	74.0	232
2000[b]	56	1.014	0.03	31.1	232

[a] Cleveland open cup method.
[b] Modified with ethylene oxide.

TABLE IV

Typical Physical Properties of Trimethylolpropane-Based Polyether Triols

Av. mol. wt.	Hydroxyl no.	Sp. gr., (25°/25°)	Total unsatn., meq./g.	Viscosity, cps., 25°C.
300	561	—	0.005	—
400	422	—	0.005	625
700	240	1.027	0.005	325
1500	112	—	0.02	290
2500	67	1.005	0.04	440
4000	42	1.004	0.07	670
4500[a]	37	—	0.08	500

[a] Modified with ethylene oxide.

IV. POLYESTERS

1. General

Until the advent of urethane foams, elastomers, and coatings the familiar polyesters for plastics raw materials were usually unsaturated, designed to cure by a free radical mechanism, and were often copolymerized with monomers such as styrene. The polyesters most suitable for reaction with isocyanates, however, are those containing hydroxyl groups, so that cure proceeds by way of urethane formation. Since radical reactions are unnecessary for this cure, the preferred polyesters for urethane applications are saturated, thus avoiding unnecessary complications. While the preparation of unsaturated polyesters has been reviewed many times (e.g., ref. 20), good descriptions of the saturated polyesters for urethane uses are much rarer. An excellent review with many examples of preparations is given by Müller (137).

2. *Preparation*

The most common ingredients of polyesters for urethane applications are adipic acid, phthalic anhydride, dimerized linoleic acid ("Dimer" acid), simple glycols, and triols. The glycols used generally include ethylene, propylene, 1,3-butylene, 1,4-butylene, and diethylene glycol. The triols are usually glycerin, 1,2,6-hexanetriol, trimethylolpropane, and trimethylolethane. Pentaerythritol may be used as a suitable source of cross linking in some cases. Lactones such as caprolactone have also been used to prepare polyesters for experimental preparation of polyurethanes (97,210).

The easiest control of urethane polymer formation is obtained when the polyester contains only hydroxyl groups as reactive sites. Hence the preferred polyesters have been those with very low acid numbers and very low water content (less than 0.1%). Linear polyesters having molecular weights close to 2000 have been preferred for elastomers, slightly branched ones of similar molecular weight for flexible foam and elastic coatings, and more highly branched ones for rigid foams and the most chemically resistant coatings.

The preparation of polyesters requires the removal of water to drive the reaction at a reasonable rate and to a sufficient molecular weight. This is generally achieved either through the use of a high temperature and vacuum or sweeping with an inert gas, or by azeotropic means.

One convenient preparation of polyesters involves reaction of the components without solvents. The glycol and triol, if desired, are added to the reactor and heated with stirring to 60–90°C. The acid component is added quickly and the mixture stirred and heated at such a rate that water distills out rapidly. The hydroxyl and acid components are used in such a ratio that nearly all acid groups react and the hydroxyl groups are in sufficient excess to control the molecular weight in the desired range:

$$(n + 1)R(OH)_2 + nR'(COOH)_2 \rightarrow HO\left[RO\overset{O}{\overset{\|}{C}}R'\overset{O}{\overset{\|}{C}}O\right]_nH$$

The reaction is usually forced to completion by heating to about 200°C. while continuously flushing the system with nitrogen or carbon dioxide, or while reducing the pressure to remove water. The reaction is stopped when the acid number has been reduced to about 1–4, the water content is below 0.1%, and the hydroxyl number is in the desired range.

Branched polyesters, such as those prepared from glycerin mixed with a glycol, are usually of lower molecular weight and higher hydroxyl number than are the linear polyesters. Hence the branched polyesters usually require a shorter reaction time, but more care must be used to prevent gelation.

Catalysts such as acids (e.g., *p*-toluenesulfonic acid) or metal oxides (e.g., lead oxide) may be used to shorten the esterification time. One must take into consideration the possible effect of residual catalyst on subsequent reaction with the isocyanate, and also on any possible degradation of the urethane polymer such as hydrolysis or oxidation. Although esterification times are longer without catalysts, there are certain obvious advantages to the subsequent use of the polyesters that are free from all catalysts.

Typical characteristics of polyesters suitable for a range of applications are indicated in Table V. (Actual analyses of a number of commercially available polyesters are given in Appendix C.)

Several factors relating to the proper choice of polyester reactants are listed in Chapter VI, "The Relationships between Polymer Structure and Properties in Urethanes." Generally speaking, cross linking (from the triol component) favors the formation of thermoset polymers having good chemical and temperature resistance, high hardness, and low elongation. The use of an aromatic component (e.g., phthalic anhydride or isophthalic acid) also promotes temperature resistance and rigidity. On the other hand, more linear polyesters favor high elongation, elasticity, softness, better low temperature flexibility, and lower chemical resistance.

TABLE V

Typical Characteristics of a Range of Polyesters

Components			Hydroxyl no.	Degree of branching	Use
Acid	Glycol	Triol			
1. Adipic	Ethylene, propylene or diethylene	None	50–60	None	Elastomers
2. Adipic or "Dimer" acid	Diethylene	Glycerin or others	50–65	Slight	Flexible foams and coatinge
3. Adipic plus phthalic	Ethylene or propylene	Glycerin or others	150–200	Moderate	Semiflexible foams and coatings
4. Adipic plus phthalic	Ethylene or propylene	Glycerin or others	250–300	High	Rigid foam, chemically resistant coatings
5. Adipic plus phthalic	Ethylene or propylene	Glycerin or others	400–450	Very high	Rigid foam, wire coatings

3. *Reactions*

Certain reactions of polyesters, in addition to that with the isocyanate, are of significance with regard to urethane polymer formation and stability. In the preparation of polyesters one must guard against decarboxylation, as this will lead to nonreactive end groups, especially to be avoided in linear polyesters:

$$\text{HO}-\left[\text{RO}\overset{\text{O}}{\overset{\|}{\text{C}}}\text{R}'\overset{\text{O}}{\overset{\|}{\text{C}}}\text{O}\right]_n\text{RO}\overset{\text{O}}{\overset{\|}{\text{C}}}\text{R}'\text{COOH} \rightarrow \text{HO}\left[\text{RO}\overset{\text{O}}{\overset{\|}{\text{C}}}\text{R}'\overset{\text{O}}{\overset{\|}{\text{C}}}\text{O}\right]_n\text{RO}\overset{\text{O}}{\overset{\|}{\text{C}}}\text{R}'\text{H} + \text{CO}_2$$

Such decarboxylations have been found to occur at temperatures above about 290°C. for a variety of acids (110). When using catalysts for esterification one must consider the possibility that the catalyst may promote decarboxylation at temperatures much lower than 290°.

The most important reaction of the polyester chain during the life of the urethane foam, elastomer, or coating is that of hydrolysis. Under accelerated conditions of high relative humidity and elevated temperature polyester-based urethane foams degrade faster than polyether-based foams (161), presumably due to hydrolysis of ester groups:

$$\sim O\overset{O}{\overset{\|}{C}}R'\overset{O}{\overset{\|}{C}}ORO\sim + H_2O \rightarrow \sim O\overset{O}{\overset{\|}{C}}R'COOH + HORO\sim$$

It is well known that many compounds in the usual classes of acid, base, and metal catalysts promote the hydrolysis of esters. Thus it is desirable to design the entire sequence of esterification and urethane formation reactions so that no catalyst remains in the polymer which will promote hydrolysis.

Oxidation of polyester chains is usually not significant. Under extreme conditions, however, oxidation could occur, particularly if unsaturation were present, as in "Dimer" acid, if ether groups were present, as in diethylene glycol, or if alkyl groups adjacent to aromatic rings were present, as in α,α'-dihydroxyxylene. Even better stability should be realized if antioxidants were added.

During service at very high temperatures (in excess of 300°C.) one might expect some cracking to unsaturated compounds to occur:

$$\sim O\overset{O}{\overset{\|}{C}}R'\overset{O}{\overset{\|}{C}}O(CH_2)_4O\sim \underset{\Delta}{\rightarrow} \sim O\overset{O}{\overset{\|}{C}}R'\overset{O}{\overset{\|}{C}}OH + CH_2{=}CH(CH_2)_2O\sim$$

Such reactions are well known in simple esters, and have been used as preparative methods, e.g., for substituted styrenes, where temperatures of 550–575°C. were used to obtain a rapid pyrolysis (130).

Heating certain polyesters at about 300°C. has also been shown to result in the formation of small amounts of low molecular weight cyclic esters, along with a variety of unidentified distillable products (92). It is not clear whether or not these products would be formed from polyester-urethanes, however, in which hydroxyl groups of the original polyester have been converted to urethane groups.

Thus it may be concluded that the polyester backbone is one having good thermal and oxidative stability, but subject to hydrolysis under moderately vigorous conditions.

V. CASTOR OIL AND DERIVATIVES

1. Origin and Manufacture

Castor oil is obtained from the seeds of the plant *Ricinus communis,* which can be found in many tropical or subtropical areas, either growing wild or cultivated. The plant grows anywhere from 6 to 35 feet high, and exhibits distinct variations in the seed, depending upon the species, climate, and soil. The average oil content of the seed ranges from 35 to 57% on an air-dry basis. The seeds, also known as "castor beans," and the oil are imported chiefly from India and Brazil, although the United States grows a considerable quantity, particularly in the southern states.

Castor oil, a viscous liquid with a characteristic unpleasant taste, can be made odorless and tasteless by neutralization and subsequent deodorization.

Castor oil is produced either by expression or by solvent extraction. In the United States it is customary to press the cleaned seed in hydraulic presses, yielding the highest quality oil, which is freed from moisture by heating under diminished pressure. For further refining, the warm oil is treated with fuller's earth along with activated carbon and filtered. For medicinal purposes, the oil is deodorized in a vacuum deodorizer using superheated steam.

The residual oil from the seed is obtained by grinding the press cake and extracting it with solvent, followed by removal of the solvent.

The grade of castor oil is determined by the color, clearness, and acidity. There are three principal industrial grades of refined castor oil available. Some of their properties are listed in Table VI. Since the moisture content and the acid value should be very low for urethane applications, the best grade of castor oil is often preferred. The cold-pressed oil (No. 1), also presently designated as C.P. castor oil, is low in acidity, clear, and nearly colorless, while the oil obtained from solvent extraction (No. 3) ranges from yellow to dark brown or dark green. The No. 1 oil is often satisfactory for urethane foam production.

TABLE VI

Typical Properties of Castor Oil

Oil	Hydroxyl value	% Volatile (moisture)	Acid value	Color (Gardner)
DB Oil (urethane grade)	163	0.02	1	1+
No. 1 Oil	163	0.2	2	1+
No. 3 Oil	154	0.3	12	6

2. *Composition and Properties*

Castor oil (I) is a triglyceride of ricinoleic (12-hydroxyoleic) acid. About 90% of the fatty acid portion of the molecule consists of ricinoleic acid, 10% being present in form of nonhydroxy acids, con-

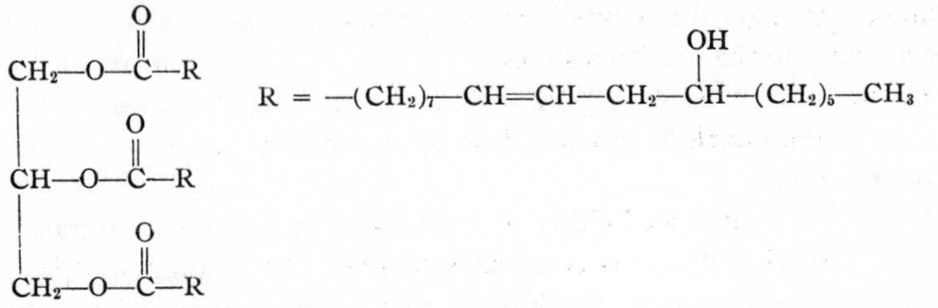

$$
\begin{array}{l}
CH_2—O—\overset{\overset{\displaystyle O}{\|}}{C}—R \\
| \\
CH—O—\overset{\overset{\displaystyle O}{\|}}{C}—R \\
| \\
CH_2—O—\overset{\overset{\displaystyle O}{\|}}{C}—R
\end{array}
\qquad
R = —(CH_2)_7—CH{=}CH—CH_2—\overset{\overset{\displaystyle OH}{|}}{C}H—(CH_2)_5—CH_3
$$

(I)

sisting largely of oleic and linoleic acids (11). Small amounts of stearic and dihydroxystearic acids are also found in some industrial grades.

Castor oil can be considered a mixture of about 70% pure glyceryl triricinoleate and 30% glyceryl diricinoleate-monooleate or -monolinoleate. Hence, from the standpoint of isocyanate utilization, it is approximately 70% tri- and 30% difunctional. Because of the long fatty acid chain, castor oil imparts nonpolar characteristics to urethane polymers which are reflected in some of the resulting polymer properties, particularly in good water resistance and flexibility. At the same time, the triol structure of castor oil produces cross linking, resulting in thermosetting resins.

As can be expected from its structure, the three secondary hydroxyl groups in the 12-position are somewhat slow to react with diisocyanates and generally require heat to give complete reaction. This can be an advantage or disadvantage, depending upon the specific application.

Because of the presence of the hydroxyl groups in the ricinoleic acid portion of the molecule, castor oil exhibits solubility characteristics different from other vegetable oils. It is soluble only in limited quantities of petroleum ether and other similar solvents at room temperature, but forms a two-phase system with larger amounts of these solvents. Castor oil is also much more soluble in alcohol and possesses a higher viscosity and specific gravity than other vegetable oils. Typical properties of castor oil and some more important derivatives have been published by various companies—Baker Castor Oil Co. (11), Spencer Kellogg and Sons (183), and others.

3. *Reactions of Castor Oil and of Ricinoleic Acid*

A. PYROLYSIS

Heating of ricinoleic acid yields decomposition products that are obtained by different types of reaction. Scission may occur with the formation of 10-undecenoic acid and heptanal as shown in the following equation (37,111):

$$\underset{\text{Ricinoleic acid}}{CH_3(CH_2)_5\underset{\displaystyle OH}{\underset{|}{CH}}{-}CH_2CH{=}CH(CH_2)_7COOH} \rightarrow \underset{\text{10-Undecenoic acid}}{CH_2{=}CH(CH_2)_8COOH} + \underset{\text{Heptanal}}{CH_3(CH_2)_5CHO}$$

Another type of pyrolytic reaction, the dehydration of castor oil and of ricinoleic acid, has been known for many years and has been extensively investigated (23,112,163). Dehydration takes place with the formation of dienoic acid as in Scheme II.

$$CH_3(CH_2)_5\underset{\displaystyle OH}{\underset{|}{CH}}CH_2CH{=}CH(CH_2)_7COOH$$

$$\swarrow -H_2O \qquad\qquad \searrow -H_2O$$

$$\underset{\text{9,12-Octadecadienoic acid (linoleic)}}{CH_3(CH_2)_4CH{=}CHCH_2CH{=}CH(CH_2)_7COOH}$$

$$\underset{\text{9,11-Octadecadienoic acid}}{CH_3(CH_2)_4CH_2CH{=}CHCH{=}CH(CH_2)_7COOH}$$

Scheme II

Both scission and dehydration may occur simultaneously or reaction conditions can be regulated to yield predominantly scission or dehydration products. High temperature decompositions (250–300°C.) appear to favor scission while dehydrating catalysts are used for the preparation of the dienoic acids. Dehydrating catalysts include activated alumina (23), and other metallic oxides (138), nonoxidizing mineral acids (197), sulfuric acid (168), activated earths (163), and others. There exists some disagreement as to the relative proportion of 9,11-conjugated and 9,12-unconjugated dienoic acids, although more recent data (73,152) indicate the presence of from 22 to 31% of conjugated acids in the dehydrated castor oil. Numerous publications deal with the various uses of dehydrated castor oil, the most important of which is as a substitute for tung oil in coating applications. Only some of the more notable references are cited here (106,191,192,201).

When castor oil is heated to high temperatures in the presence of alkali, cleavage takes place between the tenth and eleventh carbon atoms with the formation of 2-octanol or a mixture of 2-octanol and methyl hexyl ketone. At the same time, the terminal carbon atom of the residue is oxidized to yield the sodium salt of the corresponding carboxylic acid with the simultaneous evolution of hydrogen (1). Acidification of the sodium salt affords the free sebacic acid:

$$\underset{\text{Ricinoleic acid}}{CH_3(CH_2)_5\underset{\displaystyle OH}{\underset{|}{C}}HCH_2CH{=}CH(CH_2)_7COOH} \rightarrow$$

$$\underset{\text{2-Octanol}}{CH_3(CH_2)_5\underset{\displaystyle OH}{\underset{|}{C}}HCH_3} + \underset{\text{Sebacic acid}}{HOOC(CH_2)_8COOH}$$

Heating of castor oil with strong oxidizing agents such as nitric acid or alkaline permanganate yields mainly another dibasic acid—azelaic acid (93).

B. ESTERIFICATION AND TRANSESTERIFICATION (ALCOHOLYSIS)

Modifications of castor oil and particularly of ricinoleic acid through esterification have resulted in products that are of considerable interest as polyols for various urethane applications (11,132,147).

In order to obtain derivatives of reduced unit weight per hydroxyl group and increased reactivity, ricinoleic or 12-hydroxystearic acid was reacted with di- and polyhydric alcohols, e.g., ethylene and propylene glycol, glycerol, and pentaerythritol (132). The resulting monoesters had an average functionality of two (ethylene and propylene glycol), three (glycerol), or four (pentaerythritol). In addition to increasing the number of hydroxyl groups, the introduction of primary alcohol groups through the esterification reaction confers greater reactivity to the molecule. Longer chain glycols such as neopentyl glycol and ricinoleic alcohol were also used to give the corresponding difunctional esters.

Transesterification (alcoholysis) was also used to decrease the unit weight per hydroxyl group and to reduce the average distance between cross-linking sites (157,195). This reaction is demonstrated in the alcoholysis of castor oil with glycerol as shown in equation (9).

$$\begin{array}{c} CH_2OCOR \\ | \\ CHOCOR \\ | \\ CH_2OCOR \\ \text{Castor oil} \end{array} + \begin{array}{c} CH_2OH \\ | \\ CHOH \\ | \\ CH_2OH \\ \text{Glycerol} \end{array} \xrightarrow[\text{catalyst}]{\text{heat}} \begin{array}{c} CH_2OCOR \\ | \\ CHOH \\ | \\ CH_2OH \\ \text{Monoglyceride} \end{array} + \begin{array}{c} CH_2OCOR \\ | \\ CHOCOR \\ | \\ CH_2OH \\ \text{Diglyceride} \end{array}$$

$$R = -(CH_2)_7CH{=}CHCH_2CH(OH)(CH_2)_5CH_3 \qquad (9)$$

C. HYDROGENATION

Partial or complete hydrogenation of castor oil yields glycerides in which the 12-hydroxyoleic acid units are either partly or fully reduced to 12-hydroxystearic acid units ("Castor Wax") (11). When the hydrogenation is carried to complete saturation of the olefinic bonds, a wax that melts at 86°C. is obtained.

The conditions under which the hydrogenation is carried out are of the utmost importance because hydrogenation at high temperatures brings about removal of hydroxyl groups, resulting in the partial formation of stearic instead of hydroxystearic esters (26,144).

D. OXIDATION

Blown castor oils are prepared by passing air or oxygen through castor oil at temperatures of 80 to 130°C. with or without catalysts. Complex reactions take place during this process, including polymerization, resulting in an increase of viscosity, specific gravity, and saponification value of the oil. These products are used primarily as plasticizers in lacquers, for artificial leather, and in adhesives, and are very useful resins for the preparation of urethane coatings.

Oxidation of castor oil and ricinoleic acid to form dibasic acids has been discussed under "Pyrolysis" (Section V-3-A).

E. ADDITION OF SULFUR COMPOUNDS

The reaction of elementary sulfur and sulfur compounds such as sulfuric acid, chlorosulfonic acid, sulfur monochloride, and others, with fatty acids and fatty acid derivatives containing unsaturated bonds has been extensively investigated. The most important of these is the sulfation of castor oil and of ricinoleic acid. Reaction with sulfuric acid produces the so-called "sulfonated" castor oil or "Turkey red oil," which has found use since about 1877 as a dye assistant and as emulsifier. The reaction of concentrated sulfuric acid with ricinoleic acid results primarily in the sulfation of the hydroxyl group (84,140,141). Other reactions which may occur simultaneously or successively are the sulfation of the olefinic bonds, formation of lactones and lactides, possibly dehydration, and miscellaneous esterifications yielding polyricinoleates.

4. Uses

Castor oil and its derivatives, in addition to their more recent use in various polyurethane applications, have found three principal applications based on the total tonnage used. They are used for the manufacture of paints, varnishes, and lacquers, for the production of plasticizers, for the synthesis of dibasic acids, especially sebacic acid, and in lubricants, greases, hydraulic fluids, emulsifiers, cosmetics, soaps, printing inks, linoleum, oilcloth, and the like.

References

1. Adams, R., and C. S. Marvel, in *Organic Syntheses,* H. Gilman and A. H. Blatt, editors. Collective Vol. I, 2nd ed., Wiley, New York, 1946, p. 366.
2. Allen, C. F. H., and A. Bell, *Organic Syntheses,* N. L. Drake, editor, Vol. 24, Wiley, New York, 1944, p. 94.
3. Allen, T. C., and D. H. Chadwick, U. S. Pat. 2,733,254 (to Monsanto), Jan. 31, 1956.
4. American Society for Testing Materials, Philadelphia, Pa., Method D1638-59T.
5. Anderson, A. W., U. S. Pat. 2,927,918 (to Dow Chemical Co.), March 8, 1960.
6. Anderson, H. H., *J. Am. Chem. Soc.* **70,** 1220 (1948).
7. Anderson, H. H., *J. Am. Chem. Soc.* **72,** 193 (1950).
8. Anderson, H. H., *J. Am. Chem. Soc.* **72,** 196 (1950).
9. Anschütz, R., *Ann.* **359,** 202 (1908).
10. Arnold, R. G., J. A. Nelson, and J. J. Verbanc, *Chem. Revs.* **57,** 47 (1957).
11. Baker Castor Oil Co., "Castor Oil Products for Urethane Polymers," *Tech. Bulletin,* No. 31.
12. Ballard, S. A., R. C. Morris, and J. L. Van Winkle, U. S. Pat. 2,492,955 (to Shell Development Co.), Jan. 3, 1950.

13. Bank, H., *Kunststoffe* **37,** 102 (1947).
14. Barringer, C. M., "Teracol 30—Polyalkylene Ether Glycol," *Bulletin* **HR-11,** E. I. du Pont de Nemours and Co., Inc., 1956.
15. Bartlett, P. D., and S. D. Ross, *J. Am. Chem. Soc.* **70,** 926 (1948).
16. Baumann, G. F., and S. Steingiser, *J. Appl. Polymer Sci.* **1,** 251 (1959).
17. Belg. Pat. 584,738 (to Union Carbide), March 16, 1960.
18. Bennet, W. B., J. H. Saunders, and E. E. Hardy, *J. Am. Chem. Soc.* **75,** 2101 (1953).
19. Benoit, G. J., Jr., U. S. Pat. 2,723,294 (to California Research Corp.), Nov. 8, 1955.
20. Bjorksten, J., H. Tovey, B. Harker, and J. Henning, *Polyesters and Their Applications,* Reinhold, New York, 1956.
21. Bieber, T. I., *J. Am. Chem. Soc.* **74,** 4700 (1952).
22. Birckenbach, L., and M. Linhard, *Ber.* **64B,** 961, 1076 (1931).
23. Böeseken, J., and R. Hoevers, *Rec. trav. chim.* **49,** 1165 (1930).
24. Böhme, D., F. Mott, J. Pfirschke, and H. Wollthan, U. S. Pat. 2,875,225 (to Farbenfabriken Bayer), Feb. 24, 1959.
25. Boivin, J. L., *Can. J. Chem.* **36,** 1405 (1958).
26. Bömer, A., and Fr. Brehm, *Z. Untersuch. Lebensm.* **72,** 1–34 (1936); *Chem. Abstracts* **31,** 2033 (1937).
27. Bortnick, N. M., U. S. Pat. 2,611,782 (to Rohm & Haas), June 30, 1950.
28. Bortnick, N. M., L. S. Luskin, M. D. Hurwitz, and Q. W. Rytina, *J. Am. Chem. Soc.* **78,** 4358 (1956).
29. Brandner, J. D., and R. M. Goepp, Jr., *FIAT Report* **1311,** p. 26.
30. Britton, E. C., and P. S. Petri, U. S. Pat. 2,641,614 (to Dow Chemical Co.), June 9, 1953.
31. Brit. Pat. 752,589 (to Farbenfabriken Bayer), July 11, 1956.
32. Brit. Pat. 834,158 (to Du Pont), May 4, 1960.
33. Brit. Pat. 854,958 (to Farbenfabriken Bayer), Nov. 23, 1960.
34. Buckles, R. E., and C. J. Thelen, *Anal. Chem.* **22,** 676 (1950).
35. Bunge, W., *Angew. Chem.* **72,** 1002 (1960).
36. Burgoine, E., and R. G. A. New, Brit. Pat. 574,222 (to Imperial Chemical Industries), Dec. 28, 1945.
37. Bussy, A., *Ann.* **60,** 246 (1846).
38. Cagniant, P., Buu-Hoï, *Bull. soc. chim.* **10,** 349 (1943).
39. Carlson, W. W., and L. H. Gretcher, *J. Am. Chem. Soc.* **69,** 1952 (1947).
40. Chabrier, P., *Compt. rend.* **214,** 362 (1942).
41. Chemical Safety Data Sheet SD-73, "Properties and Essential Information for Safe Handling and Use of Tolylene Diisocyanate," Manufacturing Chemists' Association, Inc., Washington, D. C., 1959.
42. Chitwood, H. C., and B. T. Freure, *J. Am. Chem. Soc.* **68,** 680 (1946).
43. Coffman, D. D., U. S. Pat. 2,334,476 (to Du Pont), Nov. 16, 1944.
44. Cowley, E. G., and J. R. Partington, *J. Chem. Soc.* **1936,** 45.
45. Cupery, M. E., U. S. Pat. 2,346,665 (to Du Pont), April 18, 1944.
46. Curme, Jr., G. O., and F. Johnston, *Glycols,* Reinhold, New York, 1952.
47. Curtius, T., G. v. Brüning, and H. Derlon, *J. prakt. Chem.* **125,** 63 (1930).
48. Curtius, T., and W. Hechtenberg, *J. prakt. Chem.* **105,** 289 (1923).

49. Dadieu, A., *Monatsh. Chem.* **57**, 437 (1931).
50. Dains, F. B., R. Q. Brewster, and C. P. Olander, in *Organic Syntheses,* H. Gilman and A. H. Blatt, editors, Collective Vol. I, 2nd ed., Wiley, New York, 1946, p. 447.
51. Davis, S., J. M. McClellan, and K. C. Frisch, paper presented at the Isocyanate Symposium of the Upper Midwest Section of the Society of Plastics Engineers, Minneapolis, Minn., Oct., 1957.
52. DeBell, J. M., W. C. Goggin, and W. E. Gloor, *German Plastics Practice,* DeBell and Richardson, Cambridge, Mass., 1946, p. 300.
53. Dege, G. J., R. L. Harris, and J. S. MacKenzie, *J. Am. Chem. Soc.* **81**, 3374 (1959).
54. DeGroote, M., U. S. Pat. 2,552,528 (to Petrolite Corp.), May 15, 1951.
55. DeGroote, M., U. S. Pats. 2,554,667 (to Petrolite Corp.), May 29, 1951, 2,679,516–17 (to Petrolite Corp.), May 25, 1954.
56. DeGroote, M., U. S. Pats. 2,626,902 (to Petrolite Corp.), Jan 27, 1953, 2,626,912–19 (to Petro'ite Corp.), Jan. 27, 1953.
57. DeGroote, M., U. S. Pats. 2,626,902–20, 22–29, 50 (to Petrolite Corp.), Jan. 27, 1953.
58. DeGroote, M., U. S. Pat. 2,626, 910 (to Petrolite Corp.), Jan. 27, 1953.
59. DeGroote, M., U. S. Pat. 2,626,911 (to Petrolite Corp.), Jan. 27, 1953.
60. DeGroote, M., U. S. Pat. 2,626,926 (to Petrolite Corp.), Jan. 27, 1953.
61. DeGroote, M., U. S. Pat. 2,652,418 (to Petrolite Corp.), Sept. 15, 1953.
62. DeGroote, M., and O. H. Pettingill, U. S. Pats. 2,819,213–20 (to Petrolite Corp.), Jan. 7, 1958.
63. DeGroote, M., and O. H Pettingill, U. S. Pats. 2,944,983–5 (to Petrolite Corp.), July 12, 1960.
64. Dickey, J. B., J. M. Straley, and T. E. Stanin, U. S. Pat. 2,394,597 (to Eastman Kodak), Feb. 12, 1946.
65. Dyson, G. M., in *Organic Syntheses,* H. Gilman and A. H. Blatt, editors, Collective Vol. I, 2nd ed., Wiley, New York, 1946, p. 165.
66. Ebert, P. E., "A Study in the Polymerization of Propylene Oxide" (Doctoral Dissertation), Univ. of Penn., 1960.
67. Eicken, S. V., *Microchem. Acta* **1958**, No. 6, 731.
68. Eyster, E. H., and R. H. Gillette, *J. Chem. Phys.* **8**, 369 (1940).
69. Eyster, E. H., R. H. Gillette, and L. O. Brockway, *J. Am. Chem. Soc.* **62**, 3236 (1940).
70. Fife, H. R., and W. J. Toussaint, U. S. Pat. 2,457,139 (to Union Carbide), Dec. 28, 1948.
71. Flory, P. J., *J. Am. Chem. Soc.* **62**, 1561 (1940).
72. Forbes, G. S., and H. H. Anderson, *J. Am. Chem. Soc.* **70**, 1043, 1222 (1948).
73. Forbes, W. C., and H. A. Neville, *Ind. Eng. Chem.* **32**, 555 (1940).
74. Frisch, K. C., and S. Davis, paper presented at the American Chemical Society Meeting, Miami, Fla., April, 1957.
75. Gattermann, L., *Ber.* **23**, 1218 (1890).
76. Gattermann, L., and A. Cantzler, *Ber.* **25**, 1086 (1892).
77. Gattermann, L., and G. Schmidt, *Ann.* 244, 30 (1888).

78. Gautier, A., *Ann.* **149,** 311 (1869).
79. Gee, G., W. C. E. Higginson, P. Levesley, and K. J. Taylor, *J. Chem. Soc.* **1959,** 1338.
80. Ger. Pat. 133,760 (to Vereinigte Chininfabriken); *Chem. Zentr.* **1902** II, 553.
81. Goubeau, J., and D. Paulin, *Chem. Ber.* **93,** 1111 (1960).
82. Goubeau, J., and H. Gräbner, *Chem. Ber.* **93,** 1379 (1960).
83. Griffin, W. C., U. S. Pat. 2,673,882 (to Atlas Powder Co.), March 30, 1954.
84. Grün, A., and M. Woldenberg, *J. Am. Chem. Soc.* **31,** 490 (1909).
85. Gurvich, S. M., *Zhur. Obshcheĭ Khim.* **25,** 1713 (1955).
86. Hardy, E. E., U. S. Pat. 2,839,559, June 17, 1958.
87. Havlik, A. J., and A. F. Hildebrandt, 134th Meeting, American Chemical Society, Chicago, Ill., Sept., 1958, *Abstracts,* p. 14T.
88. Heiss, H. L., J. H. Saunders, M. R. Morris, B. R. Davis, and E. E. Hardy, *Ind. Eng. Chem.* **46,** 1498 (1954).
89. Heiss, H. L., F. P. Combs, P. G. Gemeinhardt, J. H. Saunders, and E. E. Hardy, *Ind. Eng. Chem.* **51,** 929 (1959).
90. Hentschel, W., *Ber.,* **17,** 1284 (1884).
91. Hill, A. J., and W. M. Degnan, U. S. Pat. 2,379,486 (to American Cyanamid), July 3, 1949.
92. Hill, J. W., and W. H. Carothers, *J. Am. Chem. Soc.* **55,** 5031 (1933).
93. Hill, J. W., and W. L. McEwen, in *Organic Syntheses,* A. H. Blatt, editor, Collective Vol. 2, Wiley, New York, 1946, p. 53.
94. Hofmann, A. W., *Ber.* **3,** 653 (1870).
95. Hofmann, A. W., *Ber.* **4,** 262 (1871).
96. Horsley, L. H., and E. E. Britton, U. S. Pat. 2,733,272 (to Dow Chemical Co.), Jan. 31, 1956.
97. Hostettler, F., U. S. Pat. 2,933,477 (to Union Carbide), April 19, 1960.
98. Hurwitz, M. D., and R. W. Auten, U. S. Pats. 2,640,846, 2,728,787 (to Rohm & Haas), June 2, 1953 and Dec. 27, 1955.
99. Irwin, C. F., and F. W. Swamer, U. S. Pat. 2,757,183 (to Du Pont), July 31, 1956.
100. Iwakura, Y., and K. Nagakubo, *Bull. Tokyo Inst. Technol.* **13,** No. 1, 25 (1948); *Chem. Abstracts* **44,** 3924*e* (1950).
101. Jenkins, L. H., and D. S. Sears, U. S. Pat. 2,873,171 (to Virginia-Carolina). Feb. 10, 1959.
102. Jolliffe, B. R., and C. P. Smyth, *J. Am. Chem. Soc.* **80,** 1064 (1958).
103. Jones, G. D., J. Zomlefer, and K. Hawkins, *J. Org. Chem.* **9,** 500 (1944).
104. Jones, R. N., *J. Am. Chem. Soc.* **67,** 2127 (1945).
105. Kadesch, R. G., *J. Am. Chem. Soc.* **68,** 41 (1946).
106. Killeffer, D. H., *Ind. Eng. Chem.* **32,** 1466 (1940).
107. Kirkpatrick, W. H., U. S. Pat. 2,654,714 (to Visco Products Co.), Oct. 6, 1953.
108. Klein, D. X., U. S. Pat. 2,532,559 (to Du Pont), Dec. 5, 1950.
109. Kopper, H., and A. Pongratz, *Monatsh. Chem.* **62,** 78 (1933).
110. Korshak, V. V., and S. V. Rogozhin, *Khim. i Fiz-Khim. Vysokomolekul. Soedineniĭ, Doklady 7-oĭ Konf. po Vysokomolekul. Soedineniyam* **1952,** 11–18; *Chem. Abstracts* **48,** 3912*c* (1954).

111. Krafft, F., *Ber.* **10,** 2034 (1877) ; **13,** 1413 (1880) ; **21,** 2730 (1888)
112. Kronstein, A., *Ber.* **49,** 722 (1916).
113. Krzilkalla, H., U. S. Pat. 2,666,787 (to Badische Anilin-Sodafabrik), Jan. 19, 1954.
114. Kubitz, K. A., *Anal. Chem.* **29,** 814 (1957).
115. Kühn, B., and M. Liebert, *Ber.* **23,** 1536 (1890).
116. Leis, D. G., and E. C. Stout, U. S. Pat. 2,942,033 (to Union Carbide Corp.), June 21, 1960.
117. Levene, P. A., and A. Walti, *J. Biol. Chem.* **75,** 325 (1927).
118. Lichty, J. G., and N. V. Seeger, U. S. Pat. 2,362,648 (to Wingfoot Corp.), Nov. 14, 1944.
119. Lloyd, W. G., *J. Am. Chem. Soc.* **78,** 72 (1956).
120. Lord, S. S., Jr., *Anal. Chem.* **29,** 497 (1957).
121. Lundsted, L. G., Brit. Pat. 722,746 (to Wyandotte Chemicals Corp.), Jan. 26, 1955; Can. Pat. 558,786, June 10, 1958.
122. Lundsted, L. G., Can. Pat. 594,754 (to Wyandotte Chemicals Corp.), March 22, 1960; Brit. Pat. 800,159, Aug. 20, 1958.
123. Lundsted, L. G., U. S. Pat. 2,577,256 (to Wyandotte Chemicals Corp.), Dec. 4, 1951.
124. Lundsted, L. G., U. S. Pat. 2,674,619 (to Wyandotte Chemicals Corp.), April 6, 1954.
125. Lundsted, L. G., U. S. Pat. 2,697,118 (to Wyandotte Chemicals Corp.), April 11, 1961.
126. Lundsted, L. G., and W. K. Langdon, Brit. Pat. 776,661 (to Wyandotte Chemicals Corp.), June 12, 1957.
127. Lundsted, L. G., and W. F. Schulz, U. S. Pat. 2,697,118 (to Wyandotte Chemicals Corp.), Dec. 14, 1954.
128. Madorsky, S. L., and S. Straus, *J. Polymer Sci.* **36,** 183 (1959).
129. Marcali, K., *Anal. Chem.* **29,** 552 (1957).
130. Marvel, C. S., C. G. Overberger, R. E. Allen, H. W. Johnston, J. H. Saunders, and J. D. Young, *J. Am. Chem. Soc.* **68,** 861 (1946).
131. Meerwein, H. D., Delfs, and H. Morschel, *Angew. Chem.* **72,** 927 (1960).
132. Metz, H. M., A. Ehrlich, M. K. Smith, and T. C. Patton, *Paint, Oil, Chem. Rev.* **121,** No. 8, 6–12 (1958).
133. Monson, L. T., and W. J. Dickson, U. S. Pat. 2,766,292 (to Petrolite Corp.), Oct. 9, 1956.
134. Montagne, M., and T. Guilmart, *Bull. soc. chim.* **12,** 836 (1945).
135. Morningstar, M. G., C. S. Schollenberger, and G. E. Stueber, U. S. Pat. 2,642,449 (to Goodrich), June 16, 1953.
136. Morris, R. J., and H. E. Persinger, 135th Meeting, American Chemical Society, Boston, Mass., April 5–10, 1959, *Abstracts,* p. 28S.
137. Müller, E., in *Houben-Weyl, Methoden der organischen Chemie,* E. Müller, editor. Thieme-Verlag, Stuttgart, Vol. 14, in press.
138. Münzel, F., Fr. Pat. 830,494, Aug. 1, 1938.
139. Murbach, W. J., and A. Adicoff, *Ind. Eng. Chem.* **52,** 772 (1960).
140. Nishizawa, K., and M. Sinozaki, *J. Soc. Chem. Ind. Japan* **32,** 779 (1929).
141. Nishizawa, K., and K. Winokuti, *Chem. Umschau Gebiete Fette, Öle, Wachse u. Harze* **36,** 79 (1929).

142. Okawara, M., *J. Chem. Soc. Japan, Ind. Chem. Sect.* **55**, 335 (1952); *Chem. Abstracts* **48**, 1055g (1954).
143. Oser, v., *Ann.* (Suppl.) **1**, 253 (1861).
144. Paquot, G., and H. Richet, *Oléagineux* **3**, No. 1, 26–28 (1948); *Chem. Abstracts* **42**, 3975 (1948).
145. Patton, Jr., J. T., U. S. Pat. 2,786,080 (to Wyandotte Chemicals Corp.), March 19, 1957.
146. Patton, Jr., J. T., Can. Pat. 595,207 (to Wyandotte Chemicals Corp.), March 29, 1960; Brit. Pat. 855,010, Nov. 23, 1960.
147. Patton, T. C., A. Ehrlich, and M. K. Smith, *Rubber Age* **86**, 639 (1960).
148. Petersen, S., and H. F. Piepenbrink, in Houben-Weyl, *Methoden der organischen Chemie,* E. Müller, editor, Vol. 8, Thieme-Verlag, **Stuttgart,** 1952, p. 75.
149. Petrov, A. A., *J. Gen. Chem. (USSR)* **14**, 1038 (1944).
150. Pflueger, E., *F.A.T.I.P.E.C. Compt. rend. 4th Congr., Lucerne* 141 (1957); *Chem. Abstracts* **54**, 17908*b* (1960).
151. Price, C. C., U. S. Pat. 2,866,774 (to University of Notre Dame), Dec. 30, 1958.
152. Priest, G. W., and J. D. von Mikusch, *Ind. Eng. Chem.* **32**, 1314 (1940).
153. Piggott, H. A., and F. S. Statham, Brit. Pat. 485,761 (to Imperial Chem. Ind.), May 24, 1938.
154. Pruitt, M. E., and W. A. Rogers, Jr., U. S. Pat. 2,948,757 (to Dow Chemical Co.), Aug. 9, 1960.
155. Pyman, F. L., *J. Chem. Soc.* **103**, 852 (1913).
156. Reeve, W., and A. Sadle, *J. Am. Chem. Soc.* **72**, 1251 (1950).
157. Robinson, E. B., and R. B. Waters, *J. Oil & Colour Chemists' Assoc.* **34**, 361 (1951).
158. Roesch, R., and M. H. Gold, *J. Am. Chem. Soc.* **73**, 2959 (1951).
159. Saunders, J. H., and W. B. Bennet, U. S. Pat. 2,732,392 (to Monsanto), Jan. 24, 1956.
160. Saunders, J. H., and R. J. Slocombe, *Chem. Revs.* **43**, 203 (1948).
161. Saunders, J. H., S. Steingiser, P. G. Gemeinhardt, A. S. Morecroft, and E. E. Hardy, *Chem. and Eng. Data Series* **3**, 153 (1958).
162. Schaefer, F. C., and E. K. Drechsel, U. S. Pat. 2,640,068 (to American Cyanamid), May 26, 1953.
163. Scheiber, J., U. S. Pat. 1,942,778, Jan. 9, 1934; 1,979,495, Nov. 6, 1934.
164. Schlosser, P. H., and K. R. Gray, U. S. Pat. 2,362,217 (to Rayonier, Inc.), Nov. 7, 1944.
165. Schroeter, G., *Ber.* **42**, 2336, 3356 (1909).
166. Schroeder, A. J., U. S. Pat. 2,644,760 (to Sterling Drug, Inc.), July 7, 1953.
167. Schwarz, H., W. Kallert, C. Mühlhausen, and H. Holtschmidt, U. S. Pat. 2,844,566 (to Farbenfabriken Bayer), July 22, 1958.
168. Schwarzman, A., U. S. Pat. 2,140,271 (to Spencer Kellogg and Sons), Dec. 13, 1938.
169. Schweitzer, C. E., U. S. Pat. 2,409,712 (to Du Pont), Oct. 22, 1946.
170. Sexton, A. R., and E. C. Britton, *J. Am. Chem. Soc.* **75**, 4357 (1953).
171. Shriner, R. L., W. H. Horne, and R. F. B. Cox in *Organic Syntheses,* Collective Vol. II, A. H. Blatt, editor, Wiley, New York, 1943, p. 453.

172. Sidgwick, N. V., L. E. Sutton, and W. Thomas, *J. Chem. Soc.* **1933,** 406.
173. Siefken, W., *Ann.* **562,** 75 (1949).
174. Siggia, S., and J. G. Hanna, *Anal. Chem.* **20,** 1084 (1948).
175. Simons, D. M., and J. J. Verbanc, *J. Polymer Sci.* **44,** 303 (1960).
176. Slocombe, R. J., H. W. Flores, and T. H. Cleveland, U. S. Pat. 2,680,127 (to Monsanto), June 1, 1954.
177. Slocombe, R. J., E. E. Hardy, J. H. Saunders, and R. L. Jenkins, *J. Am. Chem. Soc.* **72,** 1888 (1950).
178. Slocombe, R. J., and J. H. Saunders, U. S. Pat. 2,773,086 (to Monsanto), Dec. 4, 1956.
179. Slotta, K. H., and L. Lorenz, *Ber.* **58B,** 1320 (1925).
180. Smith, P. A. S., in *Organic Reactions,* Vol. III, Wiley, New York, 1946, p. 337.
181. Sokata, R., T. Tsuruta, T. Saegusa, and J. Furukawa, *Makromol. Chem.* **40,** 64 (1960).
182. Sokol, H., U. S. Pat. 2,527,970 (to Heyden Chemical Corp.), Oct. 31, 1950.
183. Spencer Kellogg and Sons, Inc., bulletin, "Castor Oils."
184. Spriggs, J. S., U. S. Pat. 2,828,345 (to Dow Chemical Co.), March 25, 1958.
185. St. Pierre, L. E., and C. C. Price, *J. Am. Chem. Soc.* **78,** 3432 (1956).
186. Staff report, *Ind. Eng. Chem.* **48,** 1383 (1956).
187. Staff report, *Chem. Eng. News* **35,** No. 3, 78 (1957).
188. Stagg, H. E., *Analyst* **71,** 557 (1946).
189. Steingiser, S., W. C. Darr, and E. E. Hardy, *Anal. Chem.* **31,** 1261 (1959).
190. Swann, M. H., and G. G. Esposito, *Anal. Chem.* **30,** 107 (1958).
191. Terrill, R. L., *J. Am. Oil Chemists' Soc.* **27,** 477 (1950).
192. Terrill, R. L., in *Encyclopedia of Chemical Technology,* R. E. Kirk and D. F. Othmer, editors, Vol. III, Interscience, New York-London, 1949, pp. 236–244.
193. Tinsley, S. W. and J. T. Fitzpatrick, U. S. Pat. 2,938,058 (to Union Carbide), May 24, 1960.
194. Todd, R. W., and F. E. Fuchs, U. S. Pat. 2,597,204 (to Aquaness Corp.), May 20, 1952.
195. Toone, G. C., and G. S. Wooster, *Off. Digest* **32,** 230 (1960).
196. Toussaint, W. J., and H. R. Fife, U. S. Pat. 2,425,845 (to Union Carbide), Aug. 19, 1947.
197. Ufer, H., U. S. Pat. 1,892,258 (to I. G. Farbenindustrie), Dec. 27, 1932.
198. Vaughn, T. H., D. R. Jackson, and L. G. Lundsted, *J. Am. Oil Chemists Soc.* **29,** 240 (1952).
199. Walsh, A. D., *Proc. Roy. Soc. (London)* **A191,** 32 (1947).
200. Waltman, E., and E. Wolf, U. S. Pat. 2,346,202 (to Heberlein Patent Corp.), April 11, 1944.
201. Weaver, J. C., *Paint Ind. Mag.* **55,** 352 (1940).
202. Wenker, H., *J. Am. Chem. Soc.* **58,** 2608 (1936).
203. Wilkins, J. P., U. S. Pat. 2,764,559 (to Du Pont), Sept. 25, 1956.
204. Will, W., and O. Bielschowski, *Ber.* **15,** 1309 (1882).
205. Williamson, A. G., *Analyst* **77,** 372 (1952).
206. Wilmshurst, J. K., *J. Chem. Phys.* **28,** 733 (1958).

207. Woo, S.-C. and T.-K. Liu, *J. Chem. Phys.* **3,** 544 (1935).
208. Wurtz, A., *Ann.* **71,** 326 (1849).
209. Yale, H. L., *Chem. Revs.* **33,** 209 (1943).
210. Young, D. M., and F. Hostettler, U. S. Pat. 2,933,478 (to Union Carbide), April 19, 1960.
211. Zapp, J. A., *A.M.A. Arch. Ind. Health* **15,** 324 (1957).

III. THE REACTIONS OF ISOCYANATES AND ISOCYANATE DERIVATIVES

I. Introduction

The isocyanates, containing the highly unsaturated —N=C=O group, are very reactive with a host of compounds, and may also react with themselves. Reaction can occur with almost any compound possessing a hydrogen atom that may be replaced by sodium and can occur with a few other compounds having hydrogen atoms not readily replaced by sodium. Some reactions may occur without involving a hydrogen transfer. Thus, it is not surprising that a tremendous number of references to isocyanate reactions occurs in the literature. This chapter is a survey of those reactions which appear to have significance. Qualitative observations of catalytic effects are included as they apply to specific reactions. No attempt is made to give all references describing each reaction, but one or more key references are given for each reaction.

This chapter should serve as a semiquantitative guide to isocyanate chemistry. Of the many reactions surveyed herein, only a few have been of sufficient importance to justify detailed kinetic studies. The following chapter discusses those catalyzed and uncatalyzed reactions that have been studied kinetically, and hence will be a useful source of information for those who wish to delve more deeply into the chemistry of these compounds.

The electronic structure of the isocyanate group indicates that it should have the following resonance possibilities:

$$\text{R—}\overset{-}{\ddot{\underset{\cdot\cdot}{\text{N}}}}\text{—}\overset{+}{\text{C}}\text{=}\dot{\underset{\bullet}{\text{O}}}\text{:} \leftrightarrow \text{R—}\dot{\ddot{\text{N}}}\text{=C=}\dot{\underset{\bullet}{\text{O}}}\text{:} \leftrightarrow \text{R—}\ddot{\text{N}}\text{=}\overset{+}{\text{C}}\text{—}\overset{-}{\ddot{\underset{\cdot\cdot}{\text{O}}}}\text{:}$$

The normal reaction ultimately provides addition to the carbon-nitrogen double bond. In the reaction with those compounds having an "active hydrogen," i.e., one replaceable by sodium, the hydrogen becomes attached to the nitrogen of the isocyanate, and the remainder of the active hydrogen compound (A) becomes attached to the carbonyl carbon:

$$\mathrm{R{-}N{=}C{=}O + H{-}A \rightarrow RNH{-}\overset{\overset{\displaystyle O}{\|}}{C}{-}A}$$

In many cases this addition product is quite stable. In special cases the addition product is only moderately stable and may dissociate to form the initial reactants again, or may decompose to other products. Other reactions not involving active hydrogens usually involve an opening of the carbon-nitrogen double bond as well. The mechanisms of the isocyanate reactions are discussed in detail in Chapter IV.

In addition to the reactions of the isocyanates themselves, certain aspects of the reactions of isocyanate derivatives are clearly of interest. For example, the normal reactions of substituted urethanes and ureas are significant with regard to the stability of polymers containing these groups. For this reason pertinent reactions of the more common isocyanate derivatives are included in this chapter.

The survey of isocyanate chemistry in this and the following chapter is designed to aid the reader in using isocyanates to synthesize his anticipated product with the best control of both the desirable reaction and undesired side reactions, to aid in designing the product so that it will have the expected chemical and thermal stability, and to assist in understanding the intriguing and challenging chemical behavior of the isocyanates.

Several notable literature surveys of isocyanate reactions have appeared in recent years (12,188,199,201), and an excellent survey of reactions of aliphatic diisocyanates, with experimental details, has been published by Petersen (186).

II. Reactions of Isocyanates

In most reactions, especially with active hydrogen compounds, the aromatic isocyanates are more reactive than are the aliphatic isocyanates. In addition, substitution of electronegative groups on the aromatic ring enhances the reactivity whereas electropositive groups reduce the reactivity of the isocyanate. As would be expected, steric hindrance on either the isocyanate or the active hydrogen compound will retard the reaction. All of the reactions are subject to catalysis by acids and, usually most strongly, by bases. Certain metal compounds are exceptionally powerful catalysts. In light of the great variety of reactions possible it is fortunate that conditions that permit very selective control of the reactions actually occurring can usually be chosen. It is this wide range of reactions possible, plus the host of reactive materials available, combined with good control of the desired reactions, that permit one to "tailor make" a variety of polymers.

These generalities may serve as an introduction to this chapter; a detailed treatment of the rates of isocyanate reactions and the effect of structure and catalysts on reactivity is given in the following chapter.

1. *Reactions with Compounds Containing the N—H Group*

A. AMINO-TYPE COMPOUNDS

All compounds containing the N—H groups are potentially reactive with isocyanates; the most basic are usually the most reactive unless steric hindrance is excessive. Thus, the primary aliphatic amines are extremely reactive at 0–25°C., giving disubstituted ureas in high yields:

$$RNCO + R'NH_2 \rightarrow RNHCONHR'$$

Secondary aliphatic amines, as well as primary aromatic amines, react similarly although not quite so readily (58,169,186,205,233). The secondary aromatic amines are still less reactive:

$$RNCO + R_2NH \rightarrow RNHCONR_2$$

These reactions, being inherently fast, are not strongly influenced by many compounds that are strong catalysts for other, slower, isocyanate reactions.

Other nitrogen compounds having similar basicity react almost as readily as do the amines; for example, ammonia (58,186,243):

$$RNCO + NH_3 \rightarrow RNHCONH_2$$

hydrazines (56,90,181,186):

$$RNCO + H_2N\text{—}NHR' \rightarrow RNHCONHNHR'$$

and sodium salts of amino acids (180). At temperatures sufficiently low so that the carboxyl group does not react or other side reactions occur, the basic salts of the amino acids give the expected urea derivative:

$$ArNCO + H_2NCH_2COONa \rightarrow ArNHCONHCH_2COONa$$

Esters of amino acids give urea derivatives similarly (206). In acidic media, amino acids usually react preferentially at the carboxyl group since the ammonium ion is relatively unreactive toward isocyanates. Reaction of isocyanates with amino compounds containing other functional groups may often be complicated by reactions of the other groups. Thus, at higher temperatures both carboxyl and amino groups in an amino acid may react, and ring closures may occur (139) (eq. 1).

$$C_6H_5NCO + CH_3\underset{\displaystyle NH_2}{\underset{|}{C}}HCOOH \xrightarrow[\text{dry}]{100^\circ}$$

$$\text{(5-membered ring: } CH_3\text{—CH—C(=O)—N(}C_6H_5\text{)—C(=O)—NH—, i.e. } CH_3\text{—}\overset{}{CH}\text{ N—}C_6H_5\text{ / HN——C=O)} + C_6H_5NHCONHC_6H_5 \quad (1)$$

Another example of the participation of an additional functional group, in this case in the isocyanate itself, is in the reaction of 1-alkenyl isocyanates with amines (122,124,125). Initial reaction is normal, but rearrangement and addition to the conjugated unsaturated system may occur as shown in equation (2).

$$RCH{=}CRNCO + R'NH_2 \rightarrow RCH{=}CRNHCONHR' \rightarrow$$

$$RCH_2C(R){=}NCONHR' \xrightarrow{R'NH_2} RCH_2\underset{\displaystyle NHR'}{\underset{|}{C}}(R)NHCONHR' \rightarrow$$

$$RCH_2C(R){=}NR' + R'NHCONH_2 \quad (2)$$

$$\xrightarrow{R'NH_2} RCH_2C(R)(NHR')_2$$

Sodium salts of aminosulfonic acids, like those of the aminocarboxylic acids, give the expected urea derivatives (118).

Hydroxylamine reacts with 1 mole of phenyl isocyanate if the isocyanate is added dropwise to a large excess of cold hydroxylamine, forming the urea:

$$C_6H_5NCO + H_2NOH \rightarrow C_6H_5NHCONHOH$$

The next most reactive position is the hydroxyl group, which is sufficiently reactive that 2 moles of isocyanate are normally consumed (77).

$$2C_6H_5NCO + H_2NOH \rightarrow C_6H_5NHCONHO\overset{\displaystyle O}{\overset{\|}{C}}NHC_6H_5$$

B. AMIDES AND RELATED COMPOUNDS

The substitution of an electronegative group on the nitrogen atom of the NH group usually reduces the rate of reaction with an isocyanate. Thus, amides react at a moderate rate at about 100°C., giving the acylurea (46,83,166,186,244):

$$\mathrm{RNCO + R'CONH_2 \rightarrow RNHCONHCOR'}$$

Wiley reported yields of 85–95% for several examples when the reaction was run for 12–24 hours in refluxing benzene. He found that yields were lower when aluminum chloride or stannous chloride was present, and that triethylamine had no catalytic effect (243). The reaction of *N*-substituted amides under severe conditions show abnormal behavior, as Wiley indicated by the examples (245) shown in equations (3) to (5). Although the reaction between *p*-toluenesulfonyl isocyanate and *N*-substituted amides may give the normal

$$\mathrm{C_6H_5C(=O)NHCH_3 + C_6H_5NCO \xrightarrow{190^\circ C.} C_6H_5C(=O)NHC_6H_5} \quad (3)$$

$$\mathrm{C_6H_5C(=O)NHC_6H_5 + C_6H_5NCO \xrightarrow{200\text{-}220^\circ C.} C_6H_5C(=NC_6H_5)NHC_6H_5 + CO_2} \quad (4)$$

$$\mathrm{C_6H_4(CO)_2NH + C_6H_5NCO \xrightarrow{165\text{-}180^\circ C.} C_6H_4(CO)_2N{-}C_6H_5} \quad (5)$$

addition at moderate temperatures (148), when the reaction is run under more vigorous conditions the product is an amidine or a mixture of normal addition product and amidine (133,150) (eq. 6). Loge-

$$\mathrm{ArSO_2NCO + RCONHR' \rightarrow \left[ArSO_2NHC(=O)N(R')COR\right] \rightarrow ArSO_2N{=}C(R)NHR' + CO_2} \quad (6)$$

mann and co-workers, using a C^{14}-labeled amide, showed that the carbon of the carbon dioxide was derived from the amide (151). Amidine formation did not occur when benzoyl or phenyl isocyanate was substituted for the sulfonyl isocyanate (149).

King (133) has reported that *N,N*-dialkylamides with *p*-toluenesulfonyl isocyanate also give amidines, perhaps by way of a cyclic intermediate (eq. 7). A similar reaction between phenyl isocyanate and

$$ArSO_2NCO + HCON(CH_3)_2 \rightarrow \left[\begin{array}{l} ArSO_2N\text{—}C{=}O \\ \quad\;\; | \quad\;\; | \\ \quad\; HC\text{—}O \\ \quad\;\; | \\ \quad\; N(CH_3)_2 \end{array}\right] \xrightarrow{-CO_2} ArSO_2N{=}CHN(CH_3)_2 \quad (7)$$

excess dimethylformamide at 150°C. was observed by Weiner (241). An 86% yield of $C_6H_5N{=}CHN(CH_3)_2$ was obtained, along with carbon dioxide.

The anomalous reactions of the amides reported by Wiley (245) may be explained if one assumes the possibility of cyclic intermediates. Speculation suggests that the sequence shown in reaction (8) could

$$C_6H_5CONHCH_3 + C_6H_5NCO \rightarrow \left[\begin{array}{l} \quad C_6H_5 \\ \quad\; | \\ \quad HN\text{—}C{=}O \\ \qquad\qquad | \\ C_6H_5C\text{—}NCH_3 \\ \quad\; \| \\ \quad\; O \end{array}\right] \rightarrow \left[\begin{array}{l} C_6H_5N\text{—}C{=}O \\ \quad\; | \quad\;\; | \\ C_6H_5C\text{—}NCH_3 \\ \quad\; | \\ \quad\; OH \end{array}\right] \rightarrow$$

$$\left[\begin{array}{l} C_6H_5N \\ \quad\; \| \\ C_6H_5C \\ \quad\; | \\ \quad\; OH \end{array}\right] + CH_3NCO \rightarrow \begin{array}{l} C_6H_5CNHC_6H_5 \\ \quad\;\; \| \\ \quad\;\; O \end{array} \quad (8)$$

account for the peculiar reaction of *N*-methylbenzamide. Wiley's amidine formation from *N*-phenylbenzamide, as well as the amidine formations reported by Logemann and co-workers could all occur by way of the cyclic intermediate suggested by King, as indicated by equation (7).

The formation of *N*-phenylphthalimide, as reported by Wiley (245), could be explained if a seven-membered ring could form, even as a transition state (eq. 9).

These reaction sequences are suggested not so much as possible courses for these specific reactions but principally to emphasize the possible role of cyclic intermediates in some of the more complex reac-

$$C_6H_4(CO)_2NH + C_6H_5NCO \rightarrow [C_6H_4(CO)_2NCONHC_6H_5] \rightarrow [C_6H_4(CO)_2N(C_6H_5)C(=O)NH] \rightarrow C_6H_4(CO)_2NC_6H_5 + HNCO \quad (9)$$

tions of the isocyanates. Reactions in which one isocyanate appears to displace another isocyanate or cyanic acid are becoming somewhat more familiar, and the evolution of carbon dioxide is already a common observation. Much more research is needed to clarify the true mechanisms of these reactions, but they may be removed from the category of the "unexplainable" if one assumes a cyclic intermediate in many cases. Other examples will be apparent later in this chapter.

Like the amides of carboxylic acids, sulfonamides will add to isocyanates. The sulfonamide itself is very slow to react, so the sodium salt of the sulfonamide in an organic solvent or in aqueous alkali is normally used to provide a reasonable rate of reaction (141,186,187, 197):

$$RNCO + ArSO_2NH_2 \xrightarrow{NaOH} ArSO_2NHC(=O)NHR$$

This reaction has been of particular interest in the preparation of oral diabetics, in which butyl isocyanate and *p*-toluenesulfonamide have been used (102,182). The *N*-substituted sulfonamides do not react with isocyanates under conditions tried thus far.

C. UREAS

Ureas are important examples of other nitrogen compounds that are moderately reactive at elevated temperatures (30,140,143). The simple addition product is called a biuret:

$$RNCO + RNHCONHR \rightarrow RN(CONHR)CONHR \quad \text{(biuret)}$$

Uncatalyzed reactions with ureas generally require temperatures of about 100°C. or higher to give a moderate rate. Most tertiary amines apparently are not very active catalysts for reactions of isocyanates with ureas, but stronger bases and certain metal compounds may be strongly catalytic (see Chapter IV).

Reactions of isocyanates with ureas or related compounds at 120°C. for several hours are complicated greatly by the variety of additions and dissociations possible under these conditions. For example, Lakra and Dains (143) caused 1 mole of phenyl isocyanate to react with 1 mole of urea for four hours at 120°, and isolated the compounds listed in equation (10). These products may all be explained by

$$C_6H_5NCO + H_2NCONH_2 \rightarrow \left\{\begin{array}{l} NH_3 \\ H_2NCONH_2 \\ H_2NCONHCONH_2 \\ C_6H_5NHCONHC_6H_5 \\ C_6H_5NHCONH_2 \\ (HNCO)_3 \\ \text{phenylisocyanuric acid} \end{array}\right. \quad (10)$$

assuming more or less random dissociations and recombinations. For example, urea itself may dissociate:

$$H_2NCONH_2 \rightleftharpoons HNCO + NH_3$$

The products of this dissociation could account for the ammonia, biuret (from HNCO and urea), phenylurea (from phenyl isocyanate and ammonia), and cyanuric acid (trimerization of HNCO). The phenylisocyanuric acid apparently is a "mixed trimer" from 1 mole of isocyanate and 2 moles of cyanic acid (eq. 11). The diphenylurea

$$C_6H_5NCO + 2HNCO \rightarrow \begin{array}{ccccc} & & O & & \\ & & \| & & \\ & & C & & \\ & / & & \backslash & \\ C_6H_5N & & & & NH \\ | & & & & | \\ C & & & & C \\ /\!\!/ \quad \backslash & & & & / \quad \backslash\!\!\backslash \\ O & & N & & O \\ & & H & & \end{array} \quad (11)$$

could have been formed by the sequence of reactions shown in equations (12) to (14).

$$C_6H_5NCO + NH_3 \rightleftharpoons C_6H_5NHCONH_2 \quad (12)$$

$$C_6H_5NHCONH_2 \rightleftharpoons C_6H_5NH_2 + HNCO \quad (13)$$

$$C_6H_5NCO + C_6H_5NH_2 \rightleftharpoons C_6H_5NHCONHC_6H_5 \quad (14)$$

D. URETHANES

Urethanes are generally less reactive toward isocyanates than are ureas. In uncatalyzed systems temperatures of approximately 120–140°C. are usually required to give a significant reaction rate. The initial product of the normal addition reaction is an allophanate:

$$\mathrm{RNCO + RNHCOOR' \rightarrow \underset{\displaystyle \mathrm{CONHR}}{\mathrm{RNCOOR'}}} \quad \text{(allophanate)}$$

This reaction, like that of biuret formation, is not strongly catalyzed, if it is catalyzed at all, by most tertiary amines, but it may be catalyzed by stronger bases and certain metal compounds (see Chapter IV).

Besides simple allophanate formations, many side reactions can occur at the high reaction temperature. Lakra and Dains (143) caused phenyl isocyanate and ethyiurethane to react for six hours at 140–160°C., and isolated the compounds listed in reaction (15).

$$\mathrm{ArNCO + RO\overset{O}{\overset{\|}{C}}NH_2} \rightarrow \begin{cases} \text{(a) } \mathrm{ArNH\overset{O}{\overset{\|}{C}}NH\overset{O}{\overset{\|}{C}}OR} \\ \text{(b) } \mathrm{ArNH\underset{O}{\underset{\|}{C}}OR} \\ \text{(c) phenylisocyanuric acid} \\ \text{(d) } \mathrm{ArNH\underset{O}{\underset{\|}{C}}NH\underset{O}{\underset{\|}{C}}NH\underset{O}{\underset{\|}{C}}OR} \end{cases} \tag{15}$$

The allophanate (a) is the "normal" addition product. The urethane (b) could result from dissociation of ethylurethane to ethyl alcohol and cyanic acid, followed by addition of the ethyl alcohol to phenyl isocyanate (eqs. 16 and 17). The phenylisocyanuric acid could have

$$\mathrm{H_2N\overset{O}{\overset{\|}{C}}OC_2H_5 \rightleftharpoons HNCO + C_2H_5OH} \tag{16}$$

$$\mathrm{C_6H_5NCO + C_2H_5OH \rightarrow C_6H_5NHCOOC_2H_5} \tag{17}$$

been formed from 1 mole of phenyl isocyanate and 2 moles of cyanic acid, as observed in the reaction of phenyl isocyanate with urea. The last compound (d) could have been built stepwise by the reaction sequence (18) and (19).

$$\mathrm{HNCO + H_2NCOOC_2H_5 \rightarrow H_2N\underset{O}{\underset{\|}{C}}NH\underset{O}{\underset{\|}{C}}OC_2H_5} \tag{18}$$

$$\mathrm{C_6H_5NCO + H_2N\underset{O}{\underset{\|}{C}}NH\underset{O}{\underset{\|}{C}}OC_2H_5 \rightarrow C_6H_5NH\underset{O}{\underset{\|}{C}}NH\underset{O}{\underset{\|}{C}}NH\underset{O}{\underset{\|}{C}}OC_2H_5} \tag{19}$$

These reactions with urethanes, amides, and urea are actually the combination of isocyanate with the initial reaction products from isocyanates and alcohols, carboxylic acids, and amines, respectively. Furthermore, the active hydrogen has still not disappeared. Thus, it is probable that several moles of isocyanate can be consumed by only 1 mole of the active hydrogen compound. Such a sequence of reactions may be important with regard to distillation losses during isocyanate production.

$$\text{R'NCO} + \text{RNHCONHR} \rightarrow \text{R'NHCO}\underset{\displaystyle \text{R}}{\underset{|}{\text{N}}}\text{CONHR} \xrightarrow{\text{R'NCO}} \text{R'NHCO}\underset{\displaystyle \text{R'}}{\underset{|}{\text{N}}}\text{CO}\underset{\displaystyle \text{R}}{\underset{|}{\text{N}}}\text{CONHR} \quad (20)$$

The reactions of isocyanates with substituted ureas, urethanes, and amides are particularly important in polyurethane chemistry because, if they are permitted to occur, these reactions will lead to increased branching. Thus, a linear polyurethane prepared from a diol and a diisocyanate may be branched by allophanate formation (eq. 21).

$$\begin{array}{c}\sim\text{NCOO}\sim\sim \\ | \\ \text{H} \\ + \\ \sim\text{NCO}\end{array} \xrightarrow{140°} \begin{array}{c}\sim\text{NCOO}\sim \\ | \\ \sim\text{NHCO}\end{array} \quad (21)$$

Because of the faster relative rate of reaction of isocyanate with urea groups, a polymer containing both urea and urethane groups in approximately equal concentrations may be branched principally by biuret formation (eq. 22).

$$\sim\text{NCO} + \sim\text{NH}\overset{\text{O}}{\overset{\|}{\text{C}}}\text{NH}\sim\sim\text{NH}\overset{\text{O}}{\overset{\|}{\text{C}}}\text{O}\sim \rightarrow \sim\underset{\displaystyle \text{CONH}\sim}{\underset{|}{\text{N}}}\overset{\text{O}}{\overset{\|}{\text{C}}}\text{NH}\sim\sim\text{NH}\overset{\text{O}}{\overset{\|}{\text{C}}}\text{O}\sim \quad (22)$$

E. MISCELLANEOUS

Essentially any compound containing an NH group may be reactive with isocyanates under sufficiently vigorous conditions. Illustrative examples of additional compounds which give the expected reaction:

$$\text{RNCO} + \text{HN}\langle \rightarrow \text{RNHCON}\langle$$

include imides (186,245), amidines (189), nitramines (205), diazoamino compounds (98), phenylhydrazones (48,157), cyanamide (186,222), aminooximes, (92), sulfimides (186), acylureas (143), thioureas (143), hydrazoic acid (175), and isothioureas (143).

2. *Reactions with Compounds Containing the O—H Group*

A. ALCOHOLS

Essentially all compounds containing a hydrogen atom attached to oxygen will react under appropriate conditions with an isocyanate. The most reactive class of such compounds is the family of alcohols. With the alcohols, as with many other compounds, the effect of steric hindrance is pronounced, so that while primary alcohols react readily at 25–50°C., secondary alcohols usually react only about 0.3 as fast. Tertiary alcohols react much more slowly, approximately 0.005 as fast as the primary (59).

One tertiary alcohol, triphenylcarbinol, is so hindered sterically that it has been reported as being completely unreactive (135).

The normal reaction of an alcohol and an isocyanate gives a urethane, also called a carbamate:

$$\mathrm{RNCO + R'OH \rightarrow RNH\overset{\displaystyle O}{\overset{\|}{C}}OR'}$$

The reaction is readily catalyzed by mild and strong bases, by many metals, and, weakly, by acids (see Chapter IV).

This reaction with hydroxyl groups is perhaps the most familiar of the reactions of the isocyanates. Nearly all uses of the isocyanates, such as foam, elastomers, and coatings, utilize this reaction; the other major component of the system is normally a hydroxyl-containing resin. It is for this reason that most commercial polymers derived from isocyanates and other resins such as polyesters, polyethers, and castor oil are termed "polyurethanes."

Reactions of isocyanates with simple primary and secondary alcohols usually give a nearly quantitative yield of the urethane, which is quite stable. In contrast, reaction with tertiary alcohols is usually accompanied by olefin formation (131,201):

$$\mathrm{2C_6H_5NCO + (CH_3)_3COH \rightarrow C_6H_5NHCONHC_6H_5 + CO_2 + CH_3\underset{\displaystyle CH_3}{\underset{|}{C}}{=}CH_2}$$

Such a reaction has been used as a synthetic route to certain olefins, with the elimination tending to follow the Hofmann rule (16) (eq. 23).

$$C_6H_5NCO + C_6H_5\text{—}\underset{\underset{C_2H_5}{|}}{\overset{\overset{CH_3}{|}}{C}}\text{—}OH \xrightarrow[110\text{–}120°C.]{36\ hrs.} \underset{60\%}{C_6H_5\text{—}\underset{\underset{C_2H_5}{|}}{C}{=}CH_2} + \underset{40\%}{C_6H_5\text{—}\underset{\underset{CH_3}{|}}{C}{=}CHCH_3} \quad (23)$$

Other side reactions may occur when alcohols of a more complex structure are used. With α-hydroxy esters, ring closure between the ester and urethane may take place if a sodium catalyst is present (195) (eq. 24).

$$RR'\underset{\underset{OH}{|}}{C}\text{—}COOR + R''NCO \rightarrow \left[RR'\underset{\underset{OCNH\text{—}R''}{\underset{\|}{O}}}{C}\text{—}COOR\right] \xrightarrow{NaOR} RR'C\text{—}C(=O)\text{—}N(R)\text{—}C(=O)\text{—}O \ (\text{ring}) \quad (24)$$

Rearrangements may occur similarly in certain other urethane systems, the rearrangements occurring by typical mechanisms. One recently described example is that of the urethane from phenyl isocyanate and glycidol (126) (eq. 25). Another example of a normal

$$C_6H_5NCO + HOCH_2CH\text{—}CH_2\ (\text{epoxide, }O) \rightarrow C_6H_5NHCOOCH_2CH\text{—}CH_2\ (\text{epoxide, }O) \xrightarrow{125°}$$

$$C_6H_5N\text{—}CH_2\text{—}CHOH\text{—}CH_2\text{—}O\text{—}C(=O)\text{—}(N)\ (\text{ring}) \quad 95\% \quad (25)$$

urethane giving additional reactions under mild conditions is seen in the reactions of 1-alkenyl isocyanates with alcohols (123) (eq. 26).

$$CH_2{=}C(R)NCO + R'OH \rightarrow CH_2{=}C(R)NHCOOR' \quad (26)$$

Additional reaction products isolated are shown in equation 27. When R was alkyl, the normal urethane was the favored product. When R was hydrogen, the normal urethane resulted from the reac-

$$\underset{\text{(A)}}{\underset{\displaystyle |\atop OR'}{CH_3C(R)NHCOOR'}} \quad \underset{\text{(B)}}{H_2NCOOR'} \quad \underset{\text{(C)}}{\underset{\displaystyle |\atop OR}{CH_3C(R)NHCONHCOOR'}} \quad \underset{\text{(D)}}{CH_3CR(OR')_2} \qquad (27)$$

tion at 0°C., but (A), (B), (C), and (D) were the principal products from the reaction at 30°. Products (B) and (D) could come from reaction of (A) with alcohol; product (C) could be derived from (A) and (B).

With alcohols containing more than one type of functional group the more reactive groups normally will add first to the isocyanate, as illustrated by ethanolamine. As would be expected, the more reactive amino group reacts first, followed by the hydroxyl group (136).

B. PHENOLS

Phenols, being more acidic or less basic than the aliphatic alcohols, react more slowly with isocyanates than do the alcohols. The reaction of most isocyanates with phenols is so slow at 50–75°C. that one normally uses a catalyst such as a tertiary amine or aluminum chloride to promote this reaction (147,186):

$$RNCO + ArOH \rightarrow RNH\overset{O}{\overset{\|}{C}}OAr$$

The presence of electronegative groups on the phenol nucleus retards the reaction with isocyanates, apparently because these groups reduce the basicity of the hydroxyl group still more. Picric acid, 2,4,6-trinitrophenol, presents an extreme case of combining the steric effects of the two *ortho* substituents and the electronegative influence of the nitro groups. Reportedly, this compound does not react with phenyl isocyanate even with long heating under pressure (104).

Under extreme conditions of temperature, phenyl isocyanate will react with sodium salts of phenols to give *o*-hydroxy amides (212) (eq. 28). The sequence in reaction (29) suggests an intermolecular

$$C_6H_5NCO + p\text{-}ClC_6H_4ONa \xrightarrow[200°\,C.]{1.5\text{ hrs.}} 2\text{-}HO\text{-}5\text{-}ClC_6H_3CONHC_6H_5 \qquad (28)$$

mechanism rather than an intramolecular one for the isocyanate-sodium phenoxide reaction. None of the expected chlorosalicylanilide was found (212).

$$p\text{-}ClC_6H_4OCONHC_6H_5 + C_{10}H_7ONa\ (\alpha\text{-naphthoxide}) \xrightarrow[200^\circ]{1.5\text{ hrs.}} 1\text{-}OH\text{-}2\text{-}CONHC_6H_5\text{-}C_{10}H_6 \quad (29)$$

C. WATER

Water is usually similar to the secondary alcohols in its reactivity with isocyanates if both are soluble in the reaction medium. The reaction is not as simple as the formation of a urethane, however. The first addition product is not usually stable, losing carbon dioxide:

$$RNCO + H_2O \rightarrow [RNHCOOH] \rightarrow RNH_2 + CO_2$$

The amine thus formed reacts with the isocyanate even more rapidly than does the water; a good yield of disubstituted urea is obtained:

$$RNCO + RNH_2 \rightarrow RNHCONHR$$

The net reaction is the consumption of two equivalents of isocyanate by 1 mole of water, with the evolution of 1 mole of carbon dioxide (249,250):

$$2RNCO + H_2O \rightarrow RNHCONHR + CO_2$$

While these equations may represent the principal products of the reaction with water, the actual reaction may be more complicated. Naegeli and co-workers (168) suggested that isocyanates and water could react in any one or more of several ways (eq. 30) to give substituted ureas.

$$RNCO + H_2O \rightarrow RNHCOOH$$
$$\text{II: } RNHCOOH \xrightarrow{RNCO} (RNHCO)_2O \xrightarrow{-CO_2} RNHCONHR$$
$$\text{I: } RNHCOOH \xrightarrow{-CO_2} RNH_2 \xrightarrow{RNCO} RNHCONHR \quad (30)$$
$$\text{III: } RNH_2 \xrightarrow{RNHCOOH} [RNHCO_2^-]\,[RNH_3^+] \rightarrow RNHCONHR$$

Sequence I would be favored in those cases in which the carbamic acid is very unstable, decomposing rapidly to the amine.

When the carbamic acid is fairly stable, reaction sequence II could become increasingly important. Sequence III could be significant when the amine and the isocyanate react with each other very slowly; e.g., when steric hindrance is excessive.

A recent study of the mechanism of the isocyanate-water reaction (214) strengthens the probability of Naegeli's schemes I and II. In the dioxane solution used, at 80°C. direct loss of carbon dioxide appeared to correspond to approximately 50% of the isocyanate consumed. Decomposition of the carbamic anhydride was slow at 80°, but was rapid at 100°C. The results suggested that at reaction temperatures above 100°C. the anhydride might not be formed at all. The data from this study are discussed in more detail in Chapter IV.

The reaction between isocyanates and water is catalyzed by tertiary amines, many other bases, and certain metal compounds, as described in Chapter IV.

The reaction with water proceeds differently in the presence of strong acids or bases. For example, in the presence of hydrochloric acid, a good yield of amine hydrochloride is obtained because the amine salt is relatively unreactive toward isocyanate (168):

$$RNCO + H_2O + HCl \rightarrow RNH_2 \cdot HCl + CO_2$$

With a strong base the amine and carbonate are formed (251):

$$RNCO + H_2O + 2NaOH \rightarrow RNH_2 + Na_2CO_3$$

Isolation of the amine, rather than the urea, suggests that an intermediate may be the salt of the carbamic acid:

$$RNCO + NaOH + H_2O \rightarrow RNHCO_2Na$$

$$RNHCO_2Na + NaOH + H_2O \rightarrow RNH_2 + Na_2CO_3$$

This salt may liberate the amine at a slower rate than the aqueous alkali attacks the isocyanate, thereby accounting for the high yield of amine formed rather than the substituted urea. Additional possibilities are that the base may react directly with the isocyanate faster than does the amine, or that the base may catalyze the reaction with water, present in large excess, so much that it reacts faster than does the amine.

In systems in which water and isocyanate are not mutually soluble, e.g., in the absence of a suitable solvent, the reaction may be slow because of the poor solubility of water in the isocyanate. Thus, octadecyl isocyanate may be emulsified and lose very little of its isocyanate activity in one day (201).

Most isocyanates react with water as has been indicated; however, those few isocyanates which are derived from very weakly basic amines may behave differently. Thus substitution of nitro groups on the aromatic nucleus of phenyl isocyanate reduces the tendency toward urea formation and increases the yield of amine. A sufficient number of nitro groups will reduce the basicity of the amine and hence its reactivity so that the amine becomes less reactive toward the isocyanate than is water. Substituents *ortho* to the amino group will also reduce its rate of reaction with isocyanate because of steric factors. Thus the mononitrophenyl and 3,5-dinitrophenyl isocyanates react with water to give a mixture of the corresponding amine and urea. 2,4-Dinitrophenyl and 2,4,6-trinitrophenyl isocyanates give good yields of the corresponding amines, with little or no urea formation (168).

The reaction with water is similarly selective with diisocyanates containing one *ortho* methyl group. Thus a good yield of the corresponding urea has been prepared from 2 moles of tolylene diisocyanate and 1 mole of water (23, 185) (eq. 31).

$$2\ CH_3C_6H_3(NCO)_2 + H_2O \rightarrow H_3C{-}C_6H_3(OCN){-}NHCONH{-}C_6H_3(NCO){-}CH_3 \qquad (31)$$

The reaction of aliphatic diisocyanates with water has been used to prepare polyureas when the isocyanate groups were separated by four or more methylene groups. On the other hand (eq. 32), ethylene diisocyanate reacted with water to give complete conversion to the cyclic urea, and trimethylene diisocyanate gave a 75:25 distribution or cyclic urea and polymer (119). Cyclic ureas containing four to six-

$$OCN(CH_2)_2NCO + H_2O \rightarrow \begin{array}{c} CH_2{-}CH_2 \\ | \qquad | \\ HN \quad NH \\ \diagdown \diagup \\ C \\ \| \\ O \end{array} \qquad (32)$$

teen methylene groups have also been prepared from the corresponding diisocyanate and water, using a high dilution technique (177).

Perfluoroalkyl isocyanates react abnormally with water, giving chain shortening and amide formation (1):

$$C_3F_7NCO + H_2O \rightarrow C_2F_5CONH_2$$

The reaction of isocyanates with water is of great importance in all isocyanate chemistry, sometimes because it is greatly desired, as in the production of carbon dioxide-blown foams, and sometimes because it is an undesired side reaction. This sensitivity of the isocyanates to moisture emphasizes that the chemist should exercise great care to use carefully dried containers, to avoid exposure of the isocyanate to atmospheric moisture, and to use dry reactants, solvents, and fillers if urea and gas formation are to be avoided completely.

D. CARBOXYLIC ACIDS

Carboxylic acids, having a hydroxyl group, react fairly readily with isocyanates (62). Since the acids vary considerably in their acid strength, it is to be expected that their reactivity toward isocyanates will also vary. As a general guide, however, the carboxylic acids are usually somewhat less reactive toward isocyanates than are primary alcohols and water. The reaction is catalyzed by tertiary amines, by many other bases, and by numerous metal compounds.

As in the reaction with water, the initial addition product is not stable; its fate depends upon the structure of the acid and of the isocyanate. Aliphatic isocyanates and aliphatic acids usually give mixed anhydrides that decompose to substituted amides. Strong acids such as formic, cyanoacetic, and trichloroacetic acid behave similarly (eq. 33). On the other hand, aromatic isocyanates combined

$$RNCO + R'COOH \rightarrow \left[RNH\overset{O}{\overset{\|}{C}}{-}O{-}\overset{O}{\overset{\|}{C}}R'\right] \rightarrow RNHCOR' + CO_2 \quad (33)$$

with aliphatic acids or weak aromatic acids at moderate temperatures are more likely to give other anhydrides and, eventually, acid anhydride, urea, and carbon dioxide (eq. 34). At 160°C. the acid

$$ArNCO + R'COOH \rightarrow \left[ArNH\overset{O}{\overset{\|}{C}}{-}O{-}\overset{O}{\overset{\|}{C}}R'\right] \rightarrow$$

$$\left[ArNH\overset{O}{\overset{\|}{C}}{-}O{-}\overset{O}{\overset{\|}{C}}NHAr\right] + R'\overset{O}{\overset{\|}{C}}{-}O{-}\overset{O}{\overset{\|}{C}}R' \quad (34)$$

$$\downarrow$$

$$[ArNHCONHAr] + CO_2$$

anhydride and urea may also react to give an amide and carbon dioxide (166) (eq. 35).

$$\text{ArNHCONHAr} + \text{R}'\overset{\overset{\text{O}}{\|}}{\text{C}}\text{—O—}\overset{\overset{\text{O}}{\|}}{\text{C}}\text{R}' \rightarrow 2\text{ArNHCOR}' + \text{CO}_2 \quad (35)$$

The mixed anhydrides of aromatic isocyanates and several acids have been isolated and are fairly stable at room temperature, but decompose slowly at room temperature to carbanilide and the acid anhydride, and more rapidly at 70–100°C. The mixed anhydrides of phenyl isocyanate and aliphatic acids have been reacted with water, alcohols, and ammonia to give the aliphatic acid plus carbanilide, the urethane, and the urea, respectively (62,167). Mixed anhydrides of aliphatic diisocyanates and acrylic or methacrylic acid have been isolated. These compounds decomposed with gas evolution at their melting points, about 50–60°C. Heating for five hours at 100–150° converted these mixed anhydrides into polymers (127).

Parker and co-workers showed that an equilibrium exists in the formation of mixed anhydrides. Crystalline anhydrides were prepared in 85% yield from an excess of isocyanate with the acid, without solvent, at 5°C. Infrared studies of solutions of these anhydrides showed that dissociation had occurred (183).

Tracer studies with compounds containing a labeled carbon in the carboxyl group have shown that the carbon dioxide evolved derives its carbon from the isocyanate group rather than from the acid (85) (eq. 36).

$$\left[\text{RNH}\ \boxed{\overset{\overset{\text{O}}{\|}}{\text{C}}\text{—O}}\ \text{—}\overset{\overset{\text{O}}{\|}}{\text{C}}\text{R}'\right] \rightarrow \text{RNH}\overset{\overset{\text{O}}{\|}}{\text{C}}\text{R}' + \text{CO}_2 \quad (36)$$

In reactions of one equivalent of isocyanate with hydroxy acids one may find selective reaction, depending on the structure of the acid. Thus, a hydroxy aliphatic acid such as β-hydroxyisobutyric acid gives preferential reaction with the hydroxyl group (33) (eq. 37). On

$$\text{RNCO} + \text{HOCH}_2\underset{}{\overset{\overset{\text{CH}_3}{|}}{\text{C}}}\text{HCOOH} \rightarrow \text{RNHCOOCH}_2\overset{\overset{\text{CH}_3}{|}}{\text{C}}\text{HCOOH} \quad (37)$$

the other hand (eq. 38), with hydroxy aromatic acids, reaction with the carboxyl group is preferred (117). Mandelic acid, $C_6H_5CHOHCOOH$, has also given initial reaction at the carboxyl group rather than at the hydroxyl group (81).

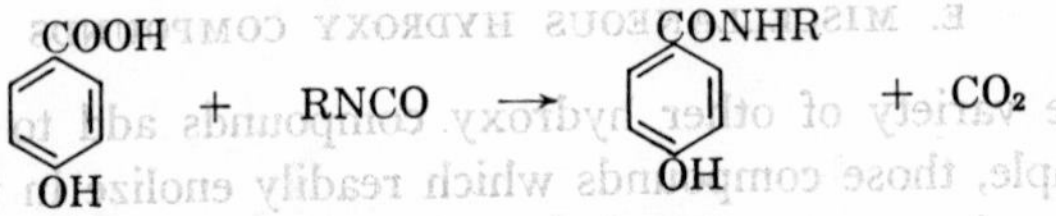

$$HOOC-C_6H_4-OH + RNCO \rightarrow RNHCO-C_6H_4-OH + CO_2 \quad (38)$$

Use has been made of a related reaction (eq. 39) to prepare an

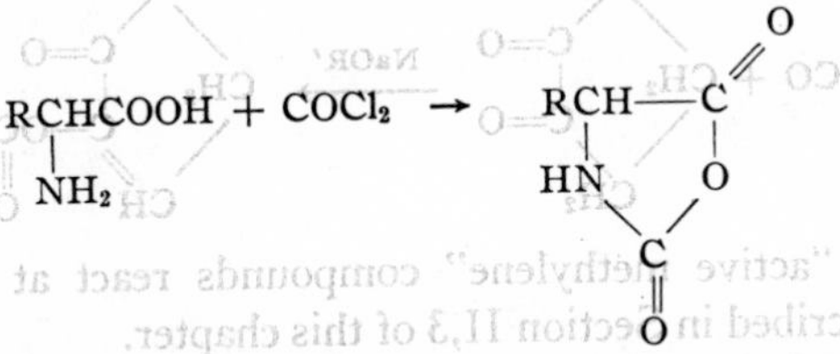

$$\underset{\displaystyle NH_2}{RCHCOOH} + COCl_2 \rightarrow \text{RCH—C(=O)—O—C(=O)—NH (ring)} \quad (39)$$

intramolecular anhydride of an isocyanate and a carboxylic acid. This cyclic anhydride is a useful monomer for the preparation of polyamides (248) (eq. 40).

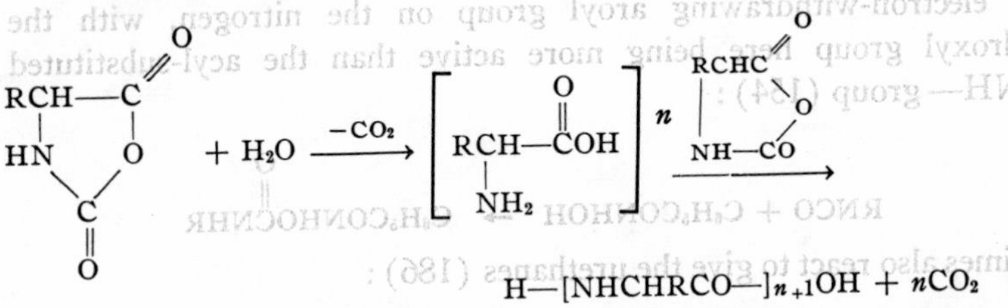

$$\text{RCH—C(=O)—O—C(=O)—NH (ring)} + H_2O \xrightarrow{-CO_2} \left[\underset{\displaystyle NH_2}{RCH}-\overset{\displaystyle O}{\overset{\|}{C}}OH \right] \xrightarrow{n\ \text{RCH—C(=O)—O—CO—NH (ring)}}$$

$$H-[NHCHRCO-]_{n+1}OH + nCO_2 \quad (40)$$

At high temperatures carboxylic acid anhydrides will react with isocyanates in a manner somewhat similar to the acids themselves. Gumpert reported that phenyl isocyanate and acetic anhydride in a pressure tube at 170–180°C. gave carbon dioxide and a product which on distillation yielded acetanilide (103,105). More recently Otvos and co-workers reported the following reaction (176):

$$\underset{(I)}{ArNCO + (CH_3\overset{*}{C}O)_2O} \rightarrow \underset{(II)}{ArN(\overset{*}{C}OCH_3)_2} + CO_2$$

With an aromatic isocyanate and acetic anhydride labeled with heavy carbon, compound II had the same activity as I, showing that the carbon of the carbon dioxide came from the isocyanate. When an aliphatic isocyanate was used, rather than an aromatic, the activity of II was less than that of I, indicating a more complex reaction.

E. MISCELLANEOUS HYDROXY COMPOUNDS

A large variety of other hydroxy compounds add to isocyanates. For example, those compounds which readily enolize in the presence of a strong base may give the urethane derivative (61) (eq. 41).

$$\text{RNCO} + \begin{matrix} & CH_2 & \\ \diagup & & \diagdown \\ CH_2 & & C{=}O \\ & & | \\ & & C{=}O \\ \diagdown & & \diagup \\ & CH_2 & \end{matrix} \xrightarrow{\text{NaOR}'} \begin{matrix} & CH_2 & \\ \diagup & & \diagdown \\ CH_2 & & C{=}O \\ & & | \\ & & C{-}O\overset{\displaystyle O}{\overset{\|}{C}}NHR \\ \diagdown & & /\!\!/ \\ & CH & \end{matrix} \qquad (41)$$

Many other "active methylene" compounds react at the methylene group, as described in Section II,3 of this chapter.

As noted previously, hydroxylamines react preferentially at the amino group if the reaction is carefully cooled and controlled, but react at both the amino and hydroxyl groups if sufficient isocyanate is present. Benzohydroxamic acid shows the deactivating effect of the electron-withdrawing aroyl group on the nitrogen, with the hydroxyl group here being more active than the acyl-substituted —NH— group (154):

$$\text{RNCO} + C_6H_5\text{CONHOH} \rightarrow C_6H_5\text{CONHO}\overset{\overset{\displaystyle O}{\|}}{C}\text{NHR}$$

Oximes also react to give the urethanes (186):

$$\text{RNCO} + \text{HON}{=}\text{CR}'_2 \rightarrow \text{RNHCOON}{=}\text{CR}'_2$$

but these are usually of limited stability, and decompose at their melting points as indicated in the following equation (96):

$$\text{RNHCOON}{=}\text{CR}'_2 \rightarrow 2\text{RCN} + \text{RNHCONHR} + CO_2$$

The reaction between dioximes and diisocyanates has been used to prepare linear polymers (50). Thermal, hydrolytic, and light stability were generally poor. Both triethylamine and cupric chloride were catalysts for the reaction; cobalt naphthenate was not.

Hydroxamic acids also react in the normal way, giving the corresponding substituted urethane (154).

Hydroperoxides add to an isocyanate, giving peroxycarbamates (172,184):

$$\text{ArNCO} + (CH_3)_3\text{COOH} \rightarrow \text{ArNH}\overset{\overset{\displaystyle O}{\|}}{C}\text{OOC}(CH_3)_3$$

These compounds may decompose by a first order, free radical mechanism and may serve as initiators of vinyl polymerizations. The results indicate that both ArNH and alkyl radicals are formed. Unlike the hydroperoxides, hydrogen peroxide gives a low yield of an azine (75). The suggested reaction sequence is as follows:

$$RNCO + H_2O_2 \rightarrow \left[RNH\overset{O}{\overset{\|}{C}}OO\overset{O}{\overset{\|}{C}}NHR\right] \rightarrow 2RNH\overset{O}{\overset{\|}{C}}O\cdot \xrightarrow{-CO_2} RNHNHR \xrightarrow{H_2O_2} RN{=}NR$$

A variety of inorganic compounds containing hydroxyl groups react to give unstable anhydrides, analogous to the reactions of isocyanates with water and with carboxylic acids. Sulfuric acid reacts with aliphatic isocyanates to give the sulfamic acid or, if water is also present, to give the amine salt (28) (eq. 42a). Phenyl isocyanate, on the other hand, gives sulfanilic acid (28) (eq. 42b). Methyl-

$$RNCO + H_2SO_4 \rightarrow \left[RNH\overset{O}{\overset{\|}{C}}OSO_3H\right] \rightarrow RNHSO_3H + CO_2 \xrightarrow{H_2O} RNH_2\cdot H_2SO_4 \quad (42a)$$

$$C_6H_5NCO + H_2SO_4 \rightarrow \left[C_6H_5NH\overset{O}{\overset{\|}{C}}OSO_3H\right] \rightarrow \left[\text{(NHCOOH)}C_6H_4\text{(SO}_3\text{H)}\right] \rightarrow {}^{+}H_3N\text{-}C_6H_4\text{-}SO_3^{-} + CO_2 \quad (42b)$$

sulfonic acid, under mild conditions gives the expected anhydride with phenyl isocyanate (eq. 43). Under more vigorous conditions, e.g.,

$$C_6H_5NCO + CH_3SO_3H \rightarrow C_6H_5NHCOOSO_2CH_3 \quad (43)$$

at 65–140°C., products of the reaction include carbon dioxide, the sulfonic acid salt of aniline, and carbanilide (179).

Derivatives of phosphorus acids containing strongly acidic hydrogens may react similarly (eq. 44). This product is not stable and

$$C_6H_5P(O)(OH)_2 + RNCO \xrightarrow{(C_2H_5)_3N} C_6H_5\overset{O}{\overset{\uparrow}{P}}(OH)\text{-}O\overset{O}{\overset{\|}{C}}NHR \quad (44)$$

loses carbon dioxide fairly readily (81). Monoesters of orthophosphoric acid also give monocarbamoyl derivatives (54). Other phosphorus acids or esters having a hydrogen attached directly to phosphorus and no strongly acidic hydrogen may react at the P—H bond, as noted in Section II,5.

Hydroxysilanes may add to the isocyanates, but the products are usually unstable. The formation of urethanes from trialkylhydroxysilanes has been reported (eq. 45). These compounds were said to be

$$\text{CH}_3\text{C}_6\text{H}_3(\text{NCO})_2 + \text{R}_3\text{SiOH} \rightarrow \text{CH}_3\text{C}_6\text{H}_3(\text{NHCOOSiR}_3)_2 \quad (45)$$

stable at their melting points, but readily hydrolyzed (13,14). On the other hand (eq. 46), triphenyl silanol has been reported to give the urea and siloxane (68). The reaction between hexamethylene

$$\text{ArNCO} + (\text{C}_6\text{H}_5)_3\text{SiOH} \rightarrow \text{ArNHCONHAr} + [(\text{C}_6\text{H}_5)_3\text{Si}]_2\text{O} \quad (46)$$

diisocyanate and a dialkylsilanediol at 120° in the presence of aluminum chloride gave products including a polyurea and polysiloxanes (215).

Boronic acids have been reported to react with diisocyanates, giving linear polymers, with the evolution of carbon dioxide (240). Boric acid also has been reacted with monoisocyanates (10) and diisocyanates (11). In the latter case polymers containing boron and nitrogen were reported.

3. Reaction with Compounds Containing the C—H Group

Compounds containing C—H bonds in which the hydrogen may readily be replaced by sodium may react with isocyanates to give substituted amides. Such compounds include malonic esters (63,186), nitroalkanes (36,155,160), acetoacetic esters (155), and acetylacetone (186). A variety of closely analogous methylene compounds contain-

$$\text{RNCO} + \text{Na}^+[\text{CH}(\text{COOC}_2\text{H}_5)_2]^- \rightarrow \text{RNHCOCH}(\text{COOC}_2\text{H}_5)_2$$

ing two activating groups (e.g., carbonyl, ester, nitrile, nitro) also react similarly (53,165,186). The *alpha* position of pyrrole (237) and the methylene group of *N*-alkyl-2-methylenedihydropyridine (204) and related compounds may react similarly (eqs. 47, 48).

$$\text{RNCO} + \text{pyrrole (N–H)} \longrightarrow \text{2-CONHR-pyrrole (N–H)} \quad (47)$$

$$\text{RNCO} + \text{1-methyl-2-methylene-1,2-dihydropyridine} (=\!CH_2,\ N\!-\!CH_3) \longrightarrow \text{1-methyl-2-(=CHCONHR)-1,2-dihydropyridine} \quad (48)$$

Isocyanates may be used (eq. 49) as acylating agents in the usual Friedel-Crafts technique, giving aryl amides (47,146). At elevated

$$\text{RNCO} + C_6H_6 \xrightarrow{AlCl_3} \text{RNHCO}-C_6H_5 \quad (49)$$

temperatures, such as 130–160°C., phenyl isocyanate may undergo a number of complex side reactions in the presence of aluminum chloride (67), therefore, moderate temperatures are preferred for this reaction.

Although not involving a reaction of the isocyanate group itself, the polymerization of isocyanatobenzyl chloride in the presence of Friedel-Crafts catalysts is an interesting example of polyisocyanate preparation (39) (eq. 50).

$$p\text{-}ClCH_2C_6H_4NCO \xrightarrow{AlCl_3} \left[(OCN)C_6H_3-CH_2-C_6H_3(OCN)-CH_2- \right]_n \quad (50)$$

Hydrogen cyanide adds to isocyanates in a normal way, analogous to hydrogen halides, as will be discussed. A tertiary amine, such as pyridine, or sodium carbonate may be used as a catalyst; the reaction is normally conducted in an appropriate solvent:

$$\text{RNCO} + \text{HCN} \rightleftarrows \text{RNH}\overset{\text{O}}{\overset{\|}{\text{C}}}\text{CN}$$

This addition may be reversed at 120–130°C. (66,186), but little practical use has been made of this reaction because of the hazards of using HCN. Without a diluent a cyclic compound was formed in one case (64) (eq. 51).

$$\text{ArNCO} + \text{HCN} \rightarrow \left[\text{ArNH}\overset{\overset{\text{O}}{\|}}{\text{C}}\text{CN}\right] \xrightarrow{\text{ArNCO}} \begin{array}{ccc} \text{ArN} & \text{—} & \overset{\overset{\text{O}}{\|}}{\text{C}} \\ | & & | \\ \text{O=C} & & \text{C=NH} \\ & \diagdown \; \diagup & \\ & \underset{\text{Ar}}{\text{N}} & \end{array} \qquad (51)$$

4. Reactions with Compounds Containing the S—H Group

Sulfur compounds usually react in a manner similar to their oxygen analogs, but slower. Thus, mercaptans and thiophenols give thiourethanes (186):

$$\text{RNCO} + \text{R'SH} \rightarrow \text{RNH}\overset{\overset{\text{O}}{\|}}{\text{C}}\text{SR'}$$

Thio compounds reacted with isocyanates include mercaptans (70,97), thiophenols (226), and mercaptobenzothiazole (207). Tertiary amines are usually strong catalysts for the reactions with sulfur compounds.

Hydrogen sulfide reacts with isocyanates, giving products analogous to those obtained from isocyanates and water (186):

$$2\text{RNCO} + \text{H}_2\text{S} \rightarrow \text{RNHCONHR} + \text{COS}$$

Metal salts of hydrogen sulfide are said to give stable, water-soluble adducts, e.g., RNHCOSNa (128).

5. Reaction with Miscellaneous Active Hydrogen Compounds

The halogen acids are among the familiar compounds that add to the isocyanates; hydrogen chloride is a normal by-product of the production of isocyanates from amines and phosgene. The halogen acids add readily, with the formation of carbamoyl halides:

$$\text{RNCO} + \text{HX} \rightleftharpoons \text{RNH}\overset{\overset{\text{O}}{\|}}{\text{C}}\text{X}$$

In addition to the reaction with hydrogen chloride, a similar reaction has been observed with hydrogen fluoride (43) and with hydrogen bromide (86).

The carbamoyl chlorides are stable at room temperature, but dissociate into the isocyanate and hydrogen chloride as the temperature is raised. Dissociation becomes nearly complete at about 90–110°C. (217). The other carbamoyl halides behave similarly.

The carbamoyl halides will react with most active hydrogen compounds in the same way as an isocyanate, except that the hydrogen halide is evolved:

$$\text{RNHCOCl} + \text{R'OH} \rightarrow \text{RNHCOOR'} + \text{HCl}$$

Disubstituted carbamoyl halides react similarly:

$$\text{R}_2\text{NCOCl} + \text{R'OH} \rightarrow \text{R}_2\text{NCOOR'} + \text{HCl}$$

The disubstituted carbamoyl chlorides are of small commercial interest as intermediates for a variety of biologically active substituted ureas and urethanes.

The acids of phosphorus and their esters that contain a P—H group and no strongly acidic hydrogen often give stable addition products with isocyanates (82,190,191,193):

$$\text{(RO)}_2\text{HPO} + \text{C}_2\text{H}_5\text{NCO} \xrightarrow{\text{NaOR}} \text{(RO)}_2\text{P(O)CONHC}_2\text{H}_5$$

In the presence of tertiary amines, phenylphosphinic and phenylphosphonic acids may add 1 mole of isocyanate, giving the amine salt of the carbamoyl derivative. Acidification gives a high yield of the acid (81) (eq. 52). Similarly, phosphines will react at the P—H group,

$$\text{C}_6\text{H}_5\text{HP(O)OH} + \text{RNCO} \xrightarrow{(\text{C}_2\text{H}_5)_3\text{N}} \text{C}_6\text{H}_5\overset{\overset{\text{O}}{\uparrow}}{\underset{\underset{\text{CONHR}}{|}}{\text{P}}}\text{OH} \qquad (52)$$

apparently until all such hydrogens have reacted (42):

$$3\text{ArNCO} + \text{PH}_3 \xrightarrow{\text{Et}_3\text{N}} \text{(ArNHCO)}_3\text{P}$$

These products are relatively stable toward hydrolysis and heat. They may decompose above 200°C., and in boiling nitrobenzene or dimethylformamide they decompose as follows:

$$2\text{(ArNHCO)}_3\text{P} \rightarrow 3\text{ArNHCONHAr} + 2\text{P} + 3\text{CO}$$

Isocyanates will react with aqueous sodium, potassium, or ammonium bisulfites to give water-soluble adducts:

$$\text{RNCO} + \text{NaHSO}_3 \rightarrow \left[\text{RNH}\overset{\overset{\text{O}}{\|}}{\text{C}}\text{SO}_3\right]^- \text{Na}^+$$

The aliphatic isocyanates give good yields of the adduct, whereas the aromatic isocyanates give considerable urea formation as well as bisulfite addition. The affinity of the aliphatic isocyanates for bisulfite is great enough to remove bisulfite from aldehyde-bisulfite addition products. The bisulfite adducts will react with amines, giving the same ureas as would be obtained from the corresponding isocyanate (186).

The possibility of a reaction between olefins and phenyl isocyanate in the presence of stannic chloride was reported by Baker and Holdsworth (18). With very rigorous efforts to keep the reactants dry, a small amount of triphenylbiuret was formed, the necessary hydrogen apparently coming from the olefin.

6. *Reaction with Unsaturated Compounds*

Staudinger and Endle observed that isocyanates have some similarity to ketenes in structure (230):

$$\underset{\text{(Ketene)}}{R{-}CH{=}C{=}O} \qquad\qquad \underset{\text{(Isocyanate)}}{R{-}N{=}C{=}O}$$

and that it is not surprising that isocyanates react with certain unsaturated compounds much as ketenes do. This early work indicated that the isocyanates, unlike ketenes, do not form four-membered rings at low temperatures with reactive unsaturated compounds such as nitrosobenzene. However, at higher temperatures (eqs. 53, 54, and 55) compounds are formed which Staudinger and Endle considered to be degradation products of the additive compounds:

$$C_6H_5NCO + C_6H_5NO \xrightarrow{120°} \left[\begin{array}{cc} C_6H_5N{-} & NC_6H_5 \\ | & | \\ C{-} & O \\ \| & \\ O & \end{array}\right] \longrightarrow C_6H_5N{=}NC_6H_5 + CO_2 \quad (53)$$

$$C_6H_5NCO + (CH_3)_2N{-}C_6H_4{-}CHO \xrightarrow{190°\ C.}$$

$$\left[\begin{array}{cc} C_6H_5N{-} & CH{-}C_6H_4{-}N(CH_3)_2 \\ | & | \\ C{-} & O \\ \| & \\ O & \end{array}\right] \longrightarrow C_6H_5N{=}CH{-}C_6H_4{-}N(CH_3)_2 + CO_2 \quad (54)$$

$$C_6H_5NCO + (CH_3)_2N-C_6H_4-\overset{S}{\overset{\|}{C}}-C_6H_4-N(CH_3)_2 \xrightarrow{170°\ C.}$$

$$\left[\begin{array}{c} C_6H_5N-C \\ | \quad | \\ C-S \\ \| \\ O \end{array}\left[C_6H_4N(CH_3)_2\right]_2\right] \rightarrow C_6H_5N{=}C\left[C_6H_4N(CH_3)_2\right]_2 + COS \quad (55)$$

More recent work has indicated several other reactions that may involve the formation of a similar four-membered ring. Some examples were discussed in the section on reactions with amides (Section II,1,B). King observed that *p*-toluenesulfonyl isocyanate reacts with sulfoxides to give sulfilimines, apparently with a cyclic intermediate (133) (eq. 56). Aldehydes reacted similarly, but the sul-

$$ArSO_2NCO + R_2SO \rightarrow \left[\begin{array}{c} R_2S-O \\ | \quad\quad | \\ ArSO_2N-C{=}O \end{array}\right] \rightarrow ArSO_2N{\leftarrow}SR_2 + CO_2 \quad (56)$$

fonylimine formed initially reacted with more aldehyde (133), as shown in equation (57).

$$ArSO_2NCO + RCHO \rightarrow \left[\begin{array}{c} ArSO_2N-C{=}O \\ | \quad\quad | \\ HC-O \\ | \\ R \end{array}\right] \xrightarrow{-CO_2} \left[\begin{array}{c} ArSO_2N \\ \| \\ CH \\ | \\ R \end{array}\right] \xrightarrow{(CH_3)_2CHCHO} \begin{array}{c} ArSO_2NH \\ | \\ RCH \\ | \\ (CH_3)_2C-CHO \end{array} \quad (57)$$

Two moles of phenylisocyanate add similarly to the C—N double bond in benzalethylamine (eq. 58) to form a diketocyanidine (106,

$$C_6H_5-CH{=}N(C_2H_5) + 2\ C_6H_5NCO \xrightarrow{180-200°\ C.} \begin{array}{c} \text{ring: } C_6H_5(H)C-N(CH_2CH_3)-C{=}O \\ | \quad\quad\quad\quad | \\ C_6H_5-N-C(=O)-N-C_6H_5 \end{array} \quad (58)$$

144). Senier and Shepheard reported methyleneaniline and phenylisocyanate add to each other (eq. 59) to form 1,3-diphenyluretidone

$$C_6H_5N{=}CH_2 + C_6H_5NCO \longrightarrow C_6H_5N\underset{\underset{O}{\overset{\|}{C}}}{\overset{CH_2}{\diamond}}NC_6H_5 \qquad (59)$$

(208). Hydrolysis of this product gave carbanilide and formaldehyde.

Staudinger and co-workers (231) found that dimethylketene would react with phenyl, α-naphthyl, and *p*-nitrophenyl isocyanates to give amorphous substances of molecular weight 3000–6000. They confirmed that dimethylketene did not react with methyl isocyanate and that *p*-anisyl isocyanate was also unreactive. Trimethylamine served as a catalyst in all of their experiments.

Diazomethane and phenylisocyanate combine (eq. 60) to yield the β-lactam, 1-phenyl-2-azetidinone (211). This is another example

$$C_6H_5NCO + 2\,CH_2N_2 \longrightarrow C_6H_5\text{-}\begin{array}{c}N\text{—}C{=}O\\ |\quad\ \ |\\ CH_2\text{—}CH_2\end{array} + 2\,N_2 \qquad (60)$$

analogous to the reaction of ketene and diazomethane, which proceeds as in reaction (61). *p*-Bromophenyl isocyanate also gave the corresponding β-lactam with diazomethane, whereas α-naphthyl, *p*-nitrophenyl, benzyl, and benzoyl isocyanates did not form β-lactams.

$$CH_2{=}C{=}O + 2CH_2N_2 \rightarrow \begin{array}{c}CH_2\text{—}C{=}O\\ |\qquad |\\ CH_2\text{—}CH_2\end{array} + 2N_2 \qquad (61)$$

Benzoyl isocyanate and diazomethane reacted in the cold (eq. 62) to give 2-phenyl-4-oxazolone in 68–70% yield (211).

$$C_6H_5\text{-}\overset{O}{\overset{\|}{C}}\text{-}NCO + CH_2N_2 \longrightarrow C_6H_5\text{-}\begin{array}{c}C{=\!=}N\\ |\qquad |\\ O\quad C{=}O\\ \diagdown CH_2 \diagup\end{array} + N_2 \qquad (62)$$

Another type of compound containing the C=N group which will combine with an isocyanate is a carbodiimide (40). In this case the addition is reversible, the complex dissociating upon attempted distillation, and the isocyanate and carbodiimide recombining in the receiver.

Slotta and Tschesche (221) reported that methyl isocyanate condensed with carbon dioxide as in reaction (63). This is a very rare

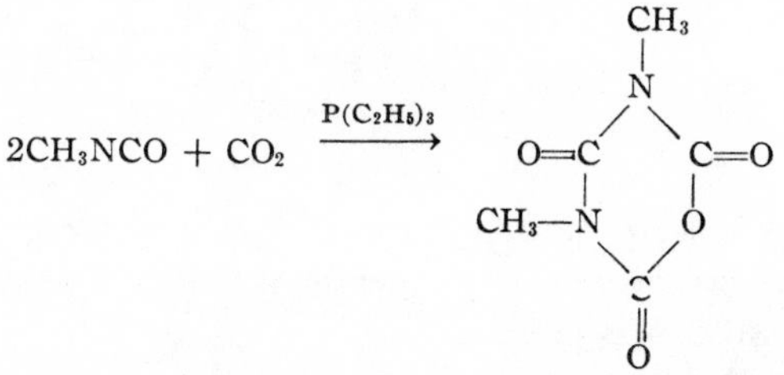

$$2CH_3NCO + CO_2 \xrightarrow{P(C_2H_5)_3} \text{cyclic product: ring } N(CH_3)\text{–}C(=O)\text{–}O\text{–}C(=O)\text{–}N(CH_3)\text{–}C(=O)\text{–} \qquad (63)$$

observation of carbon dioxide entering into a reaction with the isocyanate, rather than being evolved from such a reaction. No reaction was obtained, however, with carbon oxysulfide, carbon disulfide, phenyl isothiocyanate, acetonitrile, nitromethane, quinone, acetylene, ethylene, or amylene under the influence of triethylphosphine. With aldehydes, aldoketenes, carbon suboxide, and cyanic acid in the presence of triethylphosphine, only polymers of these substances and the trimer of methyl isocyanate were obtained. No condensation occurred with either dimethylketene or diphenylketene. Treatment with diazomethane gave an insoluble, amorphous substance which could not be identified.

Aluminum azide reacts with aromatic isocyanates (eq. 64) to give a cyclic structure that may be considered as a product of addition to the C—N double bond (113).

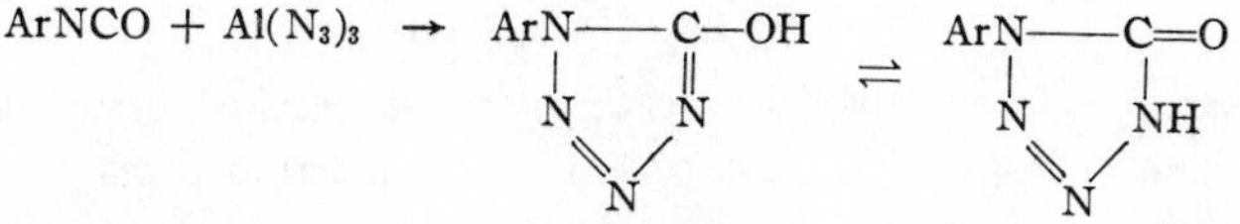

$$ArNCO + Al(N_3)_3 \rightarrow \text{ArN—C(—OH)=N—N=N— (ring)} \rightleftharpoons \text{ArN—C(=O)—NH—N=N— (ring)} \qquad (64)$$

7. *Dimerization*

As a special case of the reaction with unsaturated compounds, aromatic isocyanates may react with themselves to form dimers, "uretidine diones" (eq. 65). The reaction also is analogous to the dimerization of ketenes. Dimers of aliphatic isocyanates have not been obtained; trimerization occurs instead.

Dimerization is catalyzed vigorously by trialkylphosphines (31,84, 109,110), and more mildly by tertiary amines such as pyridine (152, 192,225). Certain aromatic isocyanates such as 4,4′-diphenylmethane

$$2ArNCO \rightarrow Ar{-}N\langle C(=O) \rangle_2 N{-}Ar \qquad (65)$$

diisocyanate dimerize slowly on standing, even without catalysts. The rate of dimerization of many other isocyanates is greatly retarded if an *ortho* substituent is present.

Molecular weight measurements of phenyl isocyanate dimer are in agreement with the dimer structure. These measurements were based on ebullioscopic methods and observed molecular weights were somewhat lower than theoretical, suggesting some dissociation in the boiling solutions (31). The crystal structure has also been determined (41), and is in agreement with the symmetrical structure as indicated.

Although the diketo structure as has been shown is generally accepted as being correct, some consideration has been given to an alternate structure (III) (88). The bulk of the evidence is in favor of the symmetrical diketo form, however.

$$R{-}N{=}C\langle O, N(R) \rangle C{=}O$$

(III)

When pyridine is used as a catalyst for dimer formation, it is most conveniently applied as the solvent medium for the reaction (225). Phosphine catalysts are much more active than pyridine and are used only in trace amounts. A convenient method of controlling phosphine-catalyzed dimerizations (21) involves the addition to the reaction mass of an alkylating agent such as benzyl chloride in an amount stoichiometrically equivalent to the substituted phosphine present. Complete deactivation of the catalyst results.

Among the phosphine catalysts the trialkyl derivatives are the most active. Dialkylaryl compounds, of which dimethylphenylphosphine is a good example, are more convenient in practice, however, because their action is more moderate, permitting better control of the exothermic dimerization reaction (227). When the phosphorus atom carries two phenyl groups, its efficiency as a catalyst is reduced, and triphenylphosphine exhibits no catalytic activity. One member of the phosphine family, 3-methyl-1-phenyl-3-phospholine, deserves special attention because of its unique activity as a catalyst for carbodiimide formation (eq. 66). The dimer is not an intermediate in this

$$2\ C_6H_5{-}NCO \xrightarrow[\text{3-methyl-1-phenyl-3-phospholine}]{\text{above } 40°\text{ C.}} C_6H_5{-}N{=}C{=}N{-}C_6H_5 + CO_2 \quad (66)$$

reaction, and the diphenylcarbodiimide is formed in nearly 90% yield. Phenylisocyanate dimer may be obtained using this catalyst only under mild conditions in dilute solution (12).

Phenyl isocyanate dimerization is a reversible reaction. The equilibrium mixture is not affected by changes in catalyst concentration. However, the conversion to dimer at equilibrium increases with decreasing temperature, with 71–74% conversion reported at 25°C. and 90% at 10°C. (12). The reaction may be forced in one direction, however, as by the precipitation of dimer from the reaction mixture, thus giving good yields at higher temperatures (216).

"Mixed dimers" have been prepared from two different isocyanates (216), and an analogous combination of α-naphthyl isocyanate and phenyl isothiocyanate apparently has been formed (eq. 67). Four

$$ArNCO + Ar'NCS \rightleftharpoons \left[ArN \underset{\underset{S}{\overset{\|}{C}}}{\overset{\overset{O}{\|}}{C}} NAr' \right] \rightleftharpoons ArNCS + Ar'NCO \quad (67)$$

products, including α-naphthyl isothiocyanate, were isolated after 14 hours of reaction at 215–225°. Formation of the "mixed dimer" as an intermediate would be a logical explanation (52). The formation of a polymeric dimer (eq. 68) by letting trimethylene diisocyanate stand for a week was reported by Iwakura and Ishizuka (121).

The preparation and properties of many dimers of mono- and diisocyanates, as well as mixed dimers of two monoisocyanates, have been reported by Siefken (216), and properties have been summarized by

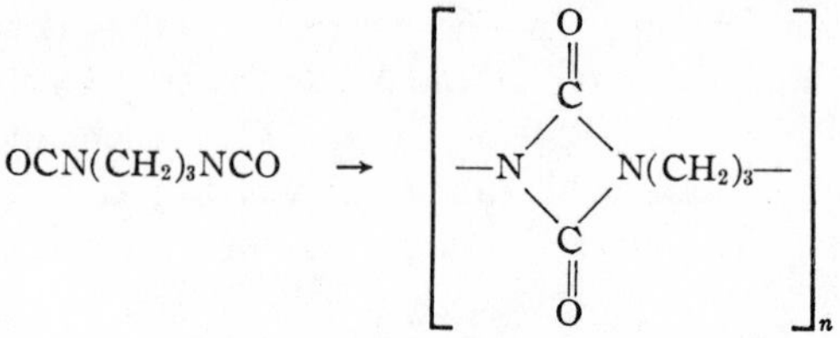

$$\mathrm{OCN(CH_2)_3NCO} \rightarrow \left[-\mathrm{N} \underset{\substack{\mathrm{C} \\ \| \\ \mathrm{O}}}{\overset{\substack{\mathrm{O} \\ \| \\ \mathrm{C}}}{\diamond}} \mathrm{N(CH_2)_3}- \right]_n \qquad (68)$$

Arnold, Nelson, and Verbanc (12). The chemistry of isocyanate dimers was also reviewed recently by Taub and McGinn (235).

8. Trimerization

Both aliphatic isocyanates and aromatic isocyanates can form trimers. This reaction is another special example of a reaction of an isocyanate with an unsaturated compound. Catalysts such as triethylphosphine, which promote dimerization of aromatic isocyanates, catalyze trimerization of the aliphatic compounds (109). Other catalysts that have been used to induce the trimerization of either aromatic or aliphatic isocyanates include calcium acetate (84), potassium acetate (111), sodium formate (111), sodium carbonate (111), sodium methoxide (155), triethylamine (112), oxalic acid (17), sodium benzoate in dimethylformamide (19), and a large number of soluble compounds of iron, sodium, potassium, magnesium, mercury, nickel, copper, zinc, aluminum, tin, vanadium, titanium, and chromium (107), titanium tetrabutyrate (142), and oxygen (134). Friedel-Crafts catalysts are also effective in bringing about polymerization (25). Perhaps because of steric hindrance, *tert*-butyl isocyanate reportedly does not trimerize, even with triethylphosphine (37). Similarly, the presence of *ortho* substituents on an aromatic isocyanate greatly reduces its ease of trimerization.

The generally accepted structure for the trimer is that of a trisubstituted isocyanurate (eq. 69). Phenyl isocyanate trimer of this

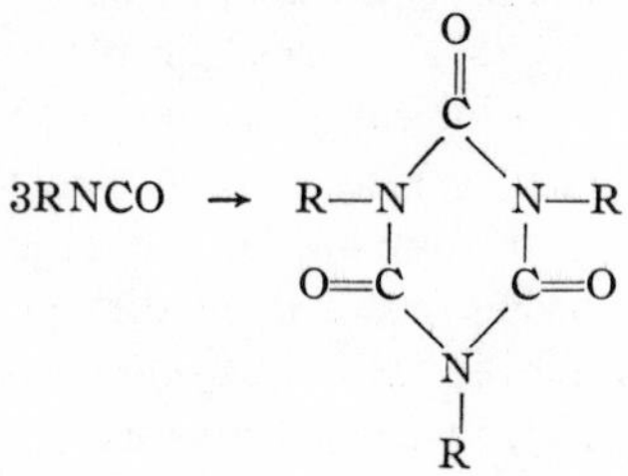

$$3\mathrm{RNCO} \rightarrow \text{R—N(C=O)N(R)(C=O)N(R)(C=O) ring: } \begin{array}{c} \mathrm{O} \\ \| \\ \mathrm{C} \\ \mathrm{R{-}N} \quad \mathrm{N{-}R} \\ | \qquad\quad | \\ \mathrm{O{=}C} \quad \mathrm{C{=}O} \\ \mathrm{N} \\ | \\ \mathrm{R} \end{array} \qquad (69)$$

structure was also synthesized by another route from phenylcyanamide (109), and trimethyl isocyanurate has been obtained from isocyanuric acid and diazomethane (219). The crystal structure of phenyl isocyanate trimer has been reported by Brown (41), and is in agreement with the isocyanurate structure.

Slotta and Tschesche (218) reported a different type of trimer from methyl isocyanate when triethylphosphine was the catalyst. They assigned it the structure (IV) of 3,5-dimethyl-2-methylimino-4,6-diketo-1,3,5-trioxodiazine. Prolonged heating converted it to the normal trimer.

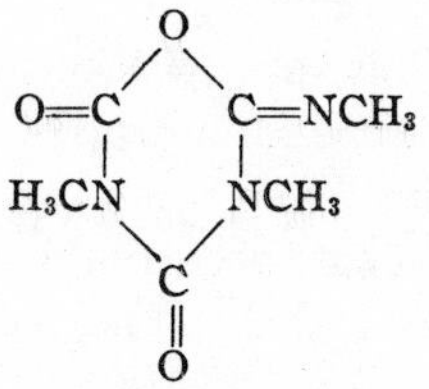

```
          O
        /   \
   O=C       C=NCH3
     |       |
  H3CN       NCH3
        \   /
          C
          ||
          O
```

(IV)

Isocyanate trimers have also been prepared by heating trimethyl cyanurate with methyl iodide or benzyl bromide (29), and by heating potassium cyanate with allyl chloride or butyl chloride plus potassium iodide (130). Heating phenyl isocyanate dimer at 250°C. without a catalyst converted it to the corresponding trimer (232).

In certain cases, at least, the formation of isocyanate trimers has been shown to utilize an addition product of an isocyanate and an active hydrogen compound as an intermediate (45,137,247). Thus, Kogon (137) has found that trimers may be obtained from the reaction between phenyl isocyanate and ethyl alcohol in the presence of a tertiary amine at 125°C. This reaction apparently requires the formation of dimer and of allophanate, with reaction of these compounds to give trimer and urethane (eqs. 70–72).

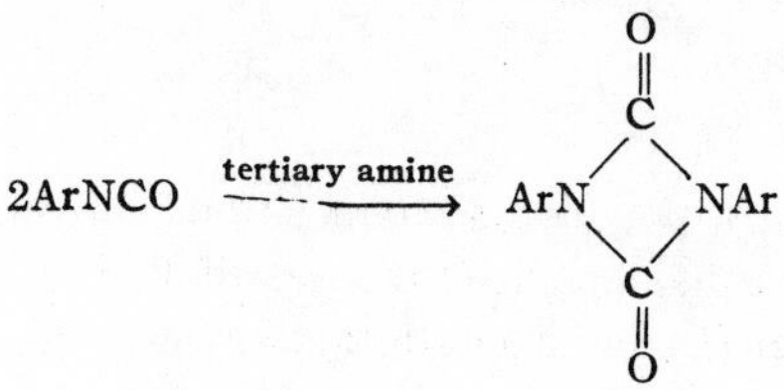

```
                              O
                              ||
                              C
                            /   \
2ArNCO --tertiary amine--> ArN     NAr        (70)
                            \   /
                              C
                              ||
                              O
```

$$ArNCO + ROH \rightarrow ArNHCOOR \xrightarrow{ArNCO} ArNH\overset{O}{\overset{\|}{C}}N(Ar)COOR \quad (71)$$

$$\text{ArN(C=O)}_2\text{NAr (dimer)} + ArNH\overset{O}{\overset{\|}{C}}N(Ar)COOR \longrightarrow \text{(ArNCO)}_3 \text{ (trimer)} + ArNHCOOR \quad (72)$$

Conditions favoring trimerization which may be similar to the use of the alcohol-tertiary amine system are the use of epoxide-tertiary amine combinations. Thus, phenyl isocyanate dissolved in 1,2-alkylene oxides gave the trimer when a drop of pyridine was added (129). Under the same conditions dimer was slowly converted to trimer. No trimerization of the isocyanate occurred in benzene, ligroin, or chloroform when pyridine was added. The trimerization in the alkylene oxide solvent may have utilized as a cocatalyst a trace of alcohol from the alkylene oxide, with reaction taking place as shown by Kogon. Trimerization has also been found to occur in the presence of ethylene carbonate and a tertiary amine (239). A complex of the trimer and the ethylene carbonate was obtained.

It is possible that trimerization generally proceeds most readily in the presence of at least trace amounts of some active hydrogen compound (HX) (eq. 73). The HX eliminated would correspond to the urethane eliminated in Kogon's mechanism.

$$RNCO + H{-}X \rightarrow RN(H)\overset{O}{\overset{\|}{C}}X \xrightarrow{RNCO} RN(H)\overset{O}{\overset{\|}{C}}N(R)\overset{O}{\overset{\|}{C}}X \xrightarrow{RNCO}$$

$$\left[\text{R–N(C=O)N(R)–C(=O)(X)–N(R)H cyclic intermediate}\right] \longrightarrow \text{(RNCO)}_3 \text{ (trimer)} + HX \quad (73)$$

An example of a polymer decomposition which apparently resulted in trimerization was reported by Swerdloff and McFarlane (234). Heating a polyurethane from tetramethylene diisocyanate and 1,4-

butanediol at 240–250°C. produced five products: tetrahydrofuran, a low molecular weight polyurethane, a low molecular weight polyurea, $H_3N^+(CH_2)_4NHCONH(CH_2)_4NHCO_2^-$, and a polymer having the elemental analysis of tetramethylene diisocyanate and assumed to be a polymer formed by trimerizing the isocyanate groups.

Trimerization is an important reaction in urethane polymer chemistry in that the trimer is relatively quite stable in the range of 150–200°C. In addition, trimerization is significant because it leads to branching of the polymer.

The chemistry of isocyanate trimers was reviewed recently by Taub and McGinn (235).

9. *Miscellaneous Reactions*

In addition to the general classes of reactions that have been discussed, isocyanates may undergo a variety of other reactions at moderate and elevated temperatures. A typical reaction at high temperatures is carbodiimide formation. For example, phenyl isocyanate on 24 hours' heating at 180°C. under pressure gives carbodiphenylimide (232):

$$2C_6H_5NCO \xrightarrow{180^\circ} C_6H_5N{=}C{=}NC_6H_5 + CO_2$$

As noted previously, phospholine oxides will catalyze carbodiimide formation (51,223), as will phospholines and phospholidines (20). Carbodiimides may be one of the ultimate decomposition products of isocyanates. It is noteworthy in polymer applications that carbodiimide formation does not change the degree of branching of the polymers.

Polymeric carbodiimides have been obtained by heating the bisneopentylurethane of diphenylmethane diisocyanate (71,72):

$$CH_2[C_6H_4NHCOOCH_2C(CH_3)_3]_2 \xrightarrow{300^\circ} \begin{array}{ll} CO_2 & 45\% \\ ROH & 91\% \\ \text{polymer} & 98\% \end{array}$$

The polymer thus obtained showed an infrared absorption at 4.7–4.8 μ, indicating the carbodiimide structure, —N=C=N—. Similarly, heating the isocyanate itself at 300°C. gave a polymeric carbodiimide (72):

$$CH_2(C_6H_4NCO)_2 \xrightarrow[45\ \text{min.}]{300^\circ} \underset{92\%}{[N{=}C{=}N{-}C_6H_4CH_2C_6H_4]_n} + CO_2$$

Polycarbodiimides have also been prepared catalytically from polyisocyanates (49), and polyurethane-polycarbodiimides have been obtained (224).

In contrast to the aromatic isocyanates, *tert*-butyl isocyanate, when heated to 180°C. does not give a carbodiimide, but does give isobutylene and cyanuric acid (37).

Another general reaction of isocyanates under milder conditions is amide formation upon treatment with an organometallic compound such as a Grignard reagent:

$$\text{RNCO} + \text{R'MgX} \xrightarrow{H_2O} \text{RNHCOR'}$$

Entemann and Johnson (74) have shown that the reactivity of the isocyanate group toward a Grignard reagent is less than that of the acetyl group, but greater than that of the fluoroformyl group:

$$CH_3CO\text{—} > \text{—}NCO > \text{—}COF$$

In contrast to the expected amide, however, Gilman and co-workers (95) obtained a 45% yield of *o*-phenylbenzohydrylaniline from the reaction between phenyl isocyanate and an excess of phenylmagnesium bromide. The proposed reaction sequence is given in equation (74).

$$C_6H_5NCO + C_6H_5MgBr \longrightarrow C_6H_5N{=}\underset{\underset{C_6H_5}{|}}{C}OMgBr \xrightarrow{C_6H_5MgBr} C_6H_5N{=}\underset{\underset{C_6H_5}{|}}{C}C_6H_5$$

$$\xrightarrow{C_6H_5MgBr} C_6H_5\overset{\overset{MgBr}{|}}{N}\text{—}CC_6H_5 \text{ (=C}_6\text{H}_5\text{ ring, } C_6H_5) \xrightarrow{H_2O} C_6H_5NHCHC_6H_5 \text{ (}o\text{-}C_6H_4C_6H_5) \qquad (74)$$

Organolithium compounds (213,238) and organothallium (94) compounds also react with isocyanates in an analogous manner.

Whereas isocyanates in the presence of alkylene oxides and tertiary amines readily polymerize (see Section II,8), Speranza and Peppel found quaternary ammonium halides to catalyze reaction of isocyanates directly with alkylene oxides (227). When ethylene oxide and phenyl isocyanate were heated with a small amount of tetraethylammonium bromide in an autoclave at 200°C. for one hour, 3-phenyl-

2-oxazolidone was obtained in 92% yield. Other oxides reacted similarly. Based on this and other work showing halide-catalyzed opening of the epoxide ring, the mechanism in equation (75) was suggested.

$$Br^- + \underset{\diagdown O \diagup}{CH_2{-}CH_2} \rightarrow [^-OCH_2CH_2Br] \xrightarrow{PhNCO} \left[Ph\overset{\ominus}{N}\overset{O}{\overset{\|}{C}}OCH_2CH_2Br \right] \rightarrow \begin{array}{c} PhN{-}C{=}O \\ | \quad\;\; | \\ H_2C \quad O \\ \diagdown \diagup \\ CH_2 \end{array} + Br^- \qquad (75)$$

Metallic sodium in dimethylformamide at —20 to —100°C. catalyzes the polymerization of monoisocyanates to give *N*-substituted "1-nylons" (209). Other anionic catalysts, especially sodium cyanide, were also effective. See reaction (76). Molecular weights as high

$$ArNCO \xrightarrow{Na} \left[\begin{array}{c} O \\ \| \\ {-}N{-}C{-} \\ | \\ Ar \end{array} \right]_n \qquad (76)$$

as 387,000 were indicated for certain of the polymers (210). Trimerization, rather than linear polymer formation, was favored as the catalyst concentration and reaction temperature were increased.

Chlorine and bromine have been reported to add to phenyl isocyanate, giving a dihalide (104) which may be rearranged to yield a mixture of the *ortho* and *para* halo-substituted aromatic isocyanates (55) (eq. 77). Both *p*-chloro- and 2,4-dichlorophenyl isocyanate

$$C_6H_5{-}NCO + X_2 \xrightarrow{20^\circ} C_6H_5{-}\overset{X}{\overset{|}{N}}{-}\overset{X}{\overset{|}{C}}{=}O \rightarrow X{-}C_6H_4{-}NH\overset{O}{\overset{\|}{C}}{-}X$$

$$\xrightarrow{90\text{-}95^\circ C.} X{-}C_6H_4{-}NCO + HX \qquad (77)$$

have been prepared by the chlorination of phenyl isocyanate in tetrachloroethane (216). Using a mercury vapor light, alkylaromatic isocyanates have been chlorinated on the alkyl group (38). Other recent patents also describe the halogenation of aromatic isocyanates (236).

Reduction of phenyl isocyanate with hydrogen and nickel at 190°C. produces methylaniline, carbanilide, aniline, methane, and carbon dioxide (198). Reduction of aromatic isocyanates with lithium aluminum hydride gives 70–90% yields of the secondary amine (76, 196,242):

$$\mathrm{ArNCO + LiAlH_4 \rightarrow ArNHCH_3}$$

Distillation of phenyl isocyanate from zinc has been reported to give aniline (103,104).

Phosphorus pentachloride converts phenyl isocyanate to a chloride which can be reduced with zinc dust to methylaniline (103,104). Phosphorus pentasulfide converts the isocyanate to the sulfur analog, phenyl isothiocyanate (156).

Photolysis of methyl isocyanate at 15–420°C. gave nitrogen, carbon monoxide, methane, ethane, hydrogen, and a polymer which was suggested to be $(CH_3N)_n$. These products indicated the intermediate formation of methyl and NCO or CH_3N radicals and carbon monoxide (22).

A reaction described as "transjointing" has been reported for phenyl isocyanate and a tertiary amine:

$$\mathrm{ArNCO + (CH_3)_2NCH_2CH_2COC_6H_5 \rightarrow ArNHCON(CH_3)_2}$$

Such a reaction was also reported with $(CH_3)_2NCH_2OR$ and $ClCH_2OR$, and apparently with $(C_2H_5)_2NCH_2OR$ (171,174):

$$\mathrm{C_6H_5NCO + (C_2H_5)_2NCH_2OBu \xrightarrow[25°C.]{ZnCl_2} \xrightarrow{H_2O} \underset{92\%}{C_6H_5NHCOOBu} + \underset{94\%}{(C_2H_5)_2NH}}$$

Isocyanates have been treated with dinitrogen tetroxide, with a variety of products being formed (15). The reaction of phenyl isocyanate with N_2O_4 in chloroform at 0–5°C. gave $C_6H_5N_2NO_3$ (V), which could couple with phenols to give phenylazophenols. If compound (V) were permitted to stand overnight, carbon dioxide was evolved and 2-nitrophenol could be isolated. Ethyl isocyanate, when treated similarly, gave carbon dioxide, nitrogen, ethylene, and ethyl nitrate.

10. Reactions of "Inorganic" Isocyanates

Thus far the "inorganic" isocyanates, represented primarily by those in which the NCO group is attached directly to a silicon atom rather than carbon, have been of academic or exploratory interest only. The chemistry of the silicon isocyanates has been studied in some detail, often with the hope of finding synthetic routes to polymers with improved temperature resistance. The reactions of the silicon isocyanates have been reviewed by O'Brien (173).

The silicon isocyanates are usually less reactive than the organic isocyanates and the most characteristic reaction is displacement of the NCO group. The fate of the NCO group is often typical of the reaction of HNCO under similar conditions. Thus, hydrolysis usually gives the silicic acid (2,78,80):

$$Si(NCO)_4 + 4H_2O \rightarrow H_4SiO_4 + 4HNCO$$

$$Si(NCO)_3F + 4H_2O \rightarrow H_4SiO_4 + HF + 3HNCO$$

The cyanic acid would be expected to hydrolyze to ammonia and carbon dioxide. The alkyl, aryl, and alkoxy silicon isocyanates are hydrolyzed less readily than are the halosilicon isocyanates. Within a particular series the rate of hydrolysis decreases as the number of isocyanate groups on the silicon atom decreases (173). Triphenylsilicon isocyanate is particularly unreactive, giving the unchanged starting compound after refluxing in ethanol, or after eight days in water (93).

Reactions of more reactive compounds with alcohols have given replacement of the isocyanate group and urethane formation from the liberated cyanic acid (80):

$$Si(NCO)_2F_2 + 6C_4H_9OH \rightarrow Si(OC_4H_9)_4 + 2C_4H_9O\overset{\overset{\displaystyle O}{\|}}{C}NH_2 + 2HF$$

Silicon tetraisocyanate has given similar replacement of the NCO, apparently followed by polymerization of the liberated HNCO (79):

$$Si(NCO)_4 + CH_3OH \rightarrow Si(NCO)_n(OCH_3)_{4-n} + (HNCO)_x$$

O'Brien (173) also obtained an allophanate from the reaction of a trialkylsilicon isocyanate and an alcohol:

$$(CH_3)_3SiNCO + ROH \rightarrow H_2NCOOR \rightarrow H_2NCONHCOOR$$

although Goubeau and Paulin (101) obtained the urethane.

In contrast to the results of the reaction of the trimethylsilicon isocyanate with alcohol in benzene, with pyridine as catalyst, O'Brien

(173) reported that a urethane was formed from that isocyanate and a glycol without a solvent or catalyst:

$$(CH_3)_3SiNCO + HO(R)OH \rightarrow (CH_3)_3SiNHCOO{-}R{-}OCONHSi(CH_3)_3$$

This result suggests that the choice between replacement of NCO or addition to NCO may be influenced greatly by traces of water in a solvent and by catalyst.

The preparation of polymers from $(C_6H_5)_2Si(OH)_2$ and $(CH_3)_2$-$Si(NCO)_2$ has been reported (246).

Amines may react with silicon isocyanates in hot benzene to give replacement of NCO, followed by addition to the HNCO (170):

$$(CH_3)_3SiNCO + RNH_2 \rightarrow RNHCONH_2$$

Using petroleum ether and a lower reaction temperature, Goubeau and Heubach (100) obtained addition of aliphatic amines to the silicon isocyanate:

$$(CH_3)_3SiNCO + R_2NH \rightarrow (CH_3)_3SiNHCONR_2$$

Grignard reagents apparently also replace the NCO group and give addition to the HNCO (173):

$$(CH_3)_3SiNCO + RMgX \rightarrow RCONH_2$$

The fate of the silicon was not established.

Redistribution reactions of halosilicon isocyanates occur at 600–700°C. without a catalyst (2,5,93) (eq. 78), but aryl, alkoxy, and most

$$Si(NCO)_2Cl_2 \rightarrow \left\{\begin{matrix} Si(NCO)_4 \\ Si(NCO)_3Cl \\ Si(NCO)_2Cl_2 \\ Si(NCO)Cl_3 \\ SiCl_4 \end{matrix}\right\} \leftarrow Si(NCO)_4 + SiCl_4 \qquad (78)$$

alkyl silicon isocyanates do not rearrange at an appreciable rate under these conditions. The methylsilicon isocyanates are an exception, undergoing random rearrangement at a slow rate, but without migration of the methyl groups (7). Silicon isocyanates will undergo exchange reactions with a number of halogen compounds in solution (4,6,8):

$$(C_3H_7)Si(NCO)_3 + AlCl_3 \rightarrow C_3H_7SiCl_3 + Al(NCO)_3$$

$$Si(NCO)_4 + C_6H_5COCl \rightarrow Si(NCO)_3Cl + C_6H_5CONCO$$

Germanium isocyanates have also been prepared, and react in ways analogous to the silicon isocyanates (3). Reactions of dimethylboron isocyanates are also characterized by displacement of the NCO group from the boron, and subsequent reaction of the liberated cyanic acid (99).

The organophosphorus isocyanates add active hydrogen compounds much as do the organic isocyanates. Thus, compounds of the type $RPO(NCO)_2$ react with alcohols and amines to give urethanes and ureas, with water to give carbon dioxide, and with resorcinol or glycols to give polymers (108,145).

Sulfuryl diisocyanate reacts with water and alcohols as do the organic isocyanates (9):

$$SO_2(NCO)_2 + H_2O \rightarrow SO_2(NH_2)_2$$

$$SO_2(NCO)_2 + ROH \rightarrow SO_2(NHCOOR)_2$$

An amide has been prepared by the following reaction (91):

$$ClSO_2NCO + ArH \xrightarrow[20\text{–}50°C.]{AlCl_3} ArCONH_2$$

11. Charts of Reactions

For convenience the reactions of the organic isocyanates are outlined in chart form in Tables I, II, and III (pages 104–106). Since most of the reactions are general for either aromatic or aliphatic isocyanates, "RNCO" has been indicated generally as the isocyanate. A few reactions, such as dimerization and ring chlorination, are specific for aromatic isocyanates. In such uses the product is indicated as a product of "ArNCO."

III. Reactions of Isocyanate Derivatives

1. Reactions of Urethanes

The urethane group is a characteristic component of polyurethanes; therefore, the reactions of simple urethanes are of direct interest to the polymer chemist. Studies of the behavior of these model compounds under a variety of conditions provide excellent clues as to the reactions of polyurethanes containing similar structures at the urethane group.

The reactions of urethanes that are of most interest in the study of polymers include thermal decompositions and reactions with active hydrogen compounds such as amines, other alcohols, and water. Some data are available on each of these reactions and on the effect of structural changes on some of these reactions.

TABLE I
Reactions with NH Compounds

$$RNCO + H{-}N\!\!<\ \rightarrow\ RN(H){-}\overset{O}{\overset{\|}{C}}{-}N\!\!<$$

		$\xrightarrow{NH_3}$	$RNHCONH_2$
$RNHCONR'_2$	$\xleftarrow{R'_2NH}$	$\xrightarrow{R'NH_2}$	$RNHCONHR'$
$RNHCONHOH$ $(RNHCONHOCONHR)$	$\xleftarrow{H_2NOH}$	$\xrightarrow{H_2N{-}NH_2}$	$RNHCONHNHCONHR$
$RNHCONH{-}R'{-}SO_3Na$	$\xleftarrow{H_2N{-}R'{-}SO_3Na}$	$\xrightarrow{H_2N{-}R'{-}CO_2Na}$	$RNHCONHR'CO_2Na$
$RNHCONHSO_2Ar$	$\xleftarrow{ArSO_2NH_2}$	$\xrightarrow{R'CONH_2}$	$RNHCONHCOR'$
$RNHCONHCONHR'$	$\xleftarrow{R'NHCONH_2}$	$\xrightarrow{H_2NCONH_2}$	$RNHCONHCONH_2$
$RNHCON(R')COOR'$	$\xleftarrow{R'NHCOOR'}$	$\xrightarrow{H_2NCOOR'}$	$RNHCONHCOOR'$
$RNHCON{=}C(R')NHCONHR$	$\xleftarrow{R'\overset{NH}{\overset{\|}{C}}NH_2}$	$\xrightarrow{(R'CO)_2NH}$	$RNHCON(COR')_2$
$RNHCON(R')N{=}NAr$	$\xleftarrow{ArN{=}N{-}NHR'}$	$\xrightarrow{R'NHNO_2}$	$RNHCON(R')NO_2$
$RNHCONHCN$ $(RNHCO)_2NCN$	$\xleftarrow{H_2NCN}$	$\xrightarrow{ArNHN{=}CHR}$	$RNHCON(Ar)N{=}CHR$
$RNHCON_3$	$\xleftarrow{HN_3}$		

TABLE II. Reactions with Other Active Hydrogen Compounds $RNCO + H—A \rightarrow RNH\overset{\|}{C}A$

With other compounds		With OH compounds	
RNHCOSR′	$\xleftarrow{R'SH}$	$\xrightarrow{R'OH}$	RNHCOOR′
RNHCOSAr	$\xleftarrow{ArSH}$	$\xrightarrow{ArOH}$	RNHCOOAr
RNHCONHR + COS	$\xleftarrow{H_2S}$	$\xrightarrow{H_2O}$	$RNHCONHR + CO_2$
$(RNHCO)_3P$	$\xleftarrow{PH_3}$	$\xrightarrow{H_2O_2}$	$(RNHCOO)_2 \rightarrow RN{=}NR + 2\ CO_2$
$RNHCOP(O)(OR')_2$	$\xleftarrow{(R'O)_2HPO}$	$\xrightarrow{R'OOH}$	$RNH\overset{O}{\overset{\|}{C}}OOR'$
RNHCOF	$\xleftarrow{HF}$		
RNHCOCl	$\xleftarrow{HCl}$	$\xrightarrow{R'COOH}$	$RNHCOR' + CO_2$ or $RNHCONHR + (R'CO)_2O + CO_2$
RNHCOBr	$\xleftarrow{HBr}$		
RNHCOCN	$\xleftarrow{HCN}$	HO–(cyclopentenone)	RNHCO–(cyclopentenone)
$RNHCOCH(COOR')_2$	$\xleftarrow{CH_2(COOR')_2}$	$\xrightarrow{}$	
RNHCOCH(CN)COOR′	$\xleftarrow{CH_2(CN)COOR'}$	$\xrightarrow{R'_2NOH}$	$RNHCOONR'_2$
$RNHCOCH(COCH_3)COOR'$	$\xleftarrow{CH_2(COCH_3)COOR'}$	$\xrightarrow{(HO)_2SO_2}$	$RNHSO_3H + CO_2$ or $H_2N—ArSO_3H$
$RNHCOCHR'NO_2$	$\xleftarrow{R'CH_2NO_2}$	$\xrightarrow{RP(O)(OH)_2}$	RP(O)(OH)OCONHR
RNHCOAr	$\xleftarrow[AlCl_3]{ArH}$		
		$\xrightarrow{R'_3SiOH}$	$RNHCOOSiR'_3$ or $RNHCONHR + R'_3SiOSiR'_3$
$RNHCOSO_3Na$	$\xleftarrow{NaHSO_3}$		

TABLE III
Other Reactions of Isocyanates

ArN–C(=O)–NAr–C(=O)– (cyclic dimer: $ArN\langle C(=O) \rangle_2 NAr$)	$\xleftarrow{\text{dimerization}}$	$\xrightarrow{ArNO}$	$RN{=}CAr + CO_2$
		$\xrightarrow{ArCHO}$	$RN{=}CHAr + CO_2$
cyclic trimer: three N(R) and three C=O in a six-membered ring	$\xleftarrow{\text{trimerization}}$	$\xrightarrow{Ar_2CS}$	$RN{=}CAr_2 + COS$
		$\xrightarrow{R'N{=}CHR'}$	RN–CHR'–NR'–C(=O)– (four-membered ring)
$\left[-N(R)-C(=O)- \right]_n$	$\xleftarrow{Na}$		
$RN{=}C{=}NR + CO_2$	$\xleftarrow{\text{heat}}$	$\xrightarrow{CH_2N_2}$	RN—C=O, CH_2—CH_2 (four-membered ring)
RNHCOR'	$\xleftarrow{R'MgX}$		
ClRNCO	$\xleftarrow[\text{light}]{Cl_2}$	$\xrightarrow[FeCl_3]{Cl_2}$	ClArNCO
$RNHCONHR + RNHCH_3$	$\xleftarrow[Ni]{H_2}$	$\xrightarrow{LiAlH_4}$	$RNHCH_3$

The thermal stability of urethanes varies greatly, depending on the structure of the urethane. Urethanes from tertiary alcohols decompose readily at temperatures as low as 50°C., whereas urethanes from many primary and secondary alcohols may undergo changes only very slowly at 150–200°C. The environment, i.e., presence of other reactants and catalysts, also greatly influences the stability of the urethanes.

Studies of the thermal decomposition of substituted urethanes have shown that three general types of reactions may take place (34,35, 71–73,143,194,234):

1. Dissociation to isocyanate and alcohol:

$$RNHCOOR' \rightleftharpoons RNCO + R'OH$$

2. *Formation of primary amine and olefin:*

$$RNHCOOCH_2CHR' \rightarrow RNH_2 + CO_2 + R'CH{=}CH_2$$

The formation of a cyclic intermediate may be a key step in this reaction (eq. 79). Dyer and Wright (73) have also proposed a reaction sequence including a cyclic structure (eq. 80).

$$\text{(cyclic intermediate: } R(H)N\text{–}C(=O)\text{–}O\text{–}CR_2\text{–}C(H)R_2\text{)} \longrightarrow RNH_2 + CO_2 + R_2C{=}CR_2 \quad (79)$$

$$\text{(cyclic intermediate: } ArNHC(\text{–}O\text{–}H)\text{–}CH_2\text{–}CH(C_6H_5)\text{–}O\text{)} \longrightarrow ArNHCOOH + C_6H_5CH{=}CH_2 \quad (80)$$

$$ArNHCOOH \rightarrow ArNH_2 + CO_2$$

3. *Formation of secondary amine:*

$$RNHCOOR' \rightarrow RN(H)R' + CO_2$$

Under the proper conditions the dissociation of a urethane has been used to prepare isocyanates in good yield. In the special case in which the urethane of a phenol is used, the dissociation may occur at temperatures as low as 150°C. The following example illustrates a typical dissociation (72):

$$C_6H_5NHCOOC_2H_5 \xrightarrow[\text{2 hrs.}]{200°\text{C.}} \underset{71\text{–}75\%}{C_6H_5NCO} + \underset{90\text{–}92\%}{C_2H_5OH}$$

The decomposition of a urethane to the primary amine and olefin is favored in cases in which the corresponding alcohol is readily dehydrated. Urethane formation and subsequent decomposition have been used to dehydrate certain alcohols, e.g., tertiary alcohols, in good yields. This type of reaction may also occur to some extent with urethanes of primary and secondary alcohols at 200–250°C. In polyurethane decompositions this reaction would cause rupture of the polymer chains.

An example of urethane decomposition with olefin and secondary as well as primary amine formation was reported by Dyer, Newborn, and Wright (72) (eq. 81).

$$C_6H_5NHCOOCH(CH_3)C_6H_5 \xrightarrow{300°C.} \begin{cases} \xrightarrow{44\%} C_6H_5NH_2 + C_6H_5CH{=}CH_2 + CO_2 \quad (35\%,\ 44\%) \\ \xrightarrow{8\%} C_6H_5NCO + C_6H_5CH(CH_3)OH \ (3\%);\ C_6H_5NCO \rightarrow (C_6H_5NH)_2CO \ (8\%) \\ \xrightarrow{24\%} C_6H_5NHCH(CH_3)C_6H_5 + CO_2 \quad (24\%) \end{cases} \tag{81}$$

Total CO_2: 84%

In addition to the three decomposition reactions, urethanes may undergo reaction with a variety of reagents which may add to a carbonyl group. It is reasonable to assume that dissociation to the isocyanate is not required, but that reaction may occur analogous to transesterification type reactions (143,194). Such reactions, with a typical active hydrogen compound (HX), and more specifically with an alcohol and with an amine, are illustrated in equations (82) to (84). The ease of displacement of OR′ apparently is greater for

$$RNH\overset{O}{\overset{\|}{C}}OR' + H{-}X \rightleftharpoons \left[RNH\overset{O}{\overset{|}{\underset{XH}{\underset{|}{C}}}}{-}OR' \right] \rightleftharpoons RNH\overset{O}{\overset{\|}{C}}X + R'OH \tag{82}$$

$$RNH\overset{O}{\overset{\|}{C}}OR' + R''OH \rightleftharpoons RNH\overset{O}{\overset{\|}{C}}OR'' + R'OH \tag{83}$$

$$RNH\overset{O}{\overset{\|}{C}}OR' + R''NH_2 \rightleftharpoons RNH\overset{O}{\overset{\|}{C}}NHR'' + R'OH \tag{84}$$

aryloxy groups than for alkoxy groups. Equilibria seem to favor urea formation more than *O*-aliphatic urethane, which in turn is favored more than *O*-aryl urethanes.

Reilly and Orchin (194) showed that dibutylamine reacted with phenyl *N*-phenylcarbamate in benzene at an appreciable rate at 40°C. and above. With the two reactants in equimolar concentrations the kinetic data did not fit a first order relation, but approximated second order kinetics, with reversal of the reaction by liberated phenol.

Urethanes from aromatic isocyanates and alcohols do not react at a significant rate with aliphatic amines at room temperature, but do so at 100 to 150°C. (116).

The reactions of urethanes in large excesses of several active hydrogen compounds have also been studied from a different viewpoint. Mukaiyama and co-workers have observed the "thermal dissociation" of urethanes at 130 to 170°C. in 10:1 molar excesses of compounds such as carboxylic acids (159,162), amines (159), and amino alcohols (161). Since the active hydrogen compound was in large excess, the fit of the kinetic data to a first-order rate equation does not rule out the possibility of a second order mechanism. Under these conditions a second order mechanism would be expected to give pseudo first order kinetics. The data were interpreted using the assumption of a rate-determining dissociation to isocyanate:

$$C_6H_5NHCOOCH_2C_6H_5 \rightleftharpoons C_6H_5NCO + C_6H_5CH_2OH$$

The isocyanate thus liberated was assumed to react very rapidly with the carboxylic acid or amino groups present. In the case of carboxylic acids, the rate of evolution of carbon dioxide fit first order kinetics with respect to isocyanate concentration. When amine or amino alcohol was present the rate of disappearance of amine fit first order kinetics similarly.

Regardless of the kinetics or the mechanism of the reaction, certain valuable relationships were found. Heating benzyl *N*-phenylurethane with a ten molar excess of dibenzylamine in tetralin for three hours at 165°C. gave a good yield of 1-phenyl-3,3-dibenzylurea. It was also found that dibutylamine reacted with this urethane under similar conditions faster than did laurylamine. Hexamethylenediamine reacted at about the same rate as laurylamine, and faster than did benzylamine. Thus, an increase in the base strength of the amine promoted the reaction with the urethane (159).

A number of substituted *N*-phenylbenzylurethanes was reacted with a ten molar excess of ethanolamine in a fifty molar quantity of benzyl alcohol at 130 to 170°C. The reaction was followed by titrating unreacted amine with standard acid. Electronegative substituents *meta* or *para* to the urethane nitrogen promoted the reaction, whereas electropostive *meta* and *para* substituents retarded the reaction. When a nitro, methyl, or chlorine group was *ortho* to the urethane nitrogen the reaction was promoted (161).

In the case of reaction with carboxylic acids, the rate of carbon dioxide evolution increased as the acid strength increased. In these experiments a ten molar excess of acid in tetralin was used as 165°C. The rate of reaction increased in the order *n*-capric acid $\simeq$ *n*-caproic acid < phenylacetic acid < chloroacetic acid.

The reaction of urethanes with alcohols was studied by Gaylord and Sroog (89) as a procedure for the synthesis of new urethanes. These authors proposed a reaction mechanism involving a carbonyl addition analogous to ester interchange.

Gaylord (87) later showed that a carbonate may result from reaction of some alcohols with certain disubstituted carbamates. *N,N*-dialkyl- and *N*-alkyl-*N*-aryl ethyl carbamates gave a new carbamate derivative upon sodium alkoxide catalyzed alcoholysis in the refluxing alcohol (eq. 85). In contrast, the *N,N*-diaryl ethyl carbamate gave

$$(C_6H_5)(CH_3)NCOOC_2H_5 + \underset{\displaystyle CH_3}{CH_3\underset{|}{C}HCH_2OH} \xrightarrow{NaOR} (C_6H_5)(CH_3)NCOOCH_2\underset{\displaystyle CH_3}{\underset{|}{C}H}CH_3 + C_2H_5OH \quad (85)$$

rise to carbonate formation in 62% yield, as in reaction (86). Only 5% of the isobutyl carbamate was isolated, and 87% of the diphenyl-

$$(C_6H_5)_2NCOOC_2H_5 + CH_3\underset{\displaystyle CH_3}{\underset{|}{C}H}CH_2OH \rightarrow (CH_3\underset{\displaystyle CH_3}{\underset{|}{C}H}CH_2O)_2CO + (C_6H_5)_2NH \quad (86)$$

amine. When benzyl alcohol was refluxed with the diphenyl ethyl carbamate the principle product was dibenzyl ether, apparently from decarboxylation of dibenzyl carbonate.

These results led Gaylord to propose that the base-catalyzed reaction of alcohols with carbamates follows one or both of the following schemes (eqs. 87,88). It was suggested that the choice will depend primarily on the relative base strength of (OR) compared to (NR_2),

$$\left[R_2N-\overset{\displaystyle O}{\overset{\|}{\underset{\displaystyle \overset{\uparrow}{R'O^{\ominus}}}{C}}}-OR\right] \longrightarrow R_2N-\overset{\displaystyle O}{\overset{\|}{C}}-OR' \quad + \quad OR^{\ominus} \quad (87)$$

$$\left[Ar_2N-\overset{\displaystyle O}{\overset{\|}{\underset{\displaystyle \overset{\uparrow}{R'O^{\ominus}}}{C}}}-OR\right] \longrightarrow R'O-\overset{\displaystyle O}{\overset{\|}{C}}-OR \quad + \quad Ar_2N^{\ominus} \quad (88)$$

the weaker base being expelled. The product of reaction (88) could react similarly with additional (OR′) to give the new carbonate, $(R'O)_2CO$.

The urethane group is subject to hydrolysis, but apparently less readily than is the ester group. In spite of the presence of urethane groups in polyether foams, the hydrolysis resistance of these polymers is excellent (202). In addition, the resistance to alkaline hydrolysis was shown to be excellent for linear polyurethanes derived from diisocyanates and aliphatic glycols (69).

2. *Reactions of Substituted Ureas*

The substituted ureas may undergo several reactions of interest to the polyurethane chemist. Like the urethanes, the ureas may dissociate at high temperatures, and may undergo carbonyl addition-type reactions, including hydrolysis.

The dissociation of a urea to the corresponding isocyanate and amine may occur, although relatively high temperatures are required for most substituted ureas. As noted (Chapter II), this reaction may be used as a preparative method for certain isocyanates in special cases:

$$RNHCONHR' \rightleftharpoons RNCO + R'NH_2$$

The dissociation of diphenylurea has been studied in some detail (26). Vapor density measurements indicated this urea to be 99% dissociated at 370°C. Also, when hydrogen chloride was added to prevent recombination of the isocyanate and amine, yields of isocyanate up to 71% were obtained, with nearly quantitative recovery of the amine salt.

The thermal stability of substituted aliphatic ureas may vary greatly with the environment. Thus, di-*tert*-alkylureas in the presence of acid catalysts may decompose to olefins, which in turn may polymerize. In the absence of catalysts di-*tert*-butylurea sublimed at 250°C., reportedly with only slight dissociation, even in the presence of alkali (35). The thermal decomposition of poly(ethylene trimethylene) urea (eq. 89) was reported to give the cyclic ureas (121).

$$\left[-NH\overset{\overset{O}{\|}}{C}NH(CH_2)_3NH\overset{\overset{O}{\|}}{C}NH(CH_2)_2-\right]_n \xrightarrow{\Delta} \underset{\text{(2-imidazolidinone)}}{HN(CH_2-CH_2)NH\!-\!C(=O)} + HN(CH_2CH_2CH_2)NH\!-\!C(=O) \qquad (89)$$

In reactions analogous to those of the urethanes, ureas may undergo typical carbonyl addition reactions (114,143,194):

$$\mathrm{RNH\overset{O}{\overset{\|}{C}}NHR' + HX \rightleftharpoons \left[RNH\overset{O}{\overset{|}{\underset{XH}{\underset{|}{C}}}}NHR'\right] \rightleftharpoons RNH\overset{O}{\overset{\|}{C}}X + R'NH_2} \quad (90)$$

$$\mathrm{RNH\overset{O}{\overset{\|}{C}}NHR' + R''NH_2 \rightleftharpoons RNH\overset{O}{\overset{\|}{C}}NHR'' + R'NH_2} \quad (91)$$

$$\mathrm{RNH\overset{O}{\overset{\|}{C}}NHR' + R''OH \rightleftharpoons RNH\overset{O}{\overset{\|}{C}}OR'' + R'NH_2} \quad (92)$$

In support of this mechanism, Reilly and Orchin (194) reacted dibutylamine and diphenylurea in equimolar quantities in refluxing anisole (152°C.). The rate data did not fit a first order relation, but did fit second order kinetics for the early part of the reaction.

Ureas have been shown to interact with each other in a manner called "dearrangement" (57,60):

$$\mathrm{RNHCONHR + R'NHCONHR' \rightleftharpoons 2RNHCONHR'}$$

Such a reaction may be assumed to involve dissociation to the amines and isocyanates followed by random recombination, and attack of free amine on urea molecules.

In studies similar to those with urethanes (see the preceding section), Mukaiyama and co-workers observed the reaction of substituted ureas with large excesses of carboxylic acids at 140–160°C. (114,163, 164,177,178) and alcohols at 160 to 190°C. (158,164). Initial dissociation to the isocyanate, followed by reaction of isocyanate with acid or alcohol, was assumed. The rates of reaction varied considerably as the solvent was changed, e.g., from anhydrous to aqueous acetic acid, or as the acid strength was changed.

The decomposition of substituted ureas in propionic acid as a solvent at 120–136°C. has also been studied by Magee and Daniels (153), with results similar to those reported by Mukaiyama and co-workers. The rate of carbon dioxide evolution was first order with regard to the concentration of substituted urea, and was faster for aryl-substituted ureas than for *sym*-dimethylurea. The results were interpreted on the assumption that the substituted urea first dissociated, and that the isocyanate thus formed reacted with the solvent acid. The evolution of carbon dioxide proceeded at a slightly slower rate when the carbonyl carbon of the substituted urea was C^{13} rather than C^{12}.

In all of these studies with a large excess of active hydrogen compound it seems probable that the reaction was actually second order, but, because of the excess of one reactant, appeared as a pseudo first-order reaction. The second order relationship reported by Reilly and Orchin (194) seems correct.

Diarylureas seem to be among the most favored reaction products in all reactions of aryl isocyanates at elevated temperatures. The formation of diphenylurea (carbanilide) has dominated many reactions of phenyl isocyanate, e.g., that with ethylurethane at 175°C. (143).

The urea group is subject to hydrolysis, but much less so than is an ester group. The resistance to hydrolysis of the diaryl-substituted urea group is illustrated by the excellent hydrolysis resistance of carbon dioxide-blown polyether foams, which contain many such urea groups (202).

3. *Reactions of Isocyanate Dimers*

Isocyanate dimers at elevated temperatures react much as do isocyanates, sometimes by prior dissociation to the isocyanate, sometimes by direct reaction between dimer and active hydrogen compound. The effects of catalysts are often similar to those with isocyanates. Thus, dimers, which may sometimes be present as trace impurities in certain isocyanates, may give nearly the same reactions as the monomeric isocyanate.

The dimers of isocyanates will dissociate to the monomers on heating. For example, the dimer of 2,4-tolylene diisocyanate dissociates rapidly and almost completely to the monomer at 175°C. This conversion of dimer to monomer has been reported to follow first order kinetics. In addition, the dissociation is promoted by catalysts such as triethylphosphine. As was noted in the discussion of the formation of dimers, an equilibrium is involved. Thus, in benzene solution in the presence of a phosphine catalyst the dimer of tolylene diisocyanate was about 25% dissociated at 25°C. and 100% dissociated at 80°C. (12).

Alcohols react with dimers to give allophanates (eq. 93) although the reaction is slow, requiring prolonged heating of the dimer in alcohol (84). The reaction is catalyzed by triethylamine, and is of second order (24).

$$\text{RN}\!\!\begin{array}{c}\overset{\displaystyle O}{\underset{}{\overset{\|}{C}}}\\ \diagup\quad\diagdown \\ \diagdown\quad\diagup \\ \underset{\displaystyle O}{\underset{\|}{C}}\end{array}\!\!\text{NR} + \text{R'OH} \rightarrow \text{RNH}\overset{\overset{\displaystyle O}{\|}}{C}\underset{\underset{\displaystyle R}{|}}{N}\text{—}\overset{\overset{\displaystyle O}{\|}}{C}\text{OR'} \tag{93}$$

Phenol does not react with phenyl isocyanate dimer at 100°C. but does react at 150°C., giving the urethane (110). It is possible that this reaction proceeds by way of regeneration of the monomer followed by combination with the phenol. Mercaptans do not react at 100 or 120°C., but at 160°C. give the thioallophanate (110), again perhaps by prior reversion of dimer to monomer.

Ammonia and aliphatic amines combine with dimers to form biurets (110,192) (eq. 94), and if the reaction is continued long enough, the

$$(\text{ArNCO})_2 + \text{RNH}_2 \rightarrow \text{ArNH}\overset{\overset{\displaystyle O}{\|}}{C}\underset{\underset{\displaystyle Ar}{|}}{N}\overset{\overset{\displaystyle O}{\|}}{C}\text{NHR} \tag{94}$$

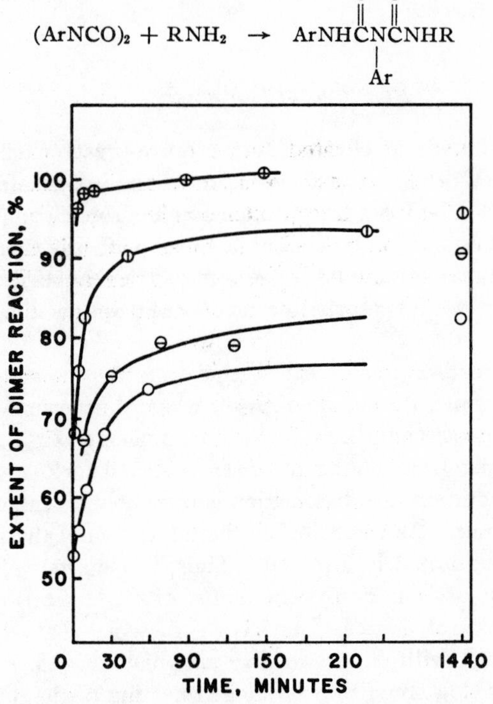

Fig. 1. Reaction of tolylene diisocyanate dimer with dibutylamine: (O) reaction at 50°C., 4:1 amine:dimer molar ratio; (⊖) 70°C., 4:1 ratio; (⦶) 130°C., 4:1 ratio: (⊕) 170–180° C., 8:1 ratio. (Taken from ref. 200.)

urea is formed. The reaction between tolylene diisocyanate dimer and dibutylamine in dichlorobenzene proceeded at the rates shown in Figure 1 (200). Thus, depending on the conditions of the analysis, a dimer could interfere with the amine equivalent analysis for an isocyanate.

Aromatic amines are less reactive toward dimers than are aliphatic amines. There is some evidence that they will not react at all below the dissociation temperature of the dimer unless a catalyst such as a trialkylphosphine is present. Hofmann prepared triphenylbiuret from phenylisocyanate dimer and aniline at 100°C., but there is evidence that his dimer was contaminated with triethylphosphine. It has been observed that phenyl isocyanate dimer and aniline do not react at 100°C.; in the presence of glacial acetic acid, however, a quantitative conversion to triphenylbiuret occurs at 25°C. within three hours (12).

Phenylhydrazine reacts with phenyl isocyanate dimer to give 1,4-diphenyl semicarbazide (65). The only product isolated from an attempted reaction between ethyl magnesium bromide or methyl magnesium iodide with phenyl isocyanate dimer was carbanilide (192).

Aside from these reactions, the isocyanate dimer may be regarded as a relatively inert compound. For example, a number of nitrophenyl and nitronaphthyl isocyanate dimers have been catalytically reduced using palladium on charcoal to give the amino derivatives of the dimer. These dimers were subsequently diazotized and coupled with suitable naphthols and phenols in aqueous medium. The dimer ring remained unchanged throughout this series of reactions (229).

Table IV lists a series of chemical reagents and their effect on phenyl isocyanate dimer (12).

TABLE IV[a]
Phenyl Isocyanate Dimer + X

X	Product
HCl (dry)	No reaction
H_2, copper chromite or Raney nickel, 125°C., 5000 p.s.i.	No reaction
$KMnO_4$ (acid)	No reaction
Glacial acetic acid	No reaction
Cl_2	*p,p'*-Dichlorophenyl isocyanate dimer
Br_2	*p*-Monobromophenyl isocyanate dimer
HNO_3	*p,p'*-Dinitrophenyl isocyanate dimer
H_2SO_4 (100%)	Sulfanilic acid

[a] Taken from ref. 12.

4. *Reactions of Isocyanate Trimers*

The isocyanate trimer ring is very stable toward heat and most chemicals; it is one of the most stable of the isocyanate derivatives. However, it has been reported that prolonged heating of phenyl isocyanate trimer at 300°C. eventually results in the formation of diphenyl carbodiimide and carbon dioxide (232). Such powerful reagents as sodium phenoxide will react at 200°C. with the trimer of phenyl isocyanate to give carbanilide and salicylanilide (212).

A complex of an alkylene carbonate and a trimer has been reported to be more reactive than the trimer alone (239). Thus, the trimer of phenyl isocyanate in complex with ethylene carbonate at 130°C. gives 3-phenyl-2-oxazolidone (eq. 95). The complex, when heated at

$$\text{ArNCO} + \begin{array}{l} CH_2\text{—O} \\ \vert \qquad\quad \diagdown \\ \vert \qquad\qquad C\text{=O} \\ \vert \qquad\quad \diagup \\ CH_2\text{—O} \end{array} \xrightarrow[70^\circ\text{C.}]{\text{tertiary amine}} \text{complex} \xrightarrow[130^\circ\text{C.}]{} \begin{array}{c} \text{ArN—C=O} \\ \diagup \qquad \diagdown \\ CH_2 \qquad\quad O \\ \diagdown \qquad \diagup \\ CH_2 \end{array} + CO_2 \qquad (95)$$

160°C. with aniline, gives the urea, and with octanol at 170°C. gives the urethane.

Heating tri(aliphatic hydrocarbon) isocyanurates to at least 120°C. under anhydrous conditions, and in the presence of hydrogen chloride, has been reported to give a low yield of the aliphatic isocyanate (203).

It has been reported that trimers give no reaction during refluxing in ethyl alcohol for several hours (137).

5. *Reactions of Carbodiimides*

The carbodiimides are those compounds containing the highly unsaturated group —N=C=N—, and in many ways are chemically analogous to the isocyanates (—N=C=O) and ketenes (—C=C=O). The normal reaction is addition of an "active hydrogen" compound to the N=C bond (eq. 96). As in the case of the addition

$$\text{R—N=C=N—R} + \text{H—A} \rightarrow \text{R—}\underset{\text{H}}{\text{N}}\text{—}\underset{\underset{\text{A}}{\vert}}{\text{C}}\text{=NR} \qquad (96)$$

products of isocyanates and active hydrogen compounds, this initial adduct may be quite stable or may rearrange or decompose to other more stable products. These reactions and the preparation of carbodiimides have been reviewed in detail by Khorana (132). A brief outline of the reactions of interest to the urethane field is given herein.

Carbodiimides are dehydrating agents, reacting readily with water to give ureas (eq. 97). In many other reactions the carbodiimides

$$\mathrm{RN{=}C{=}NR + H_2O \rightarrow \left[RNH{-}\overset{\overset{\displaystyle OH}{|}}{C}{=}NR\right] \rightarrow RNHCONHR} \qquad (97)$$

may bring about dehydration of hydroxyl compounds, as will be indicated below in the case of reaction with a carboxylic acid. Hydrogen sulfide reacts similarly to water, giving a pseudothiourea.

Alcohols and phenols are not reactive at room temperature, but when heated vigorously with the carbodiimide, will add to the N=C bond, giving ethers of pseudoureas (eqs. 98 and 99). Basic catalysts such as

$$\mathrm{RN{=}C{=}NR + ROH \rightarrow RNH\overset{\overset{\displaystyle OR}{|}}{C}{=}NR} \qquad (98)$$

$$\mathrm{RN{=}C{=}NR + ArOH \rightarrow RNH\underset{\underset{\displaystyle OAr}{|}}{C}{=}NR} \qquad (99)$$

sodium ethoxide permit addition of the alcohol to a carbodiimide under mild conditions. Mercaptans react analogously, giving ethers of pseudothioureas.

Carboxylic acids may add under very mild conditions, then rearrange (eq. 100) to acylureas in excellent yields. Urea formation and

$$\mathrm{RN{=}C{=}NR + R'COOH \rightarrow \left[RNH\underset{\underset{\displaystyle \underset{\underset{\displaystyle O}{\|}}{OCR'}}{|}}{C}{=}NR\right] \rightarrow RNH\overset{\overset{\displaystyle O}{\|}}{C}\underset{\underset{\displaystyle O{=}CR'}{|}}{N}R} \qquad (100)$$

acid anhydride formation are also possible, suggestive of the reaction between isocyanates and carboxylic acids (eq. 101). The ratios of

$$\mathrm{RNH\underset{\underset{\displaystyle \underset{\underset{\displaystyle O}{\|}}{OCR'}}{|}}{C}{=}NR \xrightarrow{H^+} \left[RNH\underset{\underset{\displaystyle \underset{\underset{\displaystyle O}{\|}}{OCR'}}{|}}{C}{=}NHR\right]^+ \xrightarrow{RCOO^-} RNHCONHR + R'\underset{\underset{\displaystyle O}{\|}}{C}O\underset{\underset{\displaystyle O}{\|}}{C}R'} \qquad (101)$$

products (acylurea, urea, anhydride) will vary with the structure of the carbodiimide and acid, the solvent used, and the reaction temperature.

Ammonia and amines react easily (eqs. 102, 103) to give substituted guanidines.

$$\mathrm{RN{=}C{=}NR + NH_3 \rightarrow RNHC(NH_2){=}NR \rightleftharpoons RNHC({=}NH)NHR} \quad (102)$$

$$\mathrm{RN{=}C{=}NR + R'NH_2 \rightarrow RNHC(NHR'){=}NR \rightleftharpoons RNHC({=}NR')NHR} \quad (103)$$

The carbodiimides may polymerize on standing at room temperature, the rate varying greatly, depending on the structure of the substituents; both dimers and trimers have been isolated. The similarity in structure between these dimers and trimers and those of isocyanate dimers and trimers is readily apparent.

Dimers:

```
ArN—C=NAr              ArN—C=O
 |   |                  |   |
ArN=C—NAr              O=C—NAr
```

Trimers:

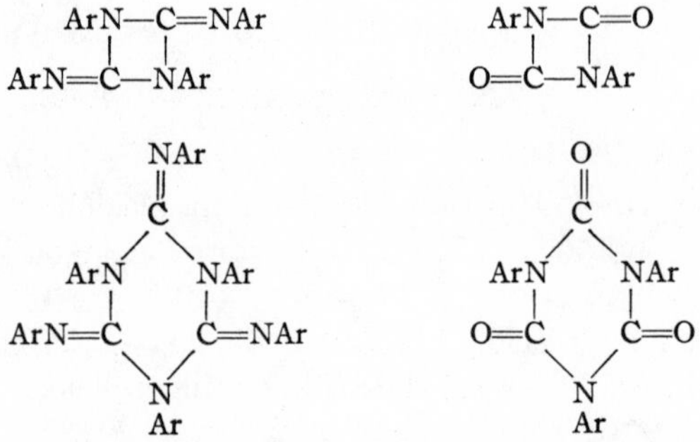

```
          NAr                     O
          ||                      ||
          C                       C
        /   \                   /   \
     ArN     NAr             ArN     NAr
      |       |               |       |
  ArN=C       C=NAr         O=C       C=O
        \   /                   \   /
          N                       N
          Ar                      Ar
   (carbodiimide)            (isocyanate)
```

6. "Splitting" of "Blocked" Isocyanates

In some fields of application a system is desired that is stable at room temperature, but that reacts at elevated temperatures as if an isocyanate were present. Particular applications of such systems include baked cōatings and wire coatings, discussed in Part II, Chapter VIII. These systems are obtained using the so-called "blocked" isocyanates or "splitters." The products have also been referred to as "disguised" and "capped" isocyanates. These blocked isocyanates are reaction products of isocyanates with certain active hydrogen compounds such that the addition product has only limited thermal stability. A typical example is the urethane from a phenol:

$$\mathrm{RNCO + ArOH \rightleftharpoons RNHCOOAr}$$

Such a urethane may dissociate at temperatures in the range of 150 to 200°C., regenerating the isocyanate. Thus, a polyisocyanate could be reacted with phenol to give a urethane that is stable at room temperature. This urethane could be dissolved in a polyester to give a mixture with indefinite storage life at room temperature. Upon heating to 150–200°C., however, the urethane would react as if it were "split," regenerating the polyisocyanate, which would then react with the polyester to give a polyurethane.

As was discussed in the sections on reactions of urethanes and ureas, one need not assume dissociation. Carbonyl additions similar to transesterification appear more reasonable:

$$\mathrm{RNH\overset{\overset{\displaystyle O}{\|}}{C}OAr} + \mathrm{R'OH} \rightleftharpoons \left[\mathrm{RNH\overset{\overset{\displaystyle O}{|}}{\underset{\underset{\displaystyle R'OH}{|}}{C}}{-}OAr}\right] \rightleftharpoons \mathrm{RNHCOOR'} + \mathrm{ArOH}$$

Such reactions of certain ureas and urethanes have been indicated to be second order, supporting such a generalized scheme (194).

The reaction may be forced to the right by the removal of a volatile component, and by the proper choice of reactants. In the system:

$$\mathrm{RNH{-}\overset{\overset{\displaystyle O}{\|}}{C}{-}X} + \mathrm{H{-}Y} \rightleftharpoons \mathrm{RNH\overset{\overset{\displaystyle O}{\|}}{C}{-}Y} + \mathrm{H{-}X}$$

reaction toward the right (at a given temperature) will be favored when R is aromatic, rather than aliphatic, when X changes in the sequence OAr>OR, and when Y changes in the sequence RNH>ArNH>RO>ArO. Thus, urethanes from aromatic isocyanates and phenols are attacked by aliphatic amines at room temperature, but not by alcohols or hydroxyl-containing polyesters. Urethanes from aromatic isocyanates and alcohols are stable at room temperature in the presence of aliphatic amines (116). These reactions appear to be subject to mild catalysis, such as by tertiary amine salts of organic acids (44) and dibutyltin dicarboxylates (115).

In some compounds having "splitter" activity, simple thermal dissociation may be a reasonably straightforward reaction, perhaps as in the case of the addition product of an isocyanate and hydrogen cyanide. Also, the dissociations of *p*-nitrophenyl and 2,4-dinitrophenyl carbanilate have been observed using infrared techniques (138). In dioxane solutions containing a tertiary amine the dissociation was apparent at room temperature:

$$\text{ArNHCOOAr}' \rightleftharpoons \text{ArNCO} + \text{Ar}'\text{OH}$$

Because of the acidic character of the nitrophenols these may well be very unusual cases. Based on the temperatures apparently required for splitting of most compounds to occur, however, and the many reactions of ureas and urethanes that are possible at 150°C. and above (see Sections III,1 and III,2 of this chapter), simple regeneration of the isocyanate in high yield seems rather unlikely in most cases.

Petersen evaluated a large number of adducts of hexamethylene diisocyanate for splitter activity (186). In this study a solution of partially hydrolyzed cellulose acetate was mixed with the adduct of the diisocyanate. The resulting mixture was coated on glass plates and cured for thirty minutes at various temperatures. The dry films were then peeled from the glass and observed for solubility in acetone and pyridine. The "splitting temperature" was taken as the lowest cure

TABLE V[a]
Results of Splitter Testing

Active hydrogen compd.	Splitting temp., °C.
HCN	120–130
Ethyl malonate	130–140
Acetylacetone	140–150
Ethyl acetoacetate	140–150
1-Phenyl-3-methyl-5-pyrazolone	150
Hydroxylamine	160
Aryl mercaptans	160
Caprolactam	>160
Pyrocatechol	>160
Aliphatic mercaptans	160–180
Monomethylaniline	170–180
Acetone oxime	180
Diphenylamine	180
Phenol	180
2,4-Diisobutylphenol	>180
Isooctylphenol	>180
4-Hydroxybiphenyl	>180
6-Hydroxytetralin	>180
α-Pyrrolidone	>180

[a] Taken from ref. 186.

temperature which gave an insoluble film. The active hydrogen compounds used in making the adducts and the corresponding splitting temperatures are shown in Table V.

One may expect somewhat lower splitting temperatures when aromatic isocyanates are substituted for the hexamethylene diisocyanate, at least in some cases. For example, a curing temperature of 150°C. is frequently used in curing polyesters with polyisocyanates blocked with phenol.

A study of similar derivatives of MDI and tetramethylene diisocyanate was made by Iwakura and Hayashi (120). Active hydrogen compounds used in preparing the splitters included phenol, *m*-cresol, diethyl malonate, ethyl acetoacetate, ethyl cyanoacetate, α-pyrrolidinone, and ε-caprolactam. Splitting tests gave results similar to those reported by Petersen.

References

1. Ahlbrecht, A. H., and D. R. Husted, U. S. Patent 2,617,817 (to Minnesota Mining), Nov. 11, 1952.
2. Anderson, H. H., *J. Am. Chem. Soc.* **66,** 934 (1944).
3. Anderson, H. H., *J. Am. Chem. Soc.* **71,** 1799 (1949).
4. Anderson, H. H., *J. Am. Chem. Soc.* **72,** 193 (1950).
5. Anderson, H. H., *J. Am. Chem. Soc.* **72,** 2091 (1950).
6. Anderson, H. H., *J. Am. Chem. Soc.* **72,** 2761 (1950).
7. Anderson, H. H., *J. Am. Chem. Soc.* **73,** 5804 (1951).
8. Anderson, H. H., *J. Am. Chem. Soc.* **75,** 1576 (1953).
9. Appel, R., and H. Gerber, *Chem. Ber.* **91,** 1200 (1958).
10. Aries, R. S., U. S. Patent 2,931,831, April 5, 1960.
11. Aries, R. S., U. S. Patent 2,945,841, July 19, 1960.
12. Arnold, R. G., J. A. Nelson, and J. J. Verbanc, *Chem. Revs.* **57,** 47 (1957).
13. Astakhin, V. V., I. P. Losev, and K. A. Andrianov, *Doklady Akad. Nauk S. S. S. R.* **113,** 581 (1957) ; *Chem. Abstracts* **51,** 14582*i* (1957).
14. Astakhin, V. V., I. P. Losev, and K. A. Andrianov, *Zhur. Obshcheĭ Khim.* **29,** 904 (1959) ; *Chem. Abstracts* **54,** 1371*f* (1960).
15. Bachman, G. B., and W. Michalowicz, *J. Org. Chem.* **23,** 1800 (1958).
16. Bailey, W. J., and F. Cesare, American Chemical Society Meeting, April 1959.
17. Bailey, J. R., and A. T. McPherson, *J. Am. Chem. Soc.* **39,** 1322 (1917).
18. Baker, J. W., and J. B. Holdsworth, *J. Chem. Soc.* **1945,** 724.
19. Balon, W. J., U. S. Patent 2,801,244 (to Du Pont), July 30, 1957.
20. Balon, W. J., U. S. Patent 2,853,518 (to Du Pont), Sept. 23, 1958.
21. Balon, W. J., and O. Stallmann, U. S. Patent 2,683,144 (to Du Pont), July 6, 1954.
22. Bamford, D. A., and C. H. Bamford, *J. Chem. Soc.* **1941,** 30.
23. Barthel, E., U. S. Patent 2,757,185 (to Du Pont), July 31, 1956.

24. Barthel, E., C. L. Kehr, E. O. Langerak, R. L. Pelley, and K. C. Smeltz, Symposium on Isocyanate Polymers, American Chemical Society Meeting, September 1956.
25. Bayer, O., B.I.O.S. Final Report No. 719 "Interview with Professer Otto Bayer," July 1946.
26. Bennett, W. B., J. H. Saunders, and E. E. Hardy, *J. Am. Chem. Soc.* **75,** 2101 (1953).
27. Berger, S. E., *Dyestuffs* **43,** 186 (1960).
28. Bieber, T. I., *J. Am. Chem. Soc.* **75,** 1405 (1953).
29. Biilmann, E., and J. Bjerrumm, *Ber.* **50,** 503 (1917).
30. Biltz, H., and A. Beck, *Ber.* **58B,** 2187 (1925).
31. Blair, J. S., and G. E. P. Smith, Jr., *J. Am. Chem. Soc.* **56,** 907 (1934).
32. Blaise, E. E., *Compt. rend.* **132,** 40 (1901).
33. Blaise, E. E., and I. Hermann, *Ann. chim. phys.* **17,** 371 (1909).
34. Blohm, H. W., and E. I. Becker, *Chem. Revs.* **51,** 471 (1952).
35. Bortnick, N., L. S. Luskin, M. D. Hurwitz, and A. W. Rytina, *J. Am. Chem. Soc.* **78,** 4358 (1956).
36. Boyd, R. N., and R. Leshin, *J. Am. Chem. Soc.* **75,** 2762 (1953).
37. Brauner, B., *Ber.* **12,** 1874 (1879).
38. Brit. Patent 752,931 (to Farbenfabriken Bayer), July 18, 1956.
39. Brit. Patent 752,952 (to Farbenfabriken Bayer), July 18, 1956.
40. Brit. Patent 795,720 (to Farbenfabriken Bayer), May 28, 1958.
41. Brown, C. J., *J. Chem. Soc.* **1955,** 2931.
42. Buckler, S. A., *J. Org. Chem.* **24,** 1460 (1959).
43. Buckley, G. D., H. A. Piggott, and J. E. Welch, *J. Chem. Soc.* **1945,** 864.
44. Bunge, W., K. H. Mielke, and F. Möller, U. S. Patent 2,886,555 (to Farbenfabriken Bayer), May 12, 1959.
45. Bunge, W., and E. Windemuth, U. S. Patent 2,952,665 (to Farbenfabriken Bayer and Mobay), Sept. 13, 1960.
46. Busch, M., G. Blume, and E. Pungs, *J. prakt. Chem.* **79,** 513 (1909).
47. Butler, J. M., *J. Am. Chem. Soc.* **71,** 2578 (1949).
48. Caldwell, W. A., J. Chapman, H. W. Goodwin, and F. J. Wilson, *J. Chem. Soc.* **1932,** 2086.
49. Campbell, T. W., U. S. Patent 2,941,966 (to Du Pont), June 21, 1960.
50. Campbell, T. W., V. S. Foldi, and R. G. Parrish, *J. Appl. Polymer Sci.* **2,** 81 (1959).
51. Campbell, T. W., and J. J. Verbanc, U. S. Patent 2,853,473 (to Du Pont), Sept. 23, 1958.
52. Case, L. C., *Nature* **183,** 675 (1959).
53. Coenen, M., *Chem. Ber.* **80,** 546 (1947).
54. Cramer, F., and M. Winter, *Chem. Ber.* **92,** 2761 (1959).
55. Curtius, T., *J. prakt. Chem.* **87,** 513 (1913).
56. Curtius, T., and A. Burkhardt, *J. prakt. Chem.* [2], **58,** 205 (1898).
57. Davis, T. L., and K. C. Blanchard, *J. Am. Chem. Soc.* **45,** 1816 (1923).
58. Davis, T. L., and F. Ebersole, *J. Am. Chem. Soc.* **56,** 885 (1934).
59. Davis, T. L., and J. M. Farnum, *J. Am. Chem. Soc.* **56,** 883 (1934).
60. Davis, T. L., and H. W. Underwood, Jr., *J. Am. Chem. Soc.* **44,** 2595 (1922).

61. Dieckmann, W., *Ber.* **35,** 3210 (1902).
62. Dieckmann, W., and F. Breest, *Ber.* **39,** 3052 (1906).
63. Dieckmann, W., J. Hoppe, and R. Stein, *Ber.* **37,** 4627 (1904).
64. Dieckmann, W., and K. Kämmerer, *Ber.* **38,** 2981 (1905).
65. Dieckmann, W., and K. Kämmerer, *Ber.* **38,** 2977 (1905).
66. Dieckmann, W., and K. Kämmerer, *Ber.* **40,** 3737 (1907).
67. Dekunikhin, N. S., and L. A. Gaeva, *Zhur. Obshcheĭ Khim.* **29,** 297 (1959); *Chem. Abstracts* **53,** 21988*a* (1959).
68. Dolgov, B., and Y. Volnov, *Zhur. Obshcheĭ Khim.,* [1], 91 (1931); *Chem. Abstracts* **25,** 4536 (1931).
69. Dyer, E., and G. W. Bartels, Jr., *J. Am. Chem. Soc.* **76,** 591 (1954).
70. Dyer, E., and J. F. Glenn, *J. Am. Chem. Soc.* **79,** 366 (1957).
71. Dyer, E., and G. E. Newborn, Jr., *J. Am. Chem. Soc.* **80,** 5495 (1958).
72. Dyer, E., G. E. Newborn, Jr., and G. C. Wright, "Thermal Degradation of Carbamates," Delaware Chemical Symposium, February 1958.
73. Dyer, E., and G. C. Wright, *J. Am. Chem. Soc.* **81,** 2138 (1959).
74. Entemann, C. E., Jr., and J. R. Johnson, *J. Am. Chem. Soc.* **55,** 2900 (1933).
75. Esser, H., K. Rastädter, and G. Reuter, *Chem. Ber.* **89,** 685 (1956).
76. Finholt, A. E., C. D. Anderson, and C. L. Agre, *J. Org. Chem.* **18,** 1338 (1953).
77. Fischer, E., *Ber.* **22,** 1930 (1889).
78. Forbes, G. S., and H. H. Anderson, *J. Am. Chem. Soc.* **62,** 761 (1940).
79. Forbes, G. S., and H. H. Anderson, *J. Am. Chem. Soc.* **66,** 1703 (1944).
80. Forbes, G. S., and H. H. Anderson, *J. Am. Chem. Soc.* **69,** 1241 (1947).
81. Fox, R. B., and W. J. Bailey, *J. Org. Chem.* **25,** 1447 (1960).
82. Fox, R. B., and D. L. Venezky, *J. Am. Chem. Soc.* **78,** 1661 (1956).
83. French, H. E., and A. F. Wirtel, *J. Am. Chem. Soc.* **48,** 1736 (1936).
84. Frentzel, W., *Ber.* **21,** 411 (1888).
85. Fry, A., *J. Am. Chem. Soc.* **75,** 2686 (1953).
86. Gal, M. H., *Bull. soc. chim.* **6,** 437 (1866).
87. Gaylord, N. G., *J. Org. Chem.* **25,** 1874 (1960).
88. Gaylord, N. G., and J. H. Crowdle, *Chem. and Ind.* **1955,** 145.
89. Gaylord, N. G., and C. E. Sroog, *J. Org. Chem.* **18,** 1632 (1953).
90. Gelderen, M. J. v., *Rec. trav. chim.* **52,** 979 (1933).
91. Ger. Patent 1,010,958 (to Farbwerke Hoechst), June 27, 1958.
92. Gheorghiu, C. V., *Bull. soc. chim.* **49,** 1205 (1931).
93. Gilman, H., B. Hofferth, and H. W. Melvin, *J. Am. Chem. Soc.* **72,** 3045 (1950).
94. Gilman, H., and R. G. Jones, *J. Am. Chem. Soc.* **61,** 1513 (1939).
95. Gilman, H., J. E. Kirby, and C. R. Kinney, *J. Am. Chem. Soc.* **51,** 2252 (1929).
96. Goldschmidt, H., *Ber.* **22,** 3101 (1889).
97. Goldschmidt, H., and A. Meissler, *Ber.* **23,** 253 (1890).
98. Goldschmidt, H., and E. Molinari, *Ber.* **21,** 2557 (1888).
99. Goubeau, J., and H. Gräbner, *Chem. Ber.* **93,** 1379 (1960).
100. Goubeau, J., and E. Heubach, *Chem. Ber.* **93,** 1117 (1960).
101. Goubeau, J., and D. Paulin, *Chem. Ber.* **93,** 1111 (1960).

102. Gryglewski, R., *Dissertationes Pharm.* **9,** 205 (1957) ; *Chem. Abstracts* **52,** 6248*b* (1958).
103. Gumpert, F., *J. prakt. Chem.* **31,** 119 (1885).
104. Gumpert, F., *J. prakt. Chem.* **32,** 278 (1885).
105. Gumpert, F., *J. prakt. Chem.* **32,** 293 (1885).
106. Hale, W. J. and N. A. Lange, *J. Am. Chem. Soc.* **41,** 379 (1919).
107. Havekoss, H., "Polymerization of Diisocyanates," O.P.B. Report 73894, Frames 4709-18, April 10, 1942.
108. Haven, A. C., Jr., *J. Am. Chem. Soc.* **78,** 842 (1956).
109. Hofmann, A. W., *Ber.* **3,** 761 (1870).
110. Hofmann, A. W., *Ber.* **4,** 246 (1871).
111. Hofmann, A. W., *Ber.* **18,** 764 (1885).
112. Hofmann, A. W., *Jahresber. Fortschritte Chem.* **1862,** 335.
113. Horwitz, J. P., B. E. Fisher and A. J. Tomasewiski, *J. Am. Chem. Soc.* **81,** 3076 (1959).
114. Hoshino, T., T. Mukuiyama and H. Hoshino, *J. Am. Chem. Soc.* **74,** 3097 (1952) ; *Bull. Chem. Soc. Japan* **25,** 392, 396 (1952) ; *Chem. Abstracts* **48,** 5132*a* (1954).
115. Hudson, G. A., Mobay Chemical Company, private communication.
116. Hudson, G. A., J. C. Hixenbaugh, E. R. Wells, J. H. Saunders and E. E. Hardy, *Offic. Dig.* **32,** 213 (1960).
117. Humnicki, W., *Roczniki Chem.* **11,** 674 (1931) ; *Chem. Abstracts* **26,** 5556 (1932).
118. Inukai, K., Y. Maki, and T. Ueda, *Rep. Gov. Ind. Research Inst., Nagoya* **1,** 176 (1952) ; *Chem. Abstracts* **50,** 3332*f* (1956).
119. Iwakura, Y., *Chem. High Polymers (Japan)* **4,** 91 (1947) ; *Chem. Abstracts* **45,** 2711 (1951).
120. Iwakura, Y., and K. Hayaski, *Yûki Gôsei Kagaku Kyôkai Shi* **16,** 533 (1958) ; *Chem. Abstracts* **53,** 1200*b* (1959).
121. Iwakura, Y., and Y. Ishizuka, *Chem. High Polymers (Japan)* **4,** 97 (1947) ; *Chem. Abstracts* **45,** 2711 (1951).
122. Iwakura, Y., M. Sato, and A. Ikegami, *Nippon Kagaku Zasshi* **80,** 632 (1959) ; *Chem. Abstracts* **55,** 5385*d* (1961).
123. Iwakura, Y., M. Sato, and A. Ikegami, *Nippon Kagaku Zasshi* **80,** 635 (1959) ; *Chem. Abstracts* **55,** 5386*a* (1961).
124. Iwakura, Y., M. Sato, and H. Munakata, *Nippon Kagaku Zasshi* **79,** 148 (1958) ; *Chem. Abstracts* **54,** 4434*e* (1960).
125. Iwakura, Y., and I. Suzuki, *Nippon Kagaku Zasshi* **77,** 64 (1956) ; *Chem. Abstracts* **52,** 281*c* (1958).
126. Iwakura, Y., and Y. Taneda, *J. Org. Chem.* **24,** 1992 (1959).
127. Iwakura, Y., and K. Yoneshima, *Nippon Kagaku Zasshi* **70,** 151 (1949) ; *Chem. Abstracts* **45,** 6583*a* (1951).
128. Jackson, H. E., Brit. Patent 599,177 (to Imperial Chemical Industry), March 5, 1948.
129. Jones, J. I., and N. G. Savill, *J. Chem. Soc.* **1957,** 4392.
130. Kaiser, D. W., and D. H. H. Church, U. S. Patent 2,536,849 (to American Cyanamid), Jan. 2, 1951.

131. Karmas, G., U. S. Patent 2,574,484 (to Ortho Pharmaceutical Corp.), Nov. 13, 1951.
132. Khorana, H. G., *Chem. Revs.* **53,** 145 (1953).
133. King, C., *J. Org. Chem.* **25,** 352 (1960).
134. Kleiner, H., H. Havekoss, and F. v. Spulak, Ger. Patent 872,618 (to Farbenfabriken Bayer), 1941.
135. Knoevenagel, E., and A. Schürenberg, *Ann.* **297,** 148 (1897).
136. Knorr, L., and P. Rössler, *Ber.* **36,** 1278 (1903).
137. Kogon, I. C., *J. Am. Chem. Soc.* **78,** 4911 (1956).
138. Kopple, K. D., *J. Am. Chem. Soc.* **79,** 6442 (1957).
139. Kuhn, B., *Ber.* **17,** 2880 (1884).
140. Kuhn, B., and E. Hentschel, *Ber.* **21,** 504 (1888).
141. Kurzer, F., *J. Chem. Soc.* **1951,** 1258; *Chem. Revs.* **50,** 1 (1952).
142. Laakso, T. M., and D. D. Reynolds, *J. Am. Chem. Soc.* **79,** 5717 (1957).
143. Lakra, H., and F. B. Dains, *J. Am. Chem. Soc.* **51,** 2220 (1929).
144. Lange, N. A., *J. Am. Chem. Soc.* **48,** 2440 (1926).
145. Lapidot, A., and M. Halmann, *J. Chem. Soc.* **1958,** 1713.
146. Leuckart, R., *Ber.* **18,** 873 (1885).
147. Leuckart, R., and M. Schmidt, *Ber.* **18,** 2339 (1885).
148. Logemann, W., and D. Artini, *Chem. Ber.* **90,** 2527 (1957).
149. Logemann, W., and D. Artini, *Chem. Ber.* **91,** 2574 (1958).
150. Logemann, W., D. Artini, and G. Tosolini, *Chem. Ber.* **91,** 2566 (1958).
151. Logemann, W., D. Artini, G. Tosolini, and F. Piccinini, *Chem. Ber.* **91,** 951 (1958).
152. Lyons, J. M., and R. H. Thompson, *J. Chem. Soc.* **1950,** 1971.
153. Magee, E. M., and F. Daniels, *J. Am. Chem. Soc.* **79,** 829 (1957).
154. Marquis, R., *Compt. rend.* **143,** 1163 (1906).
155. Michael, A., *Ber.* **38,** 22 (1905).
156. Michael, A., and G. M. Palmer, *Am. Chem. J.* **6,** 258 (1884).
157. Minunni, G., and S. D'Urso, *Gazz. chim. ital.* **58,** 808 (1928); *Chem. Abstracts* **23,** 3681 (1929).
158. Mukaiyama, T., *Bull. Chem. Soc. Japan* **28,** 253 (1955); *Chem. Abstracts* **52,** 3708*a* (1958).
159. Mukaiyama, T., and Y. Hoshino, *J. Am. Chem. Soc.* **78,** 1946 (1956).
160. Mukaiyama, T., and Y. Hoshino, *J. Am. Chem. Soc.* **82,** 5359 (1960).
161. Mukaiyama, T., and M. Iwanami, *J. Am. Chem. Soc.* **79,** 73 (1957).
162. Mukaiyama, T., S. Motoki, and Y. Hamada, *Bull. Chem. Soc. Japan* **26,** 49 (1953); *Chem. Abstracts* **48,** 3770c (1954).
163. Mukaiyama, T., S. Ozaki, and T. Hoshino, *Bull. Chem. Soc. Japan* **27,** 578 (1954); *Chem. Abstracts* **49,** 13900*f* (1955).
164. Mukaiyama, T., S. Ozaki, and Y. Kobayaski, *Bull. Chem. Soc. Japan* **29,** 51 (1956); *Chem. Abstracts* **50,** 13775*b* (1956).
165. Mumm, O., H. Hinz, and J. Diederichsen, *Ber.* **72,** 2107 (1939).
166. Naegeli, C., and A. Tyabji, *Helv. Chim. Acta* **17,** 931 (1934).
167. Naegeli, C., and A. Tyabji, *Helv. Chim. Acta* **18,** 142 (1935).
168. Naegeli, C., A. Tyabji, L. Conrad, and F. Litman, *Helv. Chim. Acta* **21,** 1100 (1938).

169. Naegeli, C., A. Tyabji, and L. Conrad, *Helv. Chim. Acta* **21,** 1127 (1938).
170. Neville, R. G., *J. Org. Chem.* **23,** 937 (1958).
171. Normura, M., T. Nishimura, and R. Oda, *Kôgyô Kwagaku Zasshi* **59,** 384 (1956); *Chem. Abstracts* **51,** 11354*i* (1957).
172. O'Brien, E. L., F. M. Beringer, and R. B. Mesrobian, *J. Am. Chem. Soc.* **79,** 6238 (1957); **81,** 1506 (1959).
173. O'Brien, J. F., "The Chemical Reactions of Silicon Isocyanates," WADC Technical Report 57-503, PB Report 131621, October 1957.
174. Oda, R., M. Nomura, S. Tanimoto, and T. Nishimura, *Bull. Inst. Chem. Research, Kyoto Univ.* **34,** 224 (1956); *Chem. Abstracts* **51,** 6528*c* (1957).
175. Olivera-Mandala, V. E., and F. Noto, *Gazy. chim. ital.* [I], **43,** 304, 514 (1913); *Chem. Abstracts* **7,** 2934,[1] 3495[7] (1913).
176. Otvos, L., J. Marton, and J. Meisel-Ágoston, *Tetrahedron Letters 1960,* No. 2, 15; *Chem. Abstracts* **54,** 12985*g* (1960).
177. Ozaki, S., T. Mukaiyama, and K. Uno, *J. Am. Chem. Soc.* **79,** 4358 (1957).
178. Ozaki, S., and T. Nagoya, *Bull. Chem. Soc. Japan* **30,** 444 (1957); *Chem. Abstracts* **52,** 3708*c* (1958).
179. Ozaki, S., and S. Shimada, *Nippon Kagaku Zasshi* **80,** 440 (1959); *Chem. Abstracts* **55,** 4397*d* (1961).
180. Paal, C., *Ber.* **27,** 974 (1894).
181. Pacilly, C. P., *Rec. trav. chim.* **55,** 101 (1936).
182. Pantlitschko, M., and F. Salvenmoser, *Monatsh. Chem.* **89,** 285 (1958); *Chem. Abstracts* **53,** 1140*i* (1959).
183. Parker, J. A., J. J. Thomas, C. L. Zeise, E. A. Peterson, and R. P. Dryden, American Chemical Society Meeting, September 1957.
184. Pedersen, C. J., *J. Org. Chem.* **23,** 252 (1958).
185. Pelley, R. L., U. S. Patent 2,757, 184 (to Du Pont), July 31, 1956.
186. Petersen, S., *Ann.* **562,** 205 (1949).
187. Petersen, S., *Ber.* **83,** 551 (1950).
188. Petersen, S., and H. F. Piepenbrink, in Houben-Weyl, *Methoden der organischen Chemie* E. Müller, editor, Thieme-Verlag, Stuttgart, Vol. 8, 1952, p. 75.
189. Pinner, A., *Ber.* **23,** 2923 (1890).
190. Pudovik, A. N., I. V. Konovalova, and R. E. Krivonosova, *Zhur. Obshcheĭ Khim.* **26,** 3110 (1956); *Chem. Abstracts* **51,** 8642*e* (1957).
191. Pudovik, A. N., and A. V. Kuznetsova, *Zhur. Obshcheĭ Khim.* **25,** 1369 (1955); *Chem. Abstracts* **50,** 4808*b* (1956).
192. Raiford, L. C., and H. B. Freyermuth, *J. Org. Chem.* **8,** 230 (1943).
193. Reetz, T., D. H. Chadwick, E. E. Hardy, and S. Kaufman, *J. Am. Chem. Soc.* **77,** 3813 (1955).
194. Reilly, C. B., and M. Orchin, "The Dissociation of Ureas, Urethanes and Biurets," Symposium on Isocyanate Polymers, American Chemical Society Meeting (1956).
195. Rekker, R. F., A. C. Faber, D. H. E. Tom, H. Verleur, and W. T. Nauta, *Rec. trav. chim.* **70,** 113 (1951).
196. Ried, W., and F. Müller, *Chem. Ber.* **85,** 470 (1952).
197. Roth, J. S., and E. F. Degering, *J. Am. Chem. Soc.* **67,** 126 (1945).

198. Sabatier, P., and A. Mailche, *Compt. rend.* **144,** 824 (1907) ; *Ann. chim.* [8], **16,** 70 (1909).
199. Saunders, J. H., *Rubber Chem. and Technol.* **32,** 337 (1959).
200. Saunders, J. H., and E. E. Hardy, *J. Am. Chem. Soc.* **75,** 5439 (1953).
201. Saunders, J. H., and R. J. Slocombe, *Chem. Revs.* **43,** 203 (1948).
202. Saunders, J. H., S. Steingiser, A. S. Morecroft, P. G. Gemeinhardt, and E. E. Hardy, *Ind. Eng. Chem. Data Series* **3,** 153 (1958).
203. Schaefer, F. C., and E. K. Drechsel, U. S. Patent 2,580,468 (to American Cyanamid), Jan. 1, 1952.
204. Schneider, W., K. Gaertner, and A. Jordan, *Ber.* **57B,** 522 (1924).
205. Scholl, R., and K. Holdermann, *Ann.* **345,** 376 (1907).
206. Schultz, E. M., *J. Am. Chem. Soc.* **69,** 1056 (1947).
207. Seeger, N. V., and T. G. Mastin, U. S. Patent 2,764,592 (to Goodyear), Sept 25, 1956.
208. Senier, A., and F. G. Shepheard, *J. Chem. Soc.* **95,** 504 (1909).
209. Shashoua, V. E., *J. Am. Chem. Soc.* **81,** 3156 (1959).
210. Shashoua, V. E., W. Sweeny, and R. F. Tietz, *J. Am. Chem. Soc.* **82,** 866 (1960).
211. Sheehan, J. C., and P. T. Izzo, *J. Am. Chem. Soc.* **71,** 4059 (1949).
212. Shilov, E. A., and M. N. Bogdanov, *Zhur. Obscheĭ Khim.* **18,** 1060 (1948) ; *Chem. Abstracts* **43,** 1351*h* (1949).
213. Shirley, D. A., and M. D. Cameron, *J. Am. Chem. Soc.* **74,** 664 (1952).
214. Shkapenko, G., G. T. Gmitter, and E. E. Gruber, *Ind. Eng. Chem.* **52,** 605 (1960).
215. Shostakovskii, M. F., V. N. Kotrelev, D. A. Kochkin, S. P. Kalinina, and V. V. Borisenko, *Zhur. Priklad. Khim.* **31,** 952 (1958) ; *Chem. Abstracts* **52,** 19911*f* (1958).
216. Siefken, W., *Ann.* **562,** 75 (1949).
217. Slocombe, R. J., E. E. Hardy, J. H. Saunders, and R. L. Jenkins, *J. Am. Chem. Soc.* **72,** 1888 (1950).
218. Slotta, K. H., and R. Tschesche, *Ber.* **60,** 295 (1927).
219. Slotta, K. H., and R. Tschesche, *Ber.* **60,** 301 (1927).
220. Slotta, K. H., and R. Tschesche, *Ber.* **60,** 1011 (1927).
221. Slotta, K. H., and R. Tschesche, *Ber.* **60** 1021 (1927).
222. Slotta, K. H., and R. Tschesche, *Ber.* **62,** 137 (1929).
223. Smeltz, K. C., U. S. Patent 2,840,589 (to Du Pont), June 24, 1958.
224. Smeltz, K. C., U. S. Patent 2,941,983 (to Du Pont), June 21, 1960.
225. Snape, H. L., *J. Chem. Soc.* **49,** 254 (1886).
226. Snape, H. L., *Ber.* **18,** 2428 (1885).
227. Speranza, G. P., and W. J. Peppel, *J. Org. Chem.* **23,** 1922 (1958).
228. Stallmann, O., U. S. Patent 2,671,082 (to Du Pont), March 2, 1954.
229. Stallmann, O., and E. O. Langerak, U. S. Patent 2,643,250 (to Du Pont), June 23, 1953.
230. Staudinger, H., and R. Endle, *Ber.* **50,** 1042 (1917).
231. Staudinger, H., F. Felix, and E. Geiger, *Helv. Chim. Acta* **8,** 314 (1925).
232. Stolle, R., *Ber.* **41,** 1125 (1908).
233. Stoutland, O., L. Helgen, and C. L. Agre, *J. Org. Chem.* **24,** 818 (1959).

234. Swerdloff, J., and S. B. McFarlane, "Thermal Degradation of Polyurethanes," American Chemical Society Meeting, September 1954.
235. Taub, B., and C. E. McGinn, *Dyestuffs* **42,** 263 (1958).
236. Tazuma, J. J., U. S. Patents 2,915,545 and 2,945,875 (to Food Machinery and Chemical Corp.) ; Dec. 1, 1959 and July 19, 1960.
237. Treibs, A., and W. Ott, *Ann.* **577,** 119 (1952).
238. Trippett, S., and D. M. Walker, *J. Chem. Soc.* **1959,** 3874.
239. Tsuzuki, R., K. Ichikawa, and M. Kase, *J. Org. Chem.* **25,** 1009 (1960).
240. Upson, R. W., U. S. Patent 2,517,944 (to Du Pont), August 8, 1950.
241. Weiner, M. L., *J. Org. Chem.* **25,** 2245 (1960).
242. Wessely, F., and W. Swoboda, *Monatsh. Chem.* **82,** 621 (1951).
243. White, H. C., and F. W. Bergstrom, *J. Org. Chem.* **7,** 497 (1942).
244. Wiley, P. F., *J. Am. Chem. Soc.* **71,** 1310 (1949).
245. Wiley, P. F., *J. Am. Chem. Soc.* **71,** 3746 (1949).
246. Wilson, J. C., M. A. Nadler, I. Katz, and A. Walti, U. S. Patent 2,932,586 (to North American Aviation), April 12, 1960.
247. Windemuth, E., W. Bunge, and O. Bayer, U. S. Patent 2,954,365 (to Farbenfabriken Bayer and Mobay), September 27, 1960.
248. Woodward, R. B., and C. H. Schramm, *J. Am. Chem. Soc.* **69,** 1551 (1947).
249. Wurtz, A., *Compt. rend.* **27,** 242 (1848).
250. Wurtz, A., *Ann.* **71,** 326 (1849).
251. Wurtz, A., *Compt. rend.* **28,** 224 (1849).

IV. KINETICS AND CATALYSIS OF THE ISOCYANATE REACTIONS

I. Introduction

It was the purpose of Chapter III to serve as an introduction to and general survey of the reactions of isocyanates and their more familiar derivatives. As shown there, a very large number of reactions of isocyanates has been observed, but only a relatively small number is of major significance in industrial operations. These more important reactions have been studied in varying degrees of thoroughness in an effort to elucidate the mechanisms of the reactions, the effect of structure on reactivity, and the role of catalysts. This chapter is a survey of information relating to those reactions which have been studied in such detail.

For convenience in comparison, all second order rate data have been expressed in terms of $k \times 10^{-4}$ l./mole sec. Because of the difficulty inherent in comparing closely the data from different laboratories, especially those obtained with different reaction conditions, comparisons are made when possible from data reported from one laboratory. In later sections of this chapter efforts are made to draw general conclusions regarding the relative reactivity of different active hydrogen compounds and effects of catalysts.

II. General Considerations

In chemical reactions the isocyanates may react as might be expected of one or more of the following resonance forms:

$$\left[R-\ddot{\underset{\cdot\cdot}{N}}^{-}-\overset{+}{C}=O \longleftrightarrow R\ddot{N}=C=O \longleftrightarrow R-\ddot{N}=\overset{+}{C}-\ddot{\underset{\cdot\cdot}{O}}^{-}: \right]$$

Such resonance structures obviously suggest the possibility of ionic reactions, with electron donors attacking the carbonyl carbon and electron acceptors attacking the oxygen or nitrogen. Catalysis by Lewis acids and bases might also be expected.

The first isocyanate reaction studied kinetically, the isocyanate-alcohol reaction, is a useful model to illustrate a general scheme of reactions. As proposed by Baker and co-workers (8–10), the reaction sequence may be pictured as in equation (1). A basic catalyst

$$\mathrm{R'NCO} + \mathrm{ROH} \rightleftharpoons \left[\begin{array}{c}\mathrm{R'N{=}C{-}\ddot{\underset{..}{O}}{:}} \\ \uparrow \\ \mathrm{O} \\ \mathrm{H}\diagup\ \ \diagdown\mathrm{R}\end{array}\right] \xrightarrow{\mathrm{ROH}} \left[\begin{array}{c}\mathrm{H}\diagdown\ \ \diagup\mathrm{R} \\ \mathrm{O} \\ \downarrow \\ \mathrm{R'{-}\ddot{\underset{..}{N}}{-}C{-}\ddot{\underset{..}{O}}{:}} \\ \uparrow \\ \mathrm{O} \\ \mathrm{R}\diagup\ \ \diagdown\mathrm{H}\end{array}\right] \rightarrow \begin{array}{c}\mathrm{R'NH\overset{O}{\overset{\|}{C}}OR} \\ + \\ \mathrm{ROH}\end{array} \quad (1)$$

could participate similarly (eq. 2). Other electron donors could also serve in a similar way as catalysts.

$$\mathrm{R'NCO} + \mathrm{R_3N{:}} \rightleftharpoons \left[\begin{array}{c}\mathrm{R'N{=}C{-}\ddot{\underset{..}{O}}{:}} \\ \uparrow \\ \ddot{\mathrm{N}} \\ \mathrm{R}\diagup\ |\ \diagdown\mathrm{R} \\ \mathrm{R}\end{array}\right] \xrightarrow{\mathrm{ROH}} \mathrm{R'NH\overset{O}{\overset{\|}{C}}OR} + \mathrm{R_3N{:}} \quad (2)$$

In addition, one might expect an acid catalyst to participate as follows:

$$\mathrm{R'NCO} + \mathrm{HA} \rightleftharpoons \left[\mathrm{R{-}N{=}C{-}\ddot{\underset{..}{O}}{:} \rightarrow H\cdot\cdot A}\right] \quad (3)$$

$$\xrightarrow{\mathrm{ROH}} \mathrm{R'NHCOOR} + \mathrm{HA}$$

Other electron-accepting materials, e.g., many metal compounds, could be expected to serve as Lewis acids and hence as catalysts. In general, however, it is found that acids are much weaker catalysts than are bases.

From these examples it is apparent that a general scheme for the reactions of isocyanates with active hydrogen compounds may be as follows:

$$\mathrm{RNCO} + \text{catalyst} \rightarrow \text{complex} \xrightarrow[\text{compound}]{\text{active hydrogen}} \text{product} + \text{catalyst}$$

One may then have as many different reactions proceeding simultaneously as there are catalyst types present. As will be discussed in regard to the later examples in this chapter, the reactions are complicated by the participation of reactant molecules (e.g., alcohol, water) and products (e.g., ureas, urethanes) as catalysts.

When a reactant molecule serves as a catalyst as well as a reactant, that specific reaction is not a second order reaction in the strictest meaning of the term. While the data may fit a second order calculation at a given concentration of reactants, the rate constant will change as the relative concentration of reactants changes.

In these reactions the structure of the isocyanate and the active hydrogen compound should play a major role in determining the rate of reaction. For example, an electron-withdrawing substituent on the isocyanate molecule should increase the partial positive charge on the isocyanate carbon and move the negative charge farther from the site of reaction, thus making attack on the carbon by an electron donor easier, and hence giving a faster reaction (eq. 4). On the other

$$\left[O_2N\text{—}C_6H_4\text{—}NCO \longleftrightarrow {}^{-}O(O)N{=}C_6H_4{=}N\text{—}\overset{+}{C}{=}O \right] \quad (4)$$

hand, an electron-donating substituent should reduce the partial positive charge on the isocyanate carbon, making attack at that point by an electron donor more difficult, thus giving a slower reaction. Experimental results confirm these expectations; i.e., electron-withdrawing substituents do increase the reactivity, whereas electron-donating substituents reduce the reactivity of an isocyanate.

The effect of substituents on the active hydrogen compound should be the oppositive to that on the isocyanate if the primary role of the active hydrogen compound is that of an electron donor. For example, with amines, electronegative groups withdraw electrons, reducing the basicity of the nitrogen, making it a poorer electron donor (eq. 5).

$$\left[O_2N\text{—}C_6H_4\text{—}\ddot{N}H_2 \longleftrightarrow {}^{-}O(O)N{=}C_6H_4{=}\overset{+}{N}H_2 \right] \quad (5)$$

Conversely, electron-donating groups would increase the basicity of the amino nitrogen.

If the primary role of the active hydrogen compound were that of a hydrogen donor, electronegative substituents should increase the rate of reaction because of the increased acidity of the active hydrogen and electropositive groups should decrease the reactivity.

Since negative substituents do decrease the reactivity of the active hydrogen compounds and positive substituents do increase the reactivity, those compounds must function primarily as electron donors, as has been shown, not as hydrogen donors.

In addition to electronic effects of substituents, steric factors are important. In aromatic compounds bulky groups in the *ortho* positions, or in aliphatic compounds branching or bulky substituents close to the site of reaction, retard the reaction. These steric factors not only affect the reactivity of both the isocyanate and the active hydrogen compound, but also influence the effectiveness of a catalyst. Since a catalyst must approach the site of reaction as closely as a reactant itself, the ease of approach and extent to which the approach is possible will be influenced by steric relations between the catalyst and one or more of the reactants, usually the isocyanate.

A critical comparison of data presented in this chapter on any given reaction will reveal discrepancies if more than one set of data are available for that reaction. In many cases the differences are small and can be ignored, in other cases they are large and cannot. Some possible reasons for the more obvious differences are noted at appropriate places in the chapter. Several generalizations at this point concerning factors affecting kinetic studies with isocyanates may be a useful guide toward evaluating data in the remainder of this chapter.

As was described in Chapter III, many reactions of the isocyanates are possible; more than one reaction may be occurring in the system under study. This possibility is most pronounced at elevated temperatures and in the presence of catalysts. In some cases equilibria may be involved. For best results the reaction system should be analyzed completely to show the rate of disappearance of all reactants and rate of formation of all products. Although such a complete study is usually difficult to accomplish, the accuracy of the conclusions may be in direct proportion to the completeness of the analysis of the total system.

The necessity of purifying all components of the reaction system cannot be overemphasized. As summarized in Section XII, a very wide range of compounds, both organic and inorganic, may catalyze one or more of the isocyanate reactions. To illustrate, in the absence of catalysts a temperature of 100°C. or higher may be required to obtain trimerization, allophanate formation, or carbodiimide formation. Each of these reactions may proceed readily at room temperature in the presence of traces of suitable catalysts. Trace impurities in resins are particularly likely sources of catalysts. Another common oversight is the very small acid (HCl) content of the isocyanate itself. Many authors have reported catalyst concentrations accurately, based on the added catalyst, but have neglected to report the acid content of the isocyanate. In many cases the acid will effectively neutralize a portion of the catalyst.

The choice of solvent may affect both the rate of an uncatalyzed reaction and the effectiveness of a catalyst. In general the solvents that readily complex with the active hydrogen compound or catalyst, e.g., by hydrogen bonding or dipole moment interaction, will provide a slower reaction than will the solvents that cannot so readily associate with reactant or catalyst. In extreme cases the solvents may even react with the isocyanate, as in the cases of dimethylformamide, dimethylacetamide (see Chapter III, Section II,1,B) and dimethyl sulfoxide. To illustrate—Sorenson (55) reported the apparent sequence (6) for the reaction between phenyl isocyanate and benzoic acid for 16 hours in refluxing dimethyl sulfoxide.

$$\mathrm{ArNCO + ArCOOH \xrightarrow{(CH_3)_2SO} ArNHCOOCOAr \xrightarrow{(CH_3)_2SO}}$$

$$\mathrm{(ArNHCO_2^-)[(CH_3)_2S \rightarrow OCOAr^+] \rightarrow ArNHCOOH + \left[CH_3{-}\underset{\underset{CH_2}{\|}}{S} \rightarrow O\overset{\overset{O}{\|}}{C}Ar \right]} \quad (6)$$

$$\mathrm{ArNHCOOH \rightarrow ArNH_2 \rightarrow \underset{(70\%\ isolated)}{ArNHCONHAr}}$$

$$\mathrm{\left[CH_3{-}\underset{\underset{CH_2}{\|}}{S} \rightarrow O\overset{\overset{O}{\|}}{C}Ar \right] \rightarrow \underset{(50\%\ isolated)}{CH_3SCH_2OCOAr}}$$

Whereas most kinetic studies have been made in dilute solution, most commercial applications utilize solvent-free systems. Since a change in a solvent may affect a rate or even relative rates in a series of reactants, one should not expect to find exactly the same kinetic results in a solvent-free system as in a dilute solution study.

The reactions of diisocyanates present a complicated mixture of reactions possible. For example, with 2,4-tolylene diisocyanate the sequences could occur as in (7). Thus the apparent reaction (1) is actually a combination of reactions (2) and (3). If reaction (3) proceeds at a significant rate, as it usually does, the initial reactivity of the diisocyanate is not a very accurate measure of the reactivity of the 4-position group. While the last 30–40% of the reaction may

$$\text{2,4-}CH_3C_6H_3(NCO)_2 + ROH \xrightarrow{(1)} \begin{cases} \xrightarrow{(2)} CH_3C_6H_3(NCO)(NHCOOR) \xrightarrow[(4)]{ROH} CH_3C_6H_3(NHCOOR)_2 \\ \xrightarrow{(3)} CH_3C_6H_3(NHCOOR)(NCO) \xrightarrow[(5)]{ROH} CH_3C_6H_3(NHCOOR)_2 \end{cases} \tag{7}$$

involve only urethane-substituted monoisocyanates, this portion of the reaction still involves two different isomers (reactions (4) and (5)). Thus, an exact analysis of the reactivity of 2,4-tolylene diisocyanate requires the synthesis of the pure urethane-substituted monoisocyanates and a study of their reactions.

In the simpler case of symmetrical diisocyanates the initial experimentally-observed rate of reaction should be divided by 2 to give the rate constant for only one of the isocyanate groups.

In addition to variations in data arising from the factors as outlined, a few anomalies remain, particularly in reactions at elevated temperatures. At this stage of knowledge one must be particularly cautious in making close predictions of relative reaction rates at temperatures of 100°C. and above.

III. Reactions with Alcohols

1. *Reactions of Monoisocyanates*

The mechanism and kinetics of the reaction of isocyanates with alcohols have been studied more thoroughly than those of any other isocyanate reaction. These studies have been of major interest primarily because of the commercial importance of this reaction: it is of fundamental significance in essentially all applications of isocyanates. Although studies have been made with both mono- and diisocyanates, those with monoisocyanates are kinetically the simplest and may be used to show the effects of molecular structure, catalyst, temperature, and solvent on the reaction. The reactions of diisocyanates with alcohols and glycols, of greater commercial importance, will be discussed in the following section.

The first quantitative study of the isocyanate-hydroxyl reaction was that of Davis and Farnum (22), who observed the relative rates of reactions of several alcohols with phenyl isocyanate in benzene at 26°C. These studies showed that among aliphatic alcohols the relative rates of reaction of primary, secondary, and tertiary alcohols are approximately 1.0, 0.3, and 0.003–0.007, respectively. These results are in agreement with the expected influence of steric hindrance due to branching of the aliphatic chain close to the site of reaction.

More detailed investigations of the isocyanate-hydroxyl reaction were reported by Baker and co-workers (8–10), who provided the theoretical basis for many of the later kinetics and mechanism studies by others. A general scheme of reaction was presented as a combination of a base (:B)-catalyzed reaction (eq. 8) and an uncatalyzed

$$[\mathrm{R{-}N{=}C{=}O} \leftrightarrow \mathrm{RN{=}\overset{+}{C}{-}\overset{-}{O}}] + :\mathrm{B} \underset{k_2}{\overset{k_1}{\rightleftharpoons}}$$

$$\left[\begin{array}{c}\mathrm{RN{=}C{-}\overset{-}{O}} \\ \uparrow \\ \underset{+}{\mathrm{B}}\end{array}\right] \xrightarrow[k_3]{\mathrm{R'OH}} \mathrm{R\overset{H}{N}COOR'} + :\mathrm{B} \qquad (8)$$

reaction (eq. 9). The transition state for the final catalyzed reaction

$$\mathrm{RNCO} + \mathrm{R'OH} \xrightarrow{k_0} \mathrm{RNHCOOR'} \qquad (9)$$

would be as in equation (10). Each aspect of this reaction was in-

$$\left[\begin{array}{c}\mathrm{H}\quad\mathrm{R'} \\ \diagdown\overset{+}{}\diagup \\ \mathrm{O} \\ \downarrow \\ \mathrm{R{-}\bar{N}{-}C{-}\bar{O}} \\ \uparrow \\ \mathrm{B^+}\end{array}\right] \qquad (10)$$

vestigated in detail, and many fine ramifications were discussed. The principal features are summarized here.

Assuming the stationary state condition, the concentration of the complex (RNCO:B) is given by:

$$(\text{complex}) = k_1(\mathrm{RNCO})(\mathrm{B})/[k_2 + k_3(\mathrm{R'OH})]$$

and the rate of disappearance of isocyanate and rate of formation of the product is:

$$-d(\mathrm{RNCO})/dt = k_0(\mathrm{R'OH})(\mathrm{RNCO}) + \{k_1k_3(\mathrm{RNCO})(\mathrm{R'OH})\ (\mathrm{B})/[k_2 + k_3(\mathrm{ROH})]\}$$

From this, the experimentally observed rate constant for any one set of conditions would be:

$$k_{\text{exp.}} = k_0 + \{k_1k_3(\text{B})/[k_2 + k_3(\text{R'OH})]\}$$

If the value of k_2 is much greater than $k_3(\text{R'OH})$, or if (R'OH) is constant in a set of experiments, this may be further simplified:

$$k_{\text{exp.}} = k_0 + k_c(\text{B})$$

in which k_c, the "catalytic rate constant," is given by:

$$k_c = k_1k_3/[k_2 + k_3(\text{R'OH})]$$

The reaction of phenyl isocyanate with methanol in dibutyl ether at 20°C. was found to be second order, but the value of the rate constant increased slowly with time, indicating catalysis by the product of the reaction. The addition of methyl carbanilate to the initial reaction mixture increased the rate of reaction, confirming catalysis by the urethane, a weak base. The rate constant for the initial uncatalyzed reaction was 0.28×10^{-4} l./mole sec.

Furthermore, the alcohol itself was found to function as a weak catalyst. Thus the value of the second order rate constant was found to increase as the alcohol/isocyanate ratio was increased, as shown in Table I. In these, as in other experiments, the progress of the reaction was followed by titration of the unreacted isocyanate with secondary amine. A similar behavior was shown with ethyl and isopropyl alcohols.

TABLE I
Effect of Alcohol Concentration on Phenyl Isocyanate-Methanol Reaction
(0.24*M* isocyanate, dibutyl ether)[a]

Alcohol concn. (moles/l.)	$k_0 \times 10^4$ (l./mole sec.)	
	20°C.	30°C.
0.12	0.10	0.27
0.24	0.28	0.48
0.48	0.43	0.73
0.96	0.78	1.60
1.92	1.27	2.28
2.4	1.45	2.53

[a] Taken from refs. 8–10.

This alcohol-catalyzed reaction may be considered to follow the general reaction sequence for base-catalyzed reactions (eq. 11).

$$\mathrm{RNCO} + \mathrm{R'OH} \underset{k_2}{\overset{k_1}{\rightleftharpoons}} \left[\begin{array}{c}\mathrm{RN{=}C{-}O} \\ \uparrow \\ \mathrm{HOR'}\end{array}\right] \xrightarrow[k_3]{\mathrm{R'OH}} \mathrm{RNHCOOR'} + \mathrm{R'OH} \qquad (11)$$

Again, assuming steady state conditions:

$$k_0 = \frac{k_1 k_3(\mathrm{R'OH})}{k_2 + k_3(\mathrm{R'OH})}$$

which may be rearranged and transposed:

$$\mathrm{R'OH}/k_0 = k_2/k_1k_3 + (\mathrm{R'OH})/k_1$$

Thus a plot of $(\mathrm{R'OH})/k_0$ against $(\mathrm{R'OH})$ should give a straight line whose slope is $1/k_1$ and whose intercept is k_2/k_1k_3. This linear relation was found for reactions with all three alcohols at each of two temperatures, without catalyst and also with catalyst. A typical relation is shown in Figure 1.

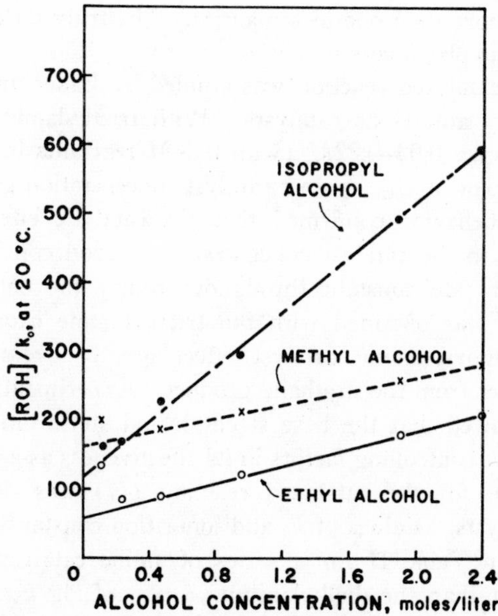

Fig. 1. Relation between rate of reaction and alcohol concentration for the phenyl isocyanate-alcohol reaction in dibutyl ether at 20°C. (Taken from refs. 8–10.)

This catalytic function of the alcohol raises doubt as to whether or not any reaction occurs by a truly uncatalyzed mechanism. The difference between a catalyzed and an uncatalyzed reaction appears to be the nature of the final transition state. For the catalyzed reaction the last step may be as in equation (12), whereas the last step for

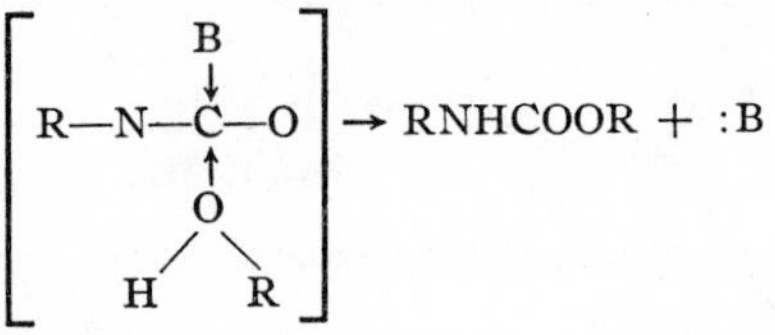

$$\left[\begin{array}{c} \mathrm{B} \\ \downarrow \\ \mathrm{R{-}N{-}C{-}O} \\ \uparrow \\ \mathrm{O} \\ \diagup \quad \diagdown \\ \mathrm{H} \qquad \mathrm{R} \end{array}\right] \rightarrow \mathrm{RNHCOOR} + :\mathrm{B} \tag{12}$$

an uncatalyzed reaction might be as in equation (13). Thus, the

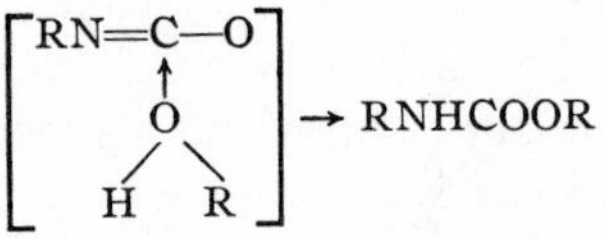

$$\left[\begin{array}{c} \mathrm{RN{=}C{-}O} \\ \uparrow \\ \mathrm{O} \\ \diagup \quad \diagdown \\ \mathrm{H} \qquad \mathrm{R} \end{array}\right] \rightarrow \mathrm{RNHCOOR} \tag{13}$$

question is more than one of semantics. The truly uncatalyzed reaction appears to play a very minor role, if any.

The base-catalyzed reaction was studied by Baker and co-workers using tertiary amines as catalysts. With triethylamine in the concentration range 0.03–0.22M (with 0.24M reactants in dibutyl ether at 20°C.) a plot of $k_{\text{exp.}}$ against catalyst concentration gave a straight line. This behavior confirmed that the catalytic effect is directly proportional to the catalyst concentration. Good consistency of the second order rate constant throughout nearly the entire course of the reaction was obtained with the triethylamine catalyst, showing that the tertiary amine catalyst effect greatly overshadowed any catalytic effect from the urethane product. Experiments with several catalysts showed that the base strength and steric hindrance of the base (:B) are controlling factors in its effectiveness as a catalyst. The rate constant for the catalyzed reaction (k_c) was determined for several catalysts. Values of k_c and ionization constants at 25°C., k_b, are shown in Table II for a series of amine catalysts. For these amines other than the dialkylanilines a plot of log k_b against log k_c gave a nearly straight line in accordance with the Brønsted relation $\log k_c = x \log k_b + C$.

TABLE II
Relation between Catalyst Strength and Base Strength for Amine Catalysts[a]

Base	Ionization const. at 25°C., k_b	$k_{exp.}$, 0.03M catalyst, $\times 10^4$ l./mole sec., 20°C.	Rate const., 20°C., k_c, $\times 10^4$ l./mole sec.
Quinoline	6.3×10^{-10}	1.7	48
Pyridine	2.3×10^{-9}	3.1	93
α-Picoline	3×10^{-8}	3.3	101
Triethylamine	5.65×10^{-4}	38	1240
Dimethylaniline	1×10^{-9}	0.33	0
Diethylaniline	4.5×10^{-8}	0.29	0
None		0.28	

[a] Taken from refs. 8–10.

Based on the assumption that resonance caused the dialkylanilines to be planar (eq. 14), calculations showed that steric hindrance due

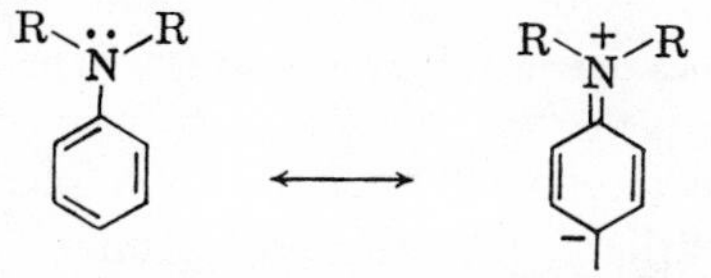

$$R_2\ddot{N}-C_6H_5 \longleftrightarrow R_2\overset{+}{N}=C_6H_5^{-} \qquad (14)$$

to the R groups prevented the nitrogen of the dialkylaniline from approaching the carbonyl carbon of the isocyanate closely enough to exert a catalytic effect.

The fact that dimethylaniline and diethylaniline were not catalysts ruled out the possibility that the catalyst functioned by assisting in removal of the proton from the alcohol as a rate-determining step. Steric hindrance could not be expected to influence such a proton removal.

The electronic effects of substituents on the reactivity of substituted phenyl isocyanates were also in agreement with the proposed mechanism. If the rate-controlling step involved attack of an electron donor on the carbonyl carbon, then electron withdrawal from the site of reaction should facilitate the reaction. Thus p-nitrophenyl isocyanate, with resonance possibilities as indicated, reinforced by inductive withdrawal of electrons by the nitro group, should be much more reactive than phenyl isocyanate (eq. 15). Conversely, electron-

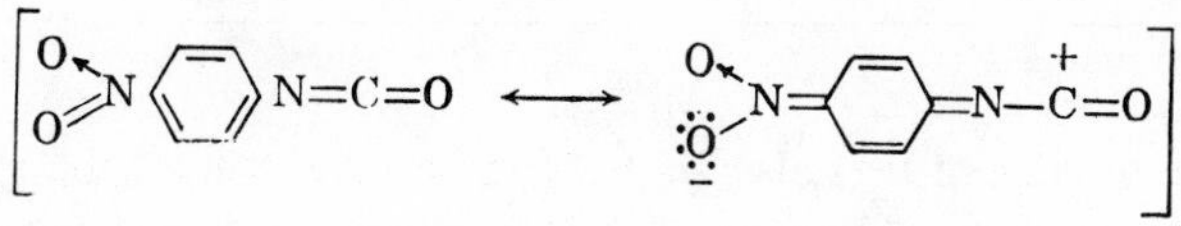

$$\left[O_2N-C_6H_4-N=C=O \longleftrightarrow {}^{-}O(O)N=C_6H_4=N-\overset{+}{C}=O \right] \qquad (15)$$

donating groups should tend to reduce the positive character of the carbonyl carbon, thus reducing the ease of attack by an electron donor, and slowing the reaction. The rates of the reactions of several aromatic isocyanates with methanol (each 0.24*M*) in dibutyl ether at 20°C., with 0.0306*M* triethylamine as catalyst, are shown in Table III, and are in agreement with the proposed electronic effects of substituents.

TABLE III

Effect of Substituents on Reactivity of Aromatic Monoisocyanates with Methanol[a] (p-RC_6H_4NCO, dibutyl ether, 20°C., 0.03*M* triethylamine, each reactant 0.24*M*)

	R =				
Constant	Cyclohexyl	CH_3O—	CH_3—	H—	NO_2—
$k_{exp.} \times 10^4$, l./mole sec.	0.035	16.5	25	37.7	5000[b]

[a] Taken from refs. 8–10.
[b] Too fast for accurate measurement, greater than 90% complete in 4 min.

The structure of the alcohol was shown to influence the rate of reaction, as indicated earlier by Davis and Farnum (22). The rate constants for the catalyzed ($k_{exp.}$, 0.03*M* triethylamine) and uncatalyzed (k_0) reactions are shown in Table IV, as are the activation energies (E_a) in kcal./mole. (The high activation energies (13 kcal.) reported for the catalyzed reaction with isopropyl and *tert*-butyl alcohols are surprising. It seems doubtful that the catalyzed reaction with isopropanol would have a higher activation energy than the uncatalyzed reaction.)

TABLE IV

Reaction of Phenyl Isocyanate with Alcohols[a]
(0.24*M* reactants in dibutyl ether)

	$k_0 \times 10^4$ l./mole sec.			$k_{exp.} \times 10^4$ l./mole sec.		
Alcohol	20°C.	30°C.	E_a	20°C.	30°C.	E_a
Methyl	0.28	0.48	10.0	34	46.5	5
Ethyl	0.48	0.85	11.0	12.7	20	7.85
Isopropyl	0.23	0.40	10.0	0.95	1.87	13
tert-Butyl	0.008	0.013	—	0.015	0.207	13

[a] Taken from refs. 8–10.

The choice of solvent was also shown to affect the rate of the isocyanate-alcohol reaction. Thus, for 0.24*M* reactants, the rate constant for the uncatalyzed phenyl isocyanate-methyl alcohol reaction was 0.28×10^{-4} l./mole sec. in dibutyl ether at 20°C., but was 1.18 for the reaction in benzene. Infrared data showed alcohol-solvent association in dibutyl ether, but not in benzene. Association of alcohol with the solvent was considered to reduce the rate primarily by reducing the magnitude of k_3. It is reasonable that attack of solvent-alcohol combinations on the isocyanate-alcohol complex should be slower than attack by unassociated alcohol.

Many investigators have subsequently studied the isocyanate-alcohol reaction and have added more data to those reported by Baker and co-workers. These amplifications have broadened the base of useful knowledge, but have added little to the fundamental understanding of the mechanism of the reaction itself.

Additional studies of the effect of isocyanate structure on reactivity were reported by Bailey and co-workers (4) and later, using the same system, by Kaplan (36). By using a large excess of 2-ethylhexanol in benzene at 28°C., and following the reaction with infrared, the relative reactivities of many substituted phenyl isocyanates were observed, as shown in Table V. Additional comparative data are given from Burkus and Eckert (14), who observed the reaction of several isocyanates with *n*-butyl alcohol in toluene, with triethylamine catalyst. The relative effect of substituent groups was calculated from observed rate data. The data of Baker and Holdsworth (9), converted to a relative rate of 1.0 for phenyl isocyanate, are also included for comparison. These results show remarkably good agreement.

Brock (13) showed that the reaction of aryl isocyanates with alcohols could be correlated by the Hammett (30) linear free energy relationship, $\log k/k_0 = \rho\Sigma\sigma$. In this series ρ is the reaction series constant, $\Sigma\sigma$ is the sum of the substituent constants, k_0 is the rate constant for the reaction of phenyl isocyanate, and k is the rate constant for the substituted phenyl isocyanate in question. The constant σ is a quantitative measure of the electronic effect of a given *meta* or *para* substituent relative to a hydrogen atom. A positive value of σ indicates an electron-withdrawing effect; a negative value indicates an electron-donating effect. The reaction constant ρ is dependent on the reaction and the conditions under which it occurs. A positive value of ρ is characteristic of reactions enhanced by electron-withdrawing substituents. A negative value of ρ is characteristic of those reactions which are promoted by electron-donating groups.

With data from published sources, with reaction temperatures in

TABLE V

Relative Effects of Substituents on Activity of Substituted Phenyl Isocyanates with Alcohols[a]

Substituent	Relative reactivity in system indicated			
	2-Ethylhexanol, benzene, 28°C.		Methanol, dibutyl ether, $(C_2H_5)_3N$ catalyst, 20°C. (9)	*n*-Butanol, toluene, $(C_2H_5)_3N$ catalyst (14)
	Bailey (4)	Kaplan (36)		
p-SO_2	>50	—	—	—
p-NO_2	>35	41	~130	—
m-NO_2	—	33	—	—
m-CF_3	—	10	—	—
m-Cl	7	7.5	—	—
m-Br	—	7.5	—	—
m-NCO	6	5	—	6-7
p-NCO	6	4	—	4
p-Cl	—	3.5	—	—
p-NHCOOR	2	1.5	—	1
p-C_6H_5	—	1.5	—	—
m-NHCOOR	2	1.5	—	2
m-CH_3O	—	1.3	—	—
None	1.0	1.0	1.0	1.0
p-*n*-C_4H_9	—	0.7	—	—
m-CH_3	0.5	0.6	—	—
p-CH_3	0.5	0.6	0.5	0.5
p-CH_3O	—	0.5	0.4	—
o-CH_3	0.08	—	—	0.17–0.25
o-CH_3O	0.04	—	—	—

[a] Data from refs. 4, 9, 14, 36.

the range of 20–39.69°C., and using several solvents, the value for ρ was calculated to be 1.69. The variation in the reaction conditions may be expected to contribute some small error to this value. Substituent constants (σ) are shown in Table VI. From these data, Brock calculated the ratio of rate constant for the 4-position group in 2,4-tolylene diisocyanate to that for the 2-position group as 2.67, much lower than that reported by several observers. It appears that this ratio may vary somewhat according to the solvent, the temperature, the active hydrogen reactant, and the catalyst, if any, but usually is approximately in the range of 3 to 10.

More recently Kaplan (36) established pseudo first order rate constants for the reaction of a number of substituted phenyl isocyanates with a large excess of 2-ethylhexanol in benzene at 28 ± 1°C. His results are shown in Table VII. His values for log k are plotted

TABLE VI
Substituent Constants for the Isocyanate-Alcohol Reaction[a]

Substituent	σ
p-NO_2	1.27[b]
m-NCO	0.43
p-NCO	0.35
p-Cl	0.23[b]
p-(CH_2—C_6H_4—NCO)	0.04
m-$NHCOOC_4H_9$ (n)	0.01–0.06
p-(CH_2—C_6H_4—$NHCOOC_2H_5$)	0.01
p-$NHCOOC_4H_9$ (n)	−0.05
p-(CH_2—C_6H_4—$NHCOOC_4H_9$)	−0.05
m-CH_3	−0.07[b]
p-CH_3	0.17[b]
p-OCH_3	−0.27[b]

[a] Taken from ref. 13.
[b] Values from Hammett (30), others calculated.

TABLE VII
Pseudo First Order Reaction Rate Constants for Substituted Phenyl Isocyanates Plus Excess 2-Ethylhexanol in Benzene at 28°C.[a]

Monosubstituent	$k \times 10^4$ sec.$^{-1}$	Disubstituents	$k \times 10^4$ sec.$^{-1}$
p-Nitro	45.5	m-Chloro, p-chloro	15.2
m-Nitro	36.3		
m-Trifluoromethyl	10.8	m-Isocyanato, p-chloro	12.2
m-Chloro	7.65		
m-Bromo	7.63	m-Chloro, p-methyl	3.99
m-Isocyanato	5.14		
p-Isocyanato	3.89	m-Isocyanato, p-methyl	2.00
p-Chloro	3.66		
p-Urethano	1.56	m-Isocyanato, p-methoxy	0.735
p-Phenyl	1.48		
m-Urethano	1.47	m-Methyl, p-methoxy	0.700
m-Methoxy	1.39		
None	1.09	m-Methyl, p-methyl	0.370
p-n-Butyl	0.712		
m-Methyl	0.695		
p-Methyl	0.660		
p-Methoxy	0.552		

[a] Taken from ref. 36.

against Hammett σ constants in Figure 2. In this study Hammett's σ value of 0.778 was used for the *para*-nitro group, rather than the alternate value of 1.27, which is sometimes preferred for aniline derivatives. The slope of the line gave a value for ρ of +1.979.

From these data σ values were calculated for four substituents as shown in Table VIII. These values are in fair agreement with the corresponding values of Brock (Table VI).

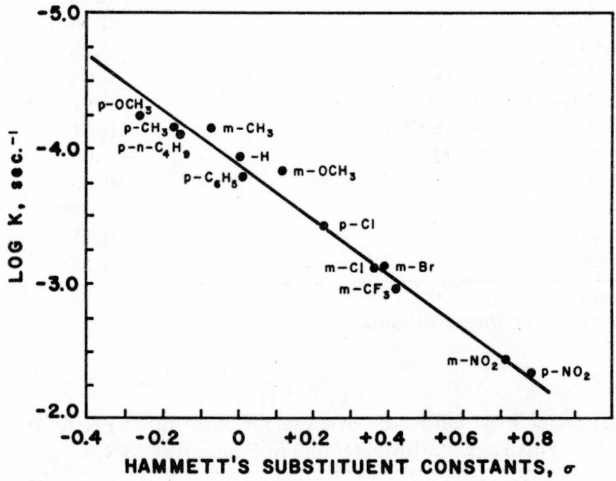

Fig. 2. Determination of the reaction constant, ρ, for the reaction of *meta*- and *para*-substituted phenyl isocyanates with 2-ethylhexanol at 28°C. (Taken from ref. 36.)

The experimental rate data for the disubstituted isocyanates of Table VII were in close agreement with values calculated from the σ constants of the corresponding groups.

TABLE VIII[a]
Calculated Sigma Values

Substituent	σ
m-NCO	+0.299
p-NCO	+0.238
p-NHCOOR[b]	+0.038
m-NHCOOR[b]	+0.025

[a] Taken from ref. 36.
[b] R = 2-ethylhexyl.

Quantitative data on the effect on rate of reaction of changes in the alcohol structure were reported by Dyer and co-workers (25). The reaction was followed by dilatometric methods and confirmed by amine and acid titration. As a part of this study it was confirmed that the rate of the isocyanate-alcohol reaction was dependent on the alcohol concentration, with the alcohol acting as a mild catalyst.

Data obtained at a 2:1 alcohol/isocyanate molar ratio in xylene are shown in Table IX. With a second order rate calculation the data gave a linear relation to 53–71% reaction in most experiments.

TABLE IX[a]
Second Order Rate Data for Reaction of Phenyl Isocyanate with Alcohols in Xylene

Alcohol	Temp., °C.	$k \times 10^4$, l./mole sec.	E_a, kcal.
1-Butanol	35	6.3	
	25	4.4	
	15	2.8	8.1
	0	1.2	
2 Butanol	25	1.4	
	15	0.8	9.9
	0	0.3	

[a] Taken from ref. 25.

An attempt was also made to obtain reaction rate constants for the reaction with tertiary alcohols. Tertiary butyl alcohol and phenyl isocpanate rapidly gave diphenylurea. α-Terpineol and phenyl isocyanate gave the desired urethane with a second order rate constant of 9×10^{-7} l./mole sec., and some diphenylurea. The temperature was not stated.

Bailey and co-workers (4) reported data for the phenyl isocyanate-alcohol reaction in benzene at 28°C. which were in good agreement with those of Dyer and co-workers (25).

The reaction of phenyl isocyanate with *n*-butanol was also reported by Morton and co-workers (42,43), using 0.5*M* reactants in dioxane, and titration with dibutylamine and acid. The rate constants at 25, 35, and 50°C. were 2.53, 4.47, and 7.57×10^{-4} l./mole sec., respectively, giving an activation energy of 9.3 kcal./mole. This activation energy was somewhat higher than that of Dyer and co-workers (25), and the rate constants were somewhat lower than the corresponding values of Dyer and co-workers. These differences may be attributed to the differences in the solvents used.

O'Brien and Pagano (46) reported an activation energy of 16 kcal./mole for the reaction between *tert*-octyl isocyanate and ethanol at 25–40°C. and 22 kcal. for reaction with 2-butanol. These relatively high activation energies are to be expected for aliphatic isocyanates, which are generally less reactive than aromatic isocyanates.

The effect of solvent on the rate of the isocyanate-alcohol reaction was confirmed by Ephraim and co-workers (26). The change from acetonitrile to benzene as a solvent was reported to change the rate of the phenyl isocyanate-methanol reaction at 20°C. by a factor of 71 in this series of experiments (approximately as much change as would be expected from substituting *p*-nitrophenyl isocyanate for phenyl isocyanate while keeping the solvent constant). Data for several alcohols and solvents are shown in Table X. The isocyanate/alcohol

TABLE X[a]

Effect of Solvent on Rate of Phenyl Isocyanate-Alcohol Reaction at 20°C.

Alcohol	Solvent	$k \times 10^{-4}$, l./mole sec.
Methanol	Toluene	1.2
	Nitrobenzene	0.45
	n-Butyl acetate	0.18
	Methyl ethyl ketone	0.05
	Dioxane	0.03
	Acetonitrile	0.017
1-Butanol	Toluene	1.4
	Methyl ethyl ketone	0.05
Isopropanol	Toluene	0.6
Methyl Cellosolve	Toluene	0.14
Ethylene glycol	Acetonitrile	0.017
	Dioxane	0.008

[a] Taken from ref. 26.

ratio was 1.0, with each being 0.25*M*. When ethylene glycol was used the isocyanate/glycol molar ratio was 2.0, with 0.25*M* isocyanate. As shown by the data in Table X, the rate of reaction decreased approximately in order of the increasing dielectric constant of the solvent and the ability of the solvent to hydrogen bond with alcohol. This behavior is in agreement with Baker's suggestion that association of the solvent with the alcohol slows the reaction of alcohol with isocyanate.

Ephraim and co-workers also confirmed that increasing the alcohol/isocyanate ratio increased the value of the calculated second order rate constant. While the reaction was always first order in isocyanate, the deviation toward higher than first order in alcohol varied with the solvent. Thus, the tendency toward higher reaction order (alcohol catalysis) changed in the order toluene > nitrobenzene > acetonitrile > methyl ethyl ketone > butyl acetate > dioxane. Catalysis by alcohol was thus less likely to occur in those solvents that would associate with the alcohol.

The large difference in rates between reactions in benzene or toluene and in dioxane is not supported by the data of Farkas and co-workers (27,28), who found approximately an eightfold difference for the uncatalyzed reaction and threefold for amine-catalyzed isocyanate-alcohol reaction. Comparisons of the data of Morton and Deisz, using dioxane (42), with those of Dyer *et al.*, using xylene (25), and Bailey *et al.*, using benzene (4), suggest that the difference in rates with the two types of solvents is usually closer to two- or threefold than the forty fold observed by Ephraim. Data from Ephraim and co-workers (26), and Baker and Holdsworth (9) are in agreement that rates may be about three times faster in benzene or toluene than in dibutyl ether.

Although reactions of aromatic isocyanates with alcohols followed second order kinetics or modified second order kinetics as outlined by Baker and Holdsworth (9), Sato (50) reported that aliphatic and alkenyl isocyanates were much more subject to alcohol and urethane catalysis. The reactions of these compounds were found to agree with the expression:

$$dx/dt = k_1(a - x)(b - x)^2 + k_2(x)(a - x)(b - x) + k_3(\text{cat.})(a - x)(b - x)$$

This equation is an expanded form of Baker's equation for the catalyzed reaction, but does not include a term for an uncatalyzed reaction. The first term of Sato's equation corresponds to alcohol catalysis, the second to urethane catalysis, and the third to the effect of an added catalyst, e.g., tertiary amine.

While a second order plot of phenyl isocyanate-methanol reaction

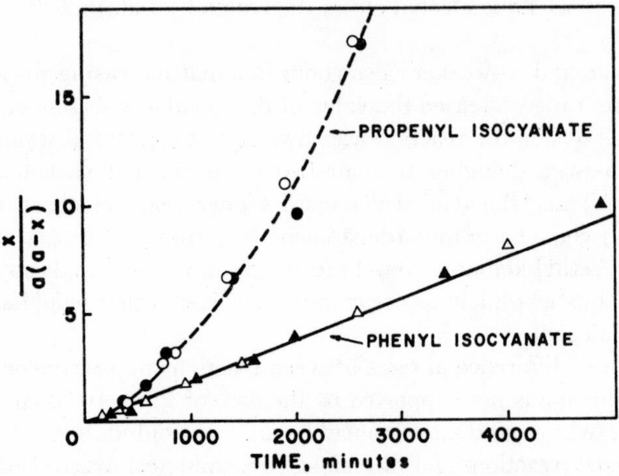

Fig. 3. Second order plot of data for isocyanate-methanol reaction in dibutyl ether at 25°C., each reactant 0.186M. No added catalyst. (Taken from ref. 50.)

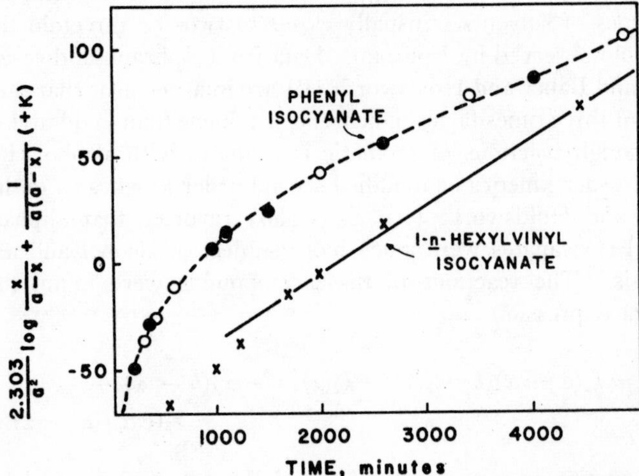

Fig. 4. Third order plot of data for the isocyanate-methanol reaction in dibutyl ether at 25°C., each reactant 0.186M. No added catalyst. (Taken from ref. 50.)

data fit a straight line, that for propenyl isocyanate-methanol did not, as shown in Figure 3. On the other hand, a third order plot based on the second term of Sato's equation showed that in the absence of added catalyst the rate for an alkenyl isocyanate fits a straight line after a time. Apparently during the first part of the reaction the first term in the equation was dominant, but as product concentration increased the second term was the controlling factor. Data for phenyl isocyanate did not fit the third order treatment as well, but behaved qualitatively similar (Fig. 4). This difference between the aliphatic and alkenyl isocyanates, on one hand, and phenyl isocyanate, on the other, was explained in part by the greater catalytic activity of aliphatic or alkenyl urethanes, compared to aryl urethanes. Catalytic constants, corresponding to k_3 in Sato's general equation, were determined as shown in Table XI. These k_3 values indicated how k_2 values might vary in

TABLE XI[a]

Urethane Catalysis of Phenyl Isocyanate-Methanol Reaction at 25°C. (Reactants and catalyst, 0.25*M* in dibutyl ether)

Urethane	$k_3 \times 10^4$, l.^{2} mole^{-2} sec.$^{-1}$
Methyl-*N*-ethylurethane	18
Methyl-*N*-vinylurethane	2.7
Methyl-*N*-phenylurethane	0.92

[a] Taken from ref. 50.

corresponding systems. Rate constants for several isocyanates were observed as shown in Table XII. Values of k_1 and k_2 were obtained

TABLE XII[a]

Third Order Rate Constants for Isocyanate-Methanol Reaction at 25°C. (0.18*M* reactants, 0.0186*M* triethylamine when used, in dibutyl ether)

Isocyanate	$k \times 10^4$, l.^{2} mole^{-2} sec.$^{-1}$		
	k_1	k_2	k_3
Ethyl	0.028	1.1	6.3
Phenyl	1.3	0.9	2166
Vinyl	4.7	31	2166
Propenyl	2.3	11	483
β-Propylvinyl	2.8	13	467
Isopropenyl	1.2	5.7	317
α-Hexylvinyl	0.28	5.0	

[a] Taken from ref. 50.

in uncatalyzed reactions; then k_3 was derived from catalyzed experiments. In agreement with earlier workers, it is readily apparent from the low k_2/k_1 ratio that phenyl isocyanate reactions are only slightly affected by urethane catalysis. It is also apparent that unsaturation close to the isocyanate group enhances isocyanate activity (k_1) in olefinic isocyanates much as in aromatic isocyanates. Thus, in systems without added catalysts the alkenyl isocyanates, having similar k_1 and larger k_2 values, should give complete reaction faster than phenyl isocyanate under the same conditions.

2. *Reactions of Diisocyanates*

The reactions of diisocyanates are usually more complicated kinetically than are those of monoisocyanates. The initial reactivity of a diisocyanate is similar to that of a monoisocyanate substituted by an activating group, in this case the second isocyanate group. As soon as one isocyanate group has reacted with an alcohol, the remaining isocyanate group has a reactivity similar to that of a monoisocyanate substituted by a urethane group. As was shown in Table V, a urethane group in the *meta* or *para* position has only a very mild activating effect, much less than an isocyanate group in the *meta* or *para* position. The reactivity of a diisocyanate having both isocyanate groups on one aromatic ring should decrease significantly as the reaction passes approximately 50% completion.

This decrease in reactivity may be even greater if another substituent is present *ortho* to one isocyanate group. As shown in Table V, an *ortho* alkyl substituent greatly decreases the reactivity of an isocyanate group.

An example illustrating these effects is 2,4-tolylene diisocyanate. The most reactive group should be the 4-position isocyanate group, which is activated by the 2-position isocyanate group. The 2-position group has similar activation initially by the 4-position isocyanate group, but compensating deactivation by the 1-position methyl group. After the 4-position isocyanate group has reacted with an alcohol the 2-position isocyanate group is even less reactive than initially because of strong deactivation by the 1-methyl, far overshadowing the very slight activating tendency of the 4-position urethane group.

In diisocyanates in which the two isocyanate groups are on different aromatic rings or are separated by aliphatic chains, the effect of one isocyanate or urethane group on a second isocyanate group is less pronounced. The effect becomes still less as the aromatic rings are separated farther and farther from each other; e.g., by progressively longer aliphatic chains.

In spite of these complicating factors, the kinetics of diisocyanate reactions has been of even greater interest than the kinetics of mono-isocyanate reactions. This enthusiasm and the need for careful studies of diisocyanate reactions have arisen from the commercial importance of the diisocyanates in the productions of urethane foams, elastomers, coatings, adhesives, and other products.

The reactions of several diisocyanates with a large excess of 2-ethyl-hexanol or a hydroxyl-terminated polyester have been reported by Bailey and co-workers (4). The polyester was a diethylene glycol adipate of molecular weight 1900. Reactions were run in benzene with the extent of reaction being followed by loss of infrared absorption at 4.4 μ, characteristic for the isocyanate group. Figure 5 illustrates the reaction of several diisocyanates with 2-ethylhexanol and of 80:20

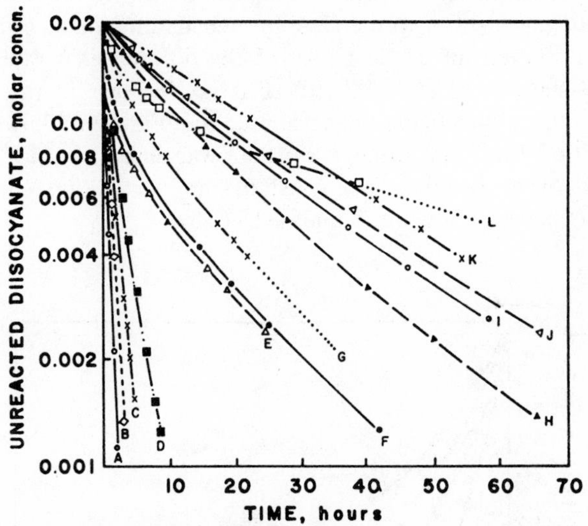

Fig. 5. Reactivity of aromatic diisocyanates with 2-ethylhexanol (A–K) and diethylene glycol adipate polyester (L), in benzene.

KEY: A. 1-Chloro-2,4-phenylene diisocyanate.
B. *m*-Phenylene diisocyanate.
C. *p*-Phenylene diisocyanate.
D. 4,4′-Diphenylmethane diisocyanate.
E. 2,4-Tolylene diisocyanate.
F. 60/40 2,4/2,6-Tolylene diisocyanate.
G. 2,6-Tolylene diisocyanate.
H. 3,3′-Dimethyl-4,4′-biphenylene diisocyanate.
I. 3,3′Dimethyl-4,4′-diphenylmethane diisocyanate.
J. 3,3′-Dimethoxy-4,4′-biphenylene diisocyante.
K. 2,2′,5,5′-Tetramethyl-4,4′-biphenylene disocyanate.
L. 80/20 2,4/2,6-Tolylene diisocyanate plus polyester.

(Taken from ref. 4.)

tolylene diisocyanate with the polyester at 28°C. A sharp decrease in the rate constant of the reaction of 2,4-tolylene diisocyanate and the 80:20 isomer ratio of tolylene diisocyanate at approximately 50% reaction is apparent. In contrast, 2,6-tolylene diisocyanate, 4,4′-diphenylmethane diisocyanate, *p*-phenylene diisocyanate, and *m*-phenylene diisocyanate show only a slight decrease in rate constant as the reaction proceeds.

A similar study of several diisocyanates and the effect of temperature on reactions with diethylene glycol adipate of molecular weight 1800 in chlorobenzene are shown in Figures 6, 7, 8, and 9. The decrease in rate constant after 50% reaction is even more apparent in the reaction of tolylene diisocyanate with the polyester at 29°C. than with 2-ethylhexanol. An increase in reaction temperature favors the slow reaction more than the fast, as would be expected if differences in activation energy accounted for at least part of the difference in rates. Thus, Figure 8 shows that at 100°C. there is no decrease in rate constant with 4,4′-diphenylmethane diisocyanate, and Figure 7 shows less decrease with 2,4-tolylene diisocyanate than was observed at 29°C.

Second order reaction rate constants and activation energies for these reactions are shown in Table XIII (41).

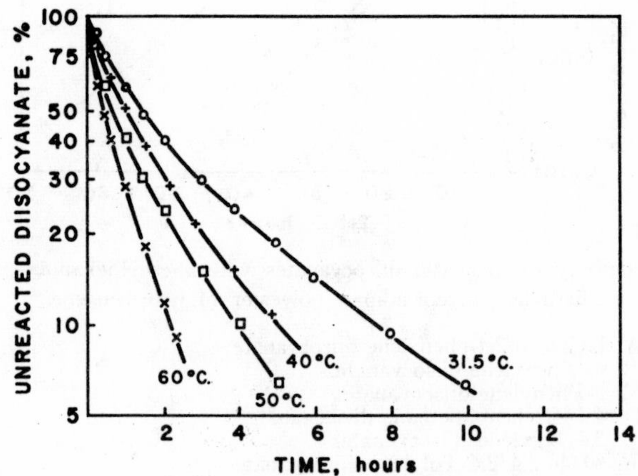

Fig. 6. Reaction of *m*-phenylene diisocyanate with diethylene glycol adipate polyester in chlorobenzene. (Taken from ref. 41.)

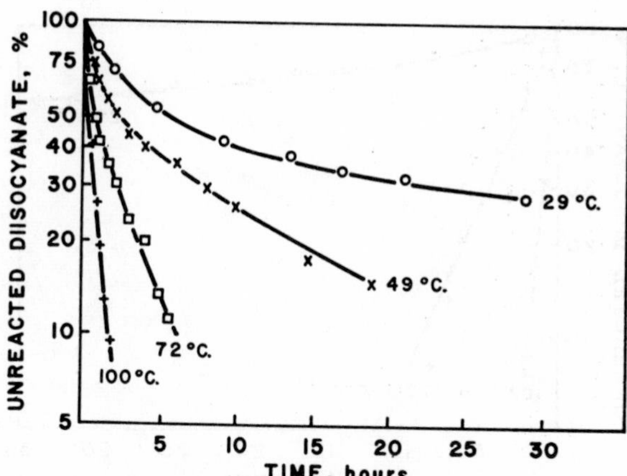

Fig. 7. Reaction of 2,4-tolylene diisocyanate with diethylene glycol adipate polyester in chlorobenzene. (Taken from ref. 41.)

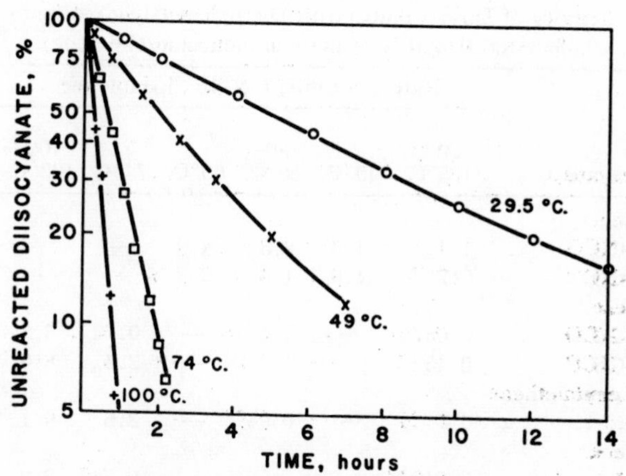

Fig. 8. Reaction of 4,4′-diphenylmethane diisocyanate with diethylene glycol adipate polyester in chlorobenzene. (Taken from ref. 41.)

The reactions of 2,4-tolylene diisocyanate and 4,4′-diphenylmethane diisocyanate with *n*-butanol in xylene were reported by Morton and co-

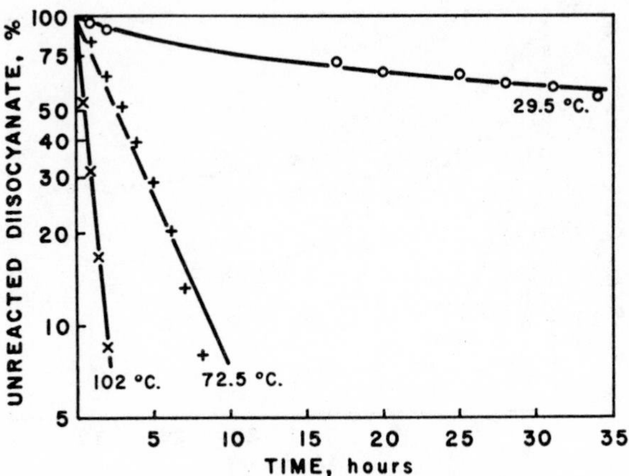

Fig. 9. Reaction of 3,3′-dimethyl-4,4′-biphenylene diisocyanate with diethylene glycol adipate polyester in chlorobenzene. (Taken from ref. 41.)

TABLE XIII[a]
Reactivity of Diisocyanates with Diethylene Glycol Adipate
(0.2*M* ester, 0.02*M* isocyanate in monochlorobenzene)

Diisocyanate	Rate constants, $k \times 10^4$, l./mole sec. 29–31.5°C.	40°C.	49–50°C.	60°C.	72–74°C.	100–102°C.	Act. energy, kcal./mole
m-Phenylene							
k for 1-NCO	1.4	1.9	2.8	4.0	—	—	7.5
k for 3-NCO	0.7	1.0	1.5	2.3	—	—	8.4
2,4-Tolylene							
k for 2-NCO	0.057	—	0.18	—	0.72	3.2	12.6
k for 4-NCO	0.45	—	1.2	—	3.4	8.5	9.3
4,4′-Diphenylmethane							
k (total)	0.34	—	0.94	—	3.6	9.1	10.5
4,4′-Tolidine							
k (total)	0.048	—	—	—	0.74	3.2	13.1

[a] Taken from ref. 41.

workers (42,43). Increasing the alcohol/isocyanate ratio increased the apparent reaction rate constants as in the case of the monoisocyanates, and a plot of (ROH)/$k_{exp.}$ against (ROH) gave a straight line with both diisocyanates. Data are shown in Table XIV, illustrating the decreased rate of reaction during the second half of the reaction with 2,4-tolylene diisocyanate.

In studying the effect of concentration of reactants (all at NCO/OH of 1:1) on the rate of reaction in xylene it was found that the rate was independent of concentration in the range of 0.1 to 0.5*N* reactants, but increased at 1.0*N* concentration (43).

TABLE XIV[a]
Reaction of *n*-Butanol with Diisocyanates in Xylene
(Initial NCO concentration 0.5*N*)

Diisocyanate	OH/NCO ratio	Temp., °C.	$k \times 10^4$, l./mole sec.		E_a, kcal./equiv.
			First 50%	Second 50%	
Tolylene	4:1	25	8.15	0.92	—
	2:1	25	5.10	0.52	—
	1:1	25	2.62	0.25	—
	1:1	35	4.22	0.44	—
	1:1	15	1.53	0.14	—
Diphenylmethane	4:1	25	5.30	—	—
	2:1	25	3.18	—	—
	1:1	25	1.89	—	—
	1:1	35	2.95	—	—
	1:1	15	1.00	—	—
Over-all					
TDI	1:1	25	2.81	—	9.2
MDI	1:1	25	3.18	—	9.6

[a] Taken from refs. 42 and 43.

Similar experiments, but using toluene as a solvent were reported by Tazuma and Latourette (57), whose data are shown in Table XV. The calculated second order rate constant for the first isocyanate group to react is shown as k_1, that for the second group as k_2. (This designation will be used throughout the remainder of this section, and should not be confused with Baker's designation of k_1 and k_2 which was noted earlier.) The ratio of k_1/k_2 is higher than was observed for 2,4-tolylene diisocyanate by Morton and Deisz (42), by Bailey and co-workers (4), and by Burkus and Eckert (14), and higher for *m*-phenylene diisocyanate than was observed by Bailey and co-workers (4) and by Burkus and Eckert (14). The higher ratios of Tazuma and Latourette (57) cannot be attributed to the higher alcohol/isocyanate ratio alone, since Bailey and co-workers also used a similarly large excess of alcohol.

TABLE XV[a]
Relative Reactivities of Aromatic Isocyanates toward *n*-Butanol in Toluene at 25°C.

Isocyanate	Concn., moles/l. Isocyanate	Alcohol	$k_1 \times 10^4$, l./mole sec.	$k_2 \times 10^4$, l./mole sec.	k_1/k_2
2,4-Tolylene diisocyanate	0.025	0.25	5.8	—	—
2,4-Tolylene diisocyanate	0.050	0.50	13	0.42	31
2,4-Tolylene diisocyanate	0.10	0.50	12	0.33	36
m-Phenylene diisocyanate	0.025	0.25	17	1.7	10
m-Phenylene diisocyanate	0.050	0.50	42	4.2	10
m-Phenylene diisocyanate	0.100	0.50	33	3.3	10
4-Chloro-1,3-phenylene diisocyanate	0.025	0.25	58	7.5	8
4,6-Dichloro-1,3-phenylene diisocyanate	0.025	0.25	84	9.2	9
2,4,6-Tribromo-1,3-phenylene diisocyanate	0.025	0.25	26	13	2
2,4,6-Trichloro-1,3-phenylene diisocyanate	0.025	0.25	34	17	2
Tetrachloro-1,3-phenylene diisocyanate	0.025	0.25	64	32	2
Phenyl isocyanate	0.05	0.25	1.8	—	—
3-Amino-2,4,6-tribromophenyl isocyanate	0.05	0.25	3.8	—	—

[a] Taken from ref. 57.

A similar study of several diisocyanates, and for comparison, three monoisocyanates, was reported by Burkus and Eckert (14). Triethylamine was included as a catalyst in all experiments. The reaction was followed by titration with dibutylamine and acid. Both energy and entropy of activation were calculated for the first group to react (rate constant, k_1) and for the second group (rate constant, k_2). It is noteworthy that in calculating values for k_1 and k_2 for 2,4-tolylene diisocyanate the initial reactivity of the 4-position isocyanate group was assumed equal to that of the 2-position group, an assumption which does not appear justified. Data are given in Table XVI. The activation energies are shown, for example for *m*-phenylene diisocyanate, as 2.4/3.4, the 2.4 value applying to the reaction of the first isocyanate group to react, the 3.4 value to the second. Entropy of activation values are shown similarly.

TABLE XVI[a]

Reaction of Isocyanates with *n*-Butanol in Toluene, Triethylamine-Catalyzed (0.05*M* isocyanate, 0.10*M* butanol, 0.03*M* triethylamine)

Isocyanate	$k \times 10^4$, l./mole sec., 24.41°C.		$k \times 10^4$, l./mole sec., 39.69°C.		E_a, kcal./mole	$-\Delta S_a$, e.u.
	k_1	k_2	k_1	k_2		
m-Phenylene diisocyanate	597	64.8	723	86.2	2.4/3.4	58.1/59.1
p-Phenylene diisocyanate	392	39.2	525	57.2	3.5/4.6	55.2/56.3
2,6-Tolylene diisocyanate	122	18	147	23.8	2.3/3.4	61.8/61.8
Durene diisocyanate	—	—	3.65	1.38	—	—
Diphenylmethane diisocyanate	—	—	160	55	—	—
3,3′-Dimethyl-4,4′-diphenylmethane diisocyanate	—	—	27.5	11.7	—	—
2,4-Tolylene diisocyanate	255	20.5	330	27.7	3.1/3.6	57.4/60.7
Hexamethylene diisocyanate	—	—	0.83	0.42	—	—
Phenyl isocyanate	52	—	67.7	—	3.1	60.7
p-Tolyl isocyanate	26	—	35	—	3.4	60.9
o-Tolyl isocyanate	7.6	—	19	—	4.3	61.4

[a] Taken from ref. 14.

While nearly all previous rate data were obtained by following the rate of disappearance of isocyanate, Kogon (39) followed the rate of formation of urethane, using infrared absorption at 6750 cm.$^{-1}$. His data for monoisocyanates and for the initial linear portion of the second order rate curve for diisocyanates are given in Table XVII. The second order plot of the uncatalyzed reaction of 2,4-tolylene diisocya-

TABLE XVII[a]

Second Order Rate Constants for the Isocyanate-Ethyl Alcohol Reaction at 28°C. (carbon tetrachloride solution)

Isocyanate	Catalyst	$k \times 10^4$, l./mole sec.
Phenyl isocyanate	0.072*M* $(C_2H_5)_3N$	43.30
p-Tolyl isocyanate	0.072*M* $(C_2H_5)_3N$	18.42
o-Tolyl isocyanate	0.072*M* $(C_2H_5)_3N$	5.16
Phenyl isocyanate	—	2.50
2,4-Tolylene diisocyanate	—	10.70
2,6-Tolylene diisocyanate	—	2.46

Taken from ref. 39.

nate was linear to about 60% reaction, and that of 2,6-tolylene diisocyanate to 30% reaction.

To throw additional light on the relative reactivity of diisocyanates at higher temperatures, Cunningham and Mastin (20) measured rates of reactions with alcohols at 115°C. To provide both primary and secondary hydroxyl groups, 1- and 2-octanol were used. Amine and acid titration were utilized in following the reaction (Table XVIII).

TABLE XVIII[a]
Second Order Reaction Rate Constants for Diisocyanates and Alcohols at 115°C., $\times 10^4$, l./mole sec.
(0.1*N* reactants, chlorobenzene)

	With 1-octanol			With 2-octanol		
Diisocyanate	Cat.[b]	Uncat.	$\frac{k_{cat.}}{k_{uncat.}}$	Cat.[b]	Uncat.	$\frac{k_{cat.}}{k_{uncat.}}$
m-Phenylene						
k_1	125	23	5.4	35	14	2.5
k_2	77	20	3.9	24	7.0	3.5
2,4-Tolylene						
k_1	51	9.0	5.6	17	5.5	3.1
k_2	26	4.5	5.9	7.7	1.2	6.7
4,4′-Diphenylmethane[c]	49	6.7	7.3	14	5.2	2.7
3,3′-Dimethylbiphenylene	17	1.8	9.5	5.8	1.2	5.0

[a] Taken from ref. 20.
[b] 0.01 *N* tri-*n*-butylamine.
[c] 97% pure.

At 115°C. the secondary alcohol was still less reactive than the primary, usually being about one-half to one-third as reactive. The relative effect of the catalyst was not consistent, but it often promoted the slower reactions more than the faster ones.

Similar data on *ortho*-substituted diisocyanates have been reported (15), where the alcohol/diisocyanate molar ratio was 5:1 (Table XIX and Fig. 10). Apparently the electronic activating effect of the *ortho* chlorine atom more than overcame its steric hindrance, so that 3,3′-dichloro-4,4′-biphenylene diisocyanate was slightly more reactive than the 4,4′-biphenylene diisocyanate.

The differences in reactivities of isocyanate groups in diisocyanates wherein one group was influenced by strong steric hindrance were shown by Case (16). The half life of the reaction was estimated at 10–20% reaction and again at 70–80%, and the two compared. This

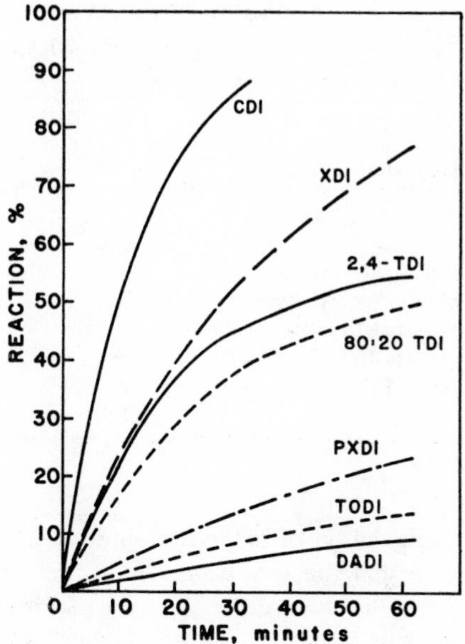

Fig. 10. Reaction of diisocyanates with *sec*-butyl alcohol at 25°C. (Taken from ref. 15.)

TABLE XIX[a]

Reactivity of 4,4′-Biphenylene Diisocyanates with *sec*-Butanol at 25°C.

Diisocyanate	$k \times 10^4$, l./mole sec.
3,3′-Dimethoxy (DADI), Fig. 10	0.063
3,3′-Dimethyl (TODI)	0.13
3,3′-Diphenyl (PXDI)	0.21
3,3′-Dichloro (CDI)	2.4
(4,4′-Biphenylene diisocyanate) (XDI)	(1.1)

[a] Taken from ref. 15.

method gives an indication of the difference in reactivity of groups in a diisocyanate (Table XX). The greatest difference was obtained when one isocyanate group was in an unhindered position on the aromatic ring and the other was on an aliphatic carbon with bulky β-substituents.

Rate data comparing the reactivity of aryl mono- and diisocyanates with benzyl type mono- and diisocyanates were reported by Ferstandig and Scherrer (29). Reactions were run in toluene at 30 and 40°C. to

TABLE XX[a]

Reactions of Diisocyanates with Isoamyl Alcohol (chlorobenzene, NCO:OH = 1:10, 0.01–0.02*M* isocyanate, 21–23°C.)

Isocyanate	Half life, min., at: 10–20%	70–80%	$\frac{T^{1/2}_{10-20}}{T^{1/2}_{70-80}}$
1-Phenoxy-2,4-phenylene diisocyanate	20	200	109
2,6-Dichloro-1,4-phenylene diisocyanate	4	100	25
2-Nitro-1,4-phenylene diisocyanate	4	30	7.5
1-*tert*-Butyl-2,4-phenylene diisocyanate	20	200	10
β-(*p*-Phenyl isocyanato)ethylisocyanate	20	70	3.5
β-(*p*-Phenyl isocyanato)butylisocyanate	80	600	7.5
β-Methyl-β-(*p*-phenyl isocyanato)propyl diisocyanate	120	18,000	150

[a] Taken from ref. 16.

provide data for calculation of activation energies. A large excess of alcohol was used so that the rate was pseudo first order. The amine titration method was used to show the rate of disappearance of isocyanate. As indicated by the data in Table XXI the benzyl type isocyanates were somewhat less reactive than corresponding arylisocyanates. In diisocyanates of the xylylene type the second isocyanate group to react did so at a rate about one-half to one-third that of the first group, similar to the behavior of diphenylmethane diisocyanate.

TABLE XXI[a]

Relative Rates of Reaction of Isocyanates with Excess Ethyl Alcohol in Toluene at 30°C.

Isocyanate	Relative rate		Act. energy, kcal.	
	First NCO	Second NCO	First NCO	Second NCO
Phenyl isocyanate	14	—	9.5	—
2,4-Tolylene diisocyanate	42	1.7	11	—
p,p'-Diphenylmethane diisocyanate	32	10	7.2	9.4
α-Naphthyl isocyanate	5.8	—	9.1	—
1,5-Naphthalene diisocyanate	38	11	5.1	9.3
Benzyl isocyanate	1.4	—	7.2	—
1,3-Xylylene diisocyanate	2.8	1.1	12.6	11.9
1,4-Xylylene diisocyanate	2.5	1.3	13.9	11.2
5-*tert*-Butyl-1,3-xylylene diisocyanate	2.7	1.0	11.8	11.9

[a] Taken from ref. 29.

Some data on the effect of structure of the hydroxyl compound on reactivity with *p*-phenylene diisocyanate were given by Cooper *et al.* (17). The system was not specified except that the temperature was 100°C. The data are very interesting for a comparison of the reactivity of several hydroxyl compounds of commercial importance (Table XXII).

TABLE XXII[a]
Reactivity of Diols with *p*-Phenylene Diisocyanate at 100°C.

Diol type	$k \times 10^4$, l./mole sec.
Polyethylene adipate	36
Polytetrahydrofuran	10–32
1,4-Butanediol	9.0
1,4-*cis*-Butenediol	4.0
1,5-Bis(β-hydroxyethoxy)naphthalene	2.5
1,4-Butynediol	0.6

[a] Taken from ref. 17.

3. *Catalysis of the Isocyanate-Hydroxyl Reaction*

The preceding sections have shown the effect of changes in structure of isocyanate and hydroxyl compound, of solvent, and of temperature on the isocyanate-hydroxyl reaction, and have indicated the role of basic catalysts. The largest commercial applications of isocyanates utilize catalyzed reactions, especially the preparation of foams. For this reason the catalysis of the isocyanate-hydroxyl reaction has been the object of extensive research.

The initial work of Baker and Holdsworth, discussed in Section II-1, outlined the role of a basic catalyst and demonstrated that an increase in base strength was accompanied by increased catalytic strength except when steric hindrance interfered. The effect of both acidic and basic catalysts was later demonstrated by Tazuma and Latourette (57). Two acids, hydrogen chloride and boron trifluoride etherate, were shown to be mild catalysts (Table XXIII). When a large excess of alcohol was present the acids had little or no catalytic effect (Table XXIV). Pyridine was a mild catalyst, even at high alcohol excess. A linear relation was found for the values of the experimentally observed rate constant and the pyridine concentration, as well as for the concentration of each acid catalyst when the alcohol concentration was low.

TABLE XXIII[a]

Acid-Catalyzed Reaction between Phenyl Isocyanate and 1-Butanol (toluene, 0.386*M* isocyanate, 25°C.)

Ratio OH/NCO	Concn., mole/l.		$k \times 10^4$, l./mole sec.
	$BF_3 \cdot OEt_2$	HCl	
1:1	0.0059	—	2.87
1:1	0.021	—	4.6, 4.8
1:1	0.032	—	5.4, 5.4
1:1	0.048	—	6.95
5:1	—	—	4.73, 4.75, 5.0
5:1	0.032	—	5.0
5:1	0.016	—	4.96
5:1	—	0.018	5.5
5:1	—	0.03	6.0, 6.0
1:1	—	0.018	4.85
1:1	—	0.031	7.2
1:1	—	0.040	8.4

[a] Taken from ref. 57.

TABLE XXIV[a]

Catalyzed Reaction between Phenyl Isocyanate and 1-Butanol (toluene, 0.009*M* isocyanate, large excess of alcohol, 25°C.)

Catalyst and concn., mole/l.			Pseudo first order $k \times 10^3$, sec.$^{-1}$
$BF_3 \cdot OEt_2$	HCl	Pyridine	
—	—	—	4.6, 4.7
—	0.0105	—	4.6, 4.8
—	0.091	—	4.6
—	0.0096	—	4.7
0.0096	—	—	4.7
0.098	—	—	4.5
—	0.0088[b]	—	4.3
—	0.0095[b]	—	4.5
—	—	0.025	5.1, 5.1
—	—	0.048	5.3, 5.5
—	—	0.099	5.9, 5.9
—	—	0.199	7.4

[a] Taken from ref. 57.
[b] Added as phenyl carbamoyl chloride.

Alzner and Frisch (1) confirmed that tertiary amines which do not have strong steric hindrance function as catalysts in direct proportion to their base strength. This study utilized phenyl isocyanate and a large excess of a polyether glycol so that the reaction was pseudo first order.

The effect of several catalysts on the reaction between 80:20 tolylene diisocyanate and a 10*M* excess of diethylene glycol adipate was reported by Bailey and co-workers (6). The catalyst concentration was 5 mole per cent based on the isocyanate. Results are given in Table XXV. In this system, *o*-chlorobenzoyl chloride did not have a catalytic effect. (In other systems with the resin containing a basic or

TABLE XXV[a]
Catalyzed Reaction between 80:20 Tolylene Diisocyanate and Diethylene Glycol Adipate at 28°C.

Catalyst	Time to indicated % reaction, hr.			
	50	60	70	80
o-Chlorobenzoyl chloride	14	28	—	—
None	10	20	—	—
Methylmorpholine	7	10	17	27
Dimethylethanolamine	5	8	13	21
Diethylcyclohexylamine	4	7	10	15
Triethylamine	2.5	4	7	11
Cobalt naphthenate	1	2	3	5

[a] Taken from ref. 6.

metallic catalyst the acid chloride would reduce the rate of the reaction between resin and isocyanate due to neutralization of the more powerfully catalytic base or metallic ion.) The results with the tertiary amine catalysts are in general agreement with the base strength of the amines. It was suggested that the cobalt catalyst functioned by coordinating with the isocyanate (as in 16). A simpler complex as proposed later by Britain and Gemeinhardt (12) may be more reasonable.

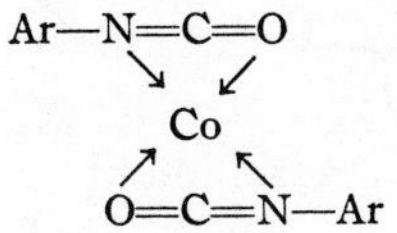

```
Ar—N=C=O
    ↘ ↙
     Co
    ↗ ↖
O=C=N—Ar
```
(16)

Research by O'Brien and Pagano (46) showed that the choice of catalyst may affect the two groups in a diisocyanate differently. With 1,8-menthane diisocyanate, the isocyanate group in the 1-position was 1.5 times more reactive toward 1-butanol than was the 8-position group when copper napthenate was used as a catalyst. With lead naphthenate the ratio was 5.8. It might be expected that the isocyanate group with less steric hindrance could coordinate with certain catalysts more easily than one with more steric hindrance, thus accounting for the difference.

The selective character of lead naphthenate with regard to selectively promoting reactions having relatively little steric strain was also shown in a comparison of reactions between menthane diisocyanate and two alcohols. The ratio of the rate constant for reaction with 1-butanol compared to that with 2-butanol at 25°C. was 26 with lead naphthenate catalyst. With a less discriminating catalyst, copper naphthenate, the ratio of rate constants was only 3.5.

The relative effectiveness of metal naphthenates for the reaction between *tert*-aliphatic isocyanates and alcohols was in the order Cu > Pb > Zn > Co > Ni > Mn. Other metal compounds which were also catalytic included ferric chloride, several metal acetates, chlorides, and nitrates.

While most tertiary amine catalysts are effective in proportion to their base strength, an exception is triethylenediamine (1,4-diaza-

TABLE XXVI[a]
Reaction of Phenyl Isocyanate with 2-Ethylhexanol at 23°C.
(0.072*M* reactants, 0.0014*M* catalyst)

Catalyst	pK	$k \times 10^4$, l./mole sec.	
		In benzene	In dioxane
None	—	0.39	0.055
Triethylamine	3.36	5.3	—
Triethylenediamine	5.40	21.7	6.0
N,N'-Dimethylpiperazine	5.71	4.3	—
N-Ethylmorpholine	6.49	1.6	—

[a] Taken from ref. 27, 28.

[2.2.2]bicyclooctane). As shown by Farkas and co-workers (*27*,*28*), this catalyst is much more powerful than would be predicted from its base strength (Table XXVI). It was suggested that the explanation may be the complete lack of steric hindrance in structure I. The rate

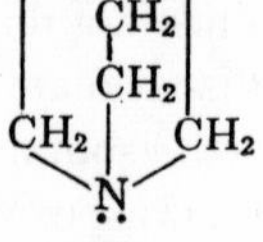

N
CH_2 CH_2
CH_2
CH_2
CH_2 CH_2
N
(I)

constant for the uncatalyzed reaction in benzene at 47°C. was 1.7; that for the triethylenediamine-catalyzed reaction was 44. Other experiments confirmed that the reaction fit second order kinetics, and that the rate of the uncatalyzed reaction was increased somewhat by an increase in alcohol concentration. In the catalyzed reaction the rate was proportional to the concentration of the catalyst and was reduced somewhat by increases in the concentration of alcohol. This latter observation suggests coordination of alcohol and catalyst.

Although previous research had shown many compounds to have catalytic activity for the isocyanate-hydroxyl reaction, none of the previously conventional catalysts was powerful enough for satisfactory commercial production of polyether-urethane foam by the "one-shot" process (see Chapter V). Research directed toward such a process led to the recognition of many metal compounds as powerful catalysts of a new order of magnitude. Chief among these were the organotin compounds, now in wide use in commercial foam processes.

The relative catalytic effect of several tin compounds was shown by Cox and Hostettler (18,34), who studied the reaction between phenyl isocyanate and methanol in dibutyl ether at 30°C. The tremendously powerful effect of certain tin compounds, compared to the more familiar catalysts, is shown in Table XXVII. It can readily be seen that tin compounds such as dibutyltin dilaurate cannot function as

TABLE XXVII[a]

Catalysis of Phenyl Isocyanate-Methanol Reaction in Dibutyl Ether at 30°C.

Catalyst	Mole % catalyst used	Rel. activity at 1.0 mole % catalyst
None	—	1
Triethylamine	1.00	11
Cobalt naphthenate	0.93	23
Benzyl trimethyl ammonium hydroxide	0.47	60
Stannous chloride	0.70	68
Tetra-*n*-butyltin	1.01	82
Stannic chloride	0.30	99
Tri-*n*-butyltin acetate	0.10	500
n-Butyltin trichloride	0.20	830
Trimethyltin hydroxide	0.041	1800
Dimethyltin dichloride	0.020	2100
Di-*n*-butyltin dilaurate	0.0094	37,000

[a] Taken from ref. 34.

simple acids or bases. The strongly basic quaternary ammonium hydroxide and the more acidic stannic chloride were much weaker catalysts.

Another interesting comparison of catalysts is shown in Table XXVIII (18). The effect of the structure of the organotin compounds on catalytic activity in these studies was summarized as follows: $R_2SnX_2 \sim R_2SnO \sim R_2SnS > RSnX_3 \sim RSnOOH \sim R_3SnX > R_4Sn$; $R = CH_3 > C_4H_9 > C_6H_5$; $X = OH > OC_4H_9 \sim SC_4H_9 \sim OCOCH_3 > Cl > F$.

TABLE XXVIII[a]
Catalysis of Phenyl Isocyanate-Butanol Reaction
(dioxane solution, 70°C.)

Catalyst	Rel. activity calcd. at 1.0 mole % catalyst
None	1.0
N-Methylmorpholine	4.0
Triethylamine	7.5
Triethylenediamine	110
Ferric acetyl acetonate	3100
Di-*n*-butyltin dichloride	56,000
Di-*n*-butyltin diacetate	55,000
Di-*n*-butyltin sulfide	21,000

[a] Taken from ref. 18.

A synergistic effect was also found when using a combination of amine and tin catalysts (18). In Table XXIX, the data illustrate a much faster reaction between phenyl isocyanate and butanol with mixed catalysts than would be expected from the individual catalyst

TABLE XXIX[a]
Synergistic Catalysis of Phenyl Isocyanate-Butanol Reaction
(dioxane, 70°C.)

Catalyst	Catalyst concn., mole %	$k \times 10^4$
None	—	0.37
Triethylamine	0.88	2.4
Dibutyltin diacetate	0.00105	20
Triethylamine plus dibutyltin diacetate	0.99 0.00098	88

[a] Taken from ref. 34.

concentrations. At very low tin catalyst concentration (0.0002 mole per cent) and high amine concentration (0.1 mole per cent) the catalytic effect of the tin was essentially lost, suggesting selective coordination of the amine with tin.

The synergistic effect of tertiary amine on tin catalyst has been confirmed by Wolfe (58).

An ingeniously simple screening method was used by Britain and Gemeinhardt (12) to evaluate catalysts for the isocyanate-hydroxyl reaction. To approximate as closely as possible actual polymerization conditions, 80:20 tolylene diisocyanate and a polyether triol of molecular weight 3000 were mixed at an NCO/OH ratio of 1.0. A 10% solution of catalyst in dry dioxane was added, the final catalyst concentration being 1% of the weight of polyether. The time for the mixture to gel at 70°C. was noted as an indication of catalytic strength. This technique used the same reactants employed in one-shot foam systems, almost completely eliminated the solvent, and was used to screen quickly hundreds of possible catalysts.

Many metallic compounds were found to be catalysts for the isocyanate-hydroxyl reaction. A list of the type compounds in a roughly decending order of catalytic activity is as follows: Bi, Pb, Sn, triethylenediamine, strong bases, Ti, Fe, Sb, U, Cd, Co, Th, Al, Hg, Zn, Ni, trialkylamines, Ce, Mo, Va, Cu, Mn, Zr, and trialkylphosphines. Arsenic, boron, calcium, and barium compounds did not show any catalytic activity within the limits of the screening test used. Results are shown in Table XXX. The effect of isocyanate structure on its

TABLE XXX[a]

Catalyst Tests for Isocyanate-Hydroxyl Reaction

Compound tested	Gelation time at 70°C., min.
A. Bismuth, Lead, Triethylenediamine, and Basic Compounds	
Blank	>240
Bismuth nitrate	1
Lead 2-ethylhexoate (24% Pb)[b]	1
Lead benzoate[b]	8
Lead oleate[b]	4
Triethylenediamine (1,4-diaza[2.2.2]bicyclooctane)	4
Sodium trichlorophenate[b]	2
Sodium propionate[b]	32
Lithium acetate[b]	60
Potassium oleate[b]	10

(*continued*)

TABLE XXX (*continued*)

Compound tested	Gelation time at 70°C., min.
B. Stannous, Stannic, and Polyalkyl Tin Compounds	
Tetrabutyltin	>240
Tributyltin chloride	200
Dibutyltin dichloride	109
Butyltin trichloride	4
Stannic chloride	3
Tributyltin *o*-phenylphenate	14
Tributyltin cyanate	5
Stannous octoate	4
Stannous oleate	8
Stannous tartrate	>240
C. Dialkyltin Compounds	
Dibutyltin di(2-ethylhexoate)	4
Dibenzyltin di(2-ethylhexoate)	5
Dibutyltin dilaurate	8
Dibutyltin diisooctylmaleate	4
Dibutyltin sulfide	20
Dibutyltin dibutoxide	3
Dibutyltin bis(*o*-phenylphenate)	3
Dibutyltin bis(acetylacetonate)	4
Di(2-ethylhexyl)tin oxide	3
D. Titanium and Iron Compounds	
Titanium tetrachloride	50
Dibutyltitanium dichloride	13
Tetrabutyl titanate	8
Butoxytitanium trichloride	16
Ferric chloride	6
Ferric 2-ethylhexoate (6% Fe)	16
Ferric acetylacetonate	16
Ferrocene	>240
E. Antimony, Uranium, Cadmium, and Cobalt Compounds	
Antimony trichloride	13
Antimony pentachloride	90
Triphenylantimony dichloride	30
Triphenylantimony	>240
Uranyl nitrate	25
Cadmium nitrate	180
Cadmium diethyldithiophosphate	30
Cobalt benzoate	32
Cobalt 2-ethylhexoate (6% Co)	12

(continued)

TABLE XXX (*continued*)

Compound tested	Gelation time at 70°C., min.
F. Thorium, Aluminum, Mercury, Zinc, and Nickel Compounds	
Thorium nitrate	32
Triphenylaluminum	32
Trioctylaluminum	32
Aluminum oleate	70
Diphenylmercury	40
Zinc 2-ethylhexoate (22% Zn)	65
Zinc naphthenate (14.5% Zn)	60
Nickelocene	50
Nickel naphthenate (6% Ni)	180
G. Tertiary Amine Compounds	
1-Methyl-4-(dimethylaminoethyl)piperazine	90
N-Ethylethylenimine	32
N,N,N',N'-Tetramethylethylenediamine	60
Triethylamine	120
2,4,6-Tri(dimethylaminomethyl)phenol	50
N-Ethylmorpholine	180
2-Methylpyrazine	>240
Dimethylaniline	>240
Nicotine	240
H. Cerium, Molybdenum, Vanadium, Copper, Manganese, and Zirconium Compounds	
Molybdenum hexacarbonyl	90
Cerium nitrate	85
Vanadium trichloride	90
Cupric 2-ethylhexoate (8% Cu)	120
Cupric acetate	90
Manganese 2-ethylhexoate (6% Mn)	120
Manganese linoresinate (8% Mn)	240
Zirconium 2-ethylhexoate (6% Zr)	240
Zirconium naphthenate (6% Zr)	240
I. Phosphorus, Arsenic, Boron, Calcium, and Barium Compounds	
Triphenylphosphine	240
Tributylphosphine	>240
Trimethylphosphite	>240
Triphenylarsine	>240
Arsenic trichloride	>240
Boron trifluoride-diethyl ether complex	>240
Pyridine borane	>240
Calcium acetate	>240
Barium acetate	>240

[a] Taken from ref. 12. [b] Isocyanate trimerization catalyst as well.

reactivity has been reviewed in the two previous sections. As previously shown, aliphatic isocyanates are generally less reactive than are the aromatic isocyanates. For example, previously published (14,29) approximate relative reaction rates of three typical isocyanates are shown in Table XXXI. Gelation tests similar to those described with

TABLE XXXI[a]

Relative Reaction Rates of Three Different Diisocyanates

$$\text{OCN—R—NCO} + \text{R'OH} \xrightarrow{k_1} \text{OCN—R—NH—CO}_2\text{R'}$$

$$\text{OCN—R—NH—CO}_2\text{R'} + \text{R'OH} \xrightarrow{k_2} \text{R'O}_2\text{C—NH—R—NH—CO}_2\text{R'}$$

—R—	k_1	k_2
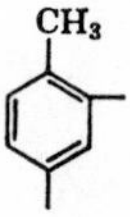 CH_3 (ring)	400	33
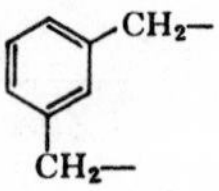 (ring) CH_2— / CH_2—	27	10
—$(CH_2)_6$—	1	0.5

[a] Taken from ref. 12.

tolylene diisocyanate were carried out using *m*-xylylene diisocyanate and the same triol, also using hexamethylene diisocyanate and triol (12). In these tests the order of strength of the catalysts was found to be different than when tolylene diisocyanate was used. Table XXXII lists the results of some catalyst screening tests with the three different diisocyanates. A list of the type compounds in decreasing order of catalytic activity for the aliphatic isocyanate-hydroxyl reaction is as follows: Bi, Fe, Sn, Pb, Ti, Sb, strong bases, Co, Zn, triethylenediamine, trialkyl amines.

The catalysts tested can be classified into three general groups. The first group of tertiary amine catalysts do not greatly affect the

TABLE XXXII[a]
Catalyst Tests with Three Different Isocyanates

Compound tested	Gelation time (min.) at 70°C. with:		
	Tolylene diisocyanate	*m*-Xylylene diisocyanate	Hexamethylene diisocyanate
Blank	>240	>240	>240
Triethylamine	120	>240	>240
Triethylenediamine	4	80	>240
Stannous octoate	4	3	4
Dibutyltin di(2-ethylhexoate)	6	3	3
Lead 2-ethylhexoate (24% Pb)	2	1	2
Sodium *o*-phenylphenate	4	6	3
Potassium oleate	10	8	3
Bismuth nitrate	1	1/2	1/2
Tetra(2-ethylhexyl) titanate	5	2	2
Stannic chloride	3	1/2	1/2
Ferric chloride	6	1/2	1/2
Ferric 2-ethylhexoate (6% Fe)	16	5	4
Cobalt 2-ethylhexoate (6% Co)	12	4	4
Zinc naphthenate (14.5% Zn)	60	6	10
Antimony trichloride	13	3	6

[a] Taken from ref. 12.

relative reaction rates of the different isocyanates. The second group includes stannous, lead, bismuth, and organotin compounds which activate the aliphatic diisocyanates more than tolylene diisocyanate so that the relative rates of the diisocyanate reactions are approximately equal. The third group has a much larger effect on the aliphatic diisocyanates so that these diisocyanates are faster to react with hydroxyl groups than tolylene diisocyanate. This last group includes zinc, cobalt, iron, stannic, antimony, and titanium compounds. An explanation of these observed effects may be found in an examination of the reaction mechanism.

A reaction mechanism for metal catalysts was proposed as shown in (17). This coordination effect, which proposes that the hydroxyl group enters on the metal side of the complex and attaches to the metal in close proximity to the isocyanate group nitrogen, can explain the fantastic catalytic actions of the metals. Obviously, the order of the metal coordination complex formation could be the reverse so that the hydroxyl compound complex forms first and the isocyanate second. It was suggested that those catalysts which caused the aliphatic isocya-

$$\mathrm{R{-}N{=}C{=}O} \xrightarrow{\mathrm{MX_2}} \left[\mathrm{R{-}N{=}C{=}}\underset{\substack{\downarrow \\ \overset{-}{\mathrm{M}}\mathrm{X_2}}}{\mathrm{O}} \leftrightarrow \mathrm{R{-}N{=}C{-}}\underset{\substack{\downarrow \\ \mathrm{MX_2}}}{\mathrm{O}} \right] \xrightarrow{\mathrm{H{-}O{-}R'}} \left[\mathrm{R{-}N{=}\overset{+}{C}{-}O} \;;\; \mathrm{H{-}\overset{+}{O}(R'){-}\overset{-2}{M}X_2} \right] \tag{17}$$

$$\left[\mathrm{R{-}\overset{+}{N}(H){=}C(OR'){-}O{-}\overset{-}{M}X_2} \updownarrow \mathrm{R{-}N(H){-}C(OR'){=}O^{+}{-}\overset{-}{M}X_2} \right] \rightarrow \mathrm{R{-}N(H){-}C(=O){-}O{-}R'} + \mathrm{MX_2}$$

nate studied to react faster than tolylene diisocyanate could perform in this manner because this aliphatic diisocyanate is not sterically hindered, whereas, the 2- and 6-positions on the tolylene diisocyanate are hindered by the methyl group in the 1-position.

It was suggested that if the metal does not have the property to complex with the incoming hydroxyl compound and the isocyanate group in such a way that the hydroxyl group and the isocyanate nitrogen are brought close together, then the only catalytic activity observed will be due to the acid or base reactions of the compound tested.

Complexing of the metal with both isocyanate and alcohol appears to be a reasonable explanation of the much greater catalytic effect on the NCO-OH reaction than on the NCO-water reaction (see Section V).

A recent report (3) of the relative strength of several catalysts for the reaction of phenyl isocyanate with poly(oxypropylene) glycol in toluene is interesting in comparison with the results of Britain and Gemeinhardt. The isocyanate concentration was $0.01M$, and the glycol, which was of 2000 molecular weight, was $0.005M$; catalyst concentration was 8.4% of the weight of isocyanate. The reaction was run at 30°C. and was followed by infrared observation of the 4.5 μ NCO band. The time to reach 50% disappearance of isocyanate is shown in Table XXXIII. In contrast to these results, Britain and Gemeinhardt's data showed approximately equal gel times at 70°C. (4–8 min.) for diethylenetriamine, dibutyltin dilaurate, stannous octoate, and three lead compounds. These differences in apparent effectiveness of diethylenetriamine and dibutyltin dilaurate in the two studies may be the result of the different reaction media used, and

TABLE XXXIII[a]
Relative Catalytic Effect on Reaction between Phenyl Isocyanate and PPG-2000 in Toluene at 30°C.

Catalyst	Time to reach 50% reaction, min.
None	>1600
Diethylenetriamine	100
Dibutyltin dilaurate	46
Stannous octoate	5
Cobalt naphthenate	31
Lead naphthenate	6

[a] Taken from ref. 3.

emphasizes the danger of trying to make precise correlations between results from dilute solution studies and reactions in essentially solvent-free systems.

IV. Reactions with Amines

In one of the first studies of the effect of structure of active hydrogen compounds on their reactivity with isocyanates, Davis and Ebersole (21) observed the relative rates of reaction of ammonia, aliphatic amines, and aniline with phenyl isocyanate. The results, as shown in Table XXXIV, are in agreement with the concept that the more basic

TABLE XXXIV[a]
Relative Reactivities of Amines with Phenyl Isocyanate in Diethyl Ether at 0°C.

Amine	Relative reactivity
NH_3	1.00
Ethylamine	9.72
n-Propylamine	8.22
n-Butylamine	9.17
n-Amylamine	9.17
Aniline	0.53

[a] Taken from ref. 21.

amines react fastest when differences in steric hindrance are not great.

A study of the effect of substituents on the reaction between aromatic isocyanates and aromatic amines by Naegeli and co-workers (45) illustrates the effect of electronic factors on the rate of this reaction. The relative rates of the reaction were observed by refluxing for one hour 0.005 mole of isocyanate and amine in 10 cc. of toluene plus 20 cc. of benzene. The yields of urea after one hour are shown in Table XXXV. A variety of organic acids and pyridine were found to be mild catalysts.

Table XXXV
Yields of Ureas from Aromatic Isocyanates and Amines

	Amine substituent, yield, %								
Isocyanate substituent	2,4-(NO_2)$_2$	2-NO_2	3,5-(NO_2)$_2$	4-NO_2	3-NO_2	3-CH_3O	H	4-CH_3	4-CH_3O
4-CH_3O	—	—	—	—	15	91	90	95	99
4-CH_3	—	—	—	0	14	90	95	98	—
H	0	0	0	0	26	92	92	100	—
3-CH_3O	—	—	—	0	46	95	—	—	—
3-NO_2	0	0.5	4	13	52	96	100	—	—
4-NO_2	0	4	8	14	61	97	100	—	—
3,5-di-NO_2	0	8	16	54	76	95	100	—	—
2-NO_2	0	0	1	8	60	98	100	—	—
2,4-di-NO_2	0	45	51	76	84	87	100	—	—

[a] Taken from ref. 45.

The effect of substituents on the reactivity of the isocyanate decreased in the order X = 2,4-(NO_2)$_2$ > 3,5-(NO_2)$_2$ > 4-NO_2 > 3-NO_2 > 2-NO_2 >> H, 4-CH_3, 3-CH_3O, 4-CH_3O, showing that electron withdrawal from the isocyanate group promotes the reaction. The effect of the substituents on the amine reactivity was in the opposite order, showing that electron withdrawal from the amine group, which reduces its basicity, reduces the rate of reaction.

In addition to the electronic factors that influence the basicity of the amino nitrogen, steric hindrance can play a powerful role in affecting the rate of reaction. Craven (2,19) showed that *ortho* substituents on either the isocyanate or the amine will strongly retard the reaction. Table XXXVI illustrates this effect, with the time required for the reaction to reach 50% completion shown as the "half life." Again, the electronic effect of substituents on the base strength of the amine is apparent, and accounts for the faster reaction of *p*-toluidine compared to aniline. The effect of an *ortho*-methyl group on the rate is noteworthy; the *ortho*-chlorine combines the electron withdrawing effect and steric hindrance. A very significant reduction in rate occurred when both isocyanate and amine contained an *ortho* methyl group. This effect is particularly important when one recognizes the similarity

TABLE XXXVI[a]
Half Lives of Reaction between ArNCO and $ArNH_2$
(each reactant 0.1*N* in dioxane, 31°C.)

Isocyanate	Amine	Dissociation const. of amine	Reaction half life, min.
Phenyl	Aniline	4.6×10^{-10}	43
Phenyl	*o*-Toluidine	3.3×10^{-10}	60
Phenyl	*p*-Toluidine	20.0×10^{-10}	5
Phenyl	*o*-Chloroaniline	0.023×10^{-10}	(<32% in 1200 min.)
o-Tolyl	Aniline		202
o-Tolyl	*o*-Toluidine		>1000
p-Tolyl	Aniline		54
p-Tolyl	*p*-Toluidine		25–30

[a] Taken from refs. 2, 19.

between reaction (18) of *o*-tolyl isocyanate with *o*-toluidine and reaction (19), one of the final reactions in systems containing tolylene diisocyanate and water. The significance of this slow reaction in the cure of urethane polymers is illustrated in Chapter V, Section II,A, on the final cure of foams.

It is noteworthy that in Craven's work the reaction was followed by titration of unreacted isocyanate with dibutylamine followed by acid to

CH_3, NCO + CH_3, NH_2 $\xrightarrow{\text{slow}}$ CH_3, NHCONH, CH_3 (18)

CH_3, NCO, NH, C=O + H_2O → CH_3, NH_2, NH, C=O + CO_2 (19a)

CH_3, NCO, NH, C=O + CH_3, NH_2, NH, C=O $\xrightarrow{\text{slow}}$ CH_3, NHCONH, CH_3, NH, C=O, NH, C=O (19b)

a bromophenol blue end point. It was reported that at concentrations below $0.02N$ the aromatic amines do not interfere with this titration. In addition, in the experiment with aniline and phenyl isocyanate, total amine was also measured by potentiometric titration with perchloric acid. The results showed that the aniline was consumed at the same rate as the isocyanate.

The retarding effect of an *ortho*-methyl group was also shown in the selective reaction of the 4-position group in 2,4-tolylene diisocyanate (eq. 20). In addition to 68% yield of the purified urea, a 32% yield of an isomer mixture was obtained (53).

$$CH_3C_6H_3(NCO)_2 + C_6H_5NH_2 \xrightarrow{25°C.} \xrightarrow[H_2O]{HCl} CH_3C_6H_3(NH_2\cdot HCl)(NHCONHC_6H_5) \; 68\% \qquad (20)$$

Perhaps because of the relatively basic nature of the amino nitrogen itself, the reaction between isocyanates and amines is not strongly catalyzed by most of the catalysts that have been studied. Perhaps the relatively fast nature of the reaction has eliminated the need for an extensive catalyst study, which may account in part for the fact that few strong catalysts have been found.

Naegeli and co-workers (45) reported that in their systems the isocyanate-amine reaction was catalyzed by tertiary amines and carboxylic acids, but not by water, inorganic acids, salts, or bases. In contrast, Craven (19) found that the typical tertiary amines and acids had little catalytic effect in the systems he studied. Certain substituted ureas appeared to catalyze the reaction to a greater extent than many tertiary amines. Typical results are shown in Table XXXVII, in which reductions of less than 5% in the half life of the reaction are not considered to be significant. Craven reported that the rate of reaction could be expressed as follows:

$$\text{rate} = k(\text{isocyanate})(\text{amine})^n$$

with the product of the reaction being catalytic in some cases. Where the product (urea) is a strong catalyst, n in this equation approaches 2.0; when the product is a very weak catalyst, n approaches 1.0. The results of the reactions between phenyl isocyanate and three amines are shown in Table XXXVIII. (Values of k apply only to the initial

TABLE XXXVII[a]

Effect of Catalysts on Half Life of Reaction between Phenyl Isocyanate and *o*-Toluidine
(each reactant 0.1*N* in dioxane, 31°C.)

Catalyst	Mole % catalyst	Decrease in $t_{1/2}$, %
Pyridine	1.0	5
Diethylcyclohexylamine	1.0	<1
Diethylcyclohexylamine	4.5	15
Sulfuric acid	1.0	0
Water	5.0	4
Acetic acid	1.0	9
n-Butyric acid	10.0	57
N-Phenyl-*N'*-*o*-tolylurea	1.0	8
N-Phenyl-*N'*-*o*-tolylurea	5.0	27
N-Phenyl-*N'*-*o*-tolylurea	10.0	38
N-Phenyl-*N'*-*o*-tolylurea	25.0	46

[a] Taken from ref. 19.

TABLE XXXVIII[a]

Reaction between Isocyanates and Amines
(each reactant 0.1*N* in dioxane, 31°C.)

Isocyanate	Amine	Catalytic action of product	Order of initial reaction	k[b]
Phenyl	*o*-Toluidine	Strong	$n^b = 1.85$	0.24
Phenyl	Aniline	Weak	$n = 1.7$	0.58
Phenyl	*p*-Toluidine	None	$n = 0.95$	1.2
p-Tolyl	*p*-Toluidine	Weak	$n = 1.7$	1.6

[a] Taken from refs. 2,19.
[b] k and n from the equation: rate = k(isocyanate)(amine)^n.

reaction, and are not true rate constant values.) The dependence of the rate on amine concentration (n) was shown to decrease as the reaction progressed.

It was also shown that adding 0.025*M* *N*-phenyl-*N'*-*o*-tolylurea to the solution of phenyl isocyanate and *o*-toluidine catalyzed the reaction so that the initial rate was as great as the ultimate rate in the absence of added urea (Fig. 11). The reaction sequence (21) was proposed as a suitable explanation of these observations (2,19). This sequence would account for catalysis by the amine reactant itself as well as catalysis by the product of the reaction, the substituted urea.

$$\mathrm{Ar'NCO + ArNH_2} \underset{k_2}{\overset{k_1}{\rightleftharpoons}} \left[\begin{array}{c}\mathrm{Ar'NCO} \\ \uparrow \\ \mathrm{ArNH_2}\end{array}\right] \xrightarrow[\text{ArNH}_2]{k_3} \mathrm{Ar'NHCONHAr + ArNH_2}; \quad \xrightarrow[\text{urea}]{k_4} \mathrm{2Ar'NHCONHAr} \tag{21}$$

Product catalysis in the reaction between phenyl isocyanate and *o*-toluidine was also reported by Ozaki and co-workers (47).

A mechanism similar to that of Arnold *et al.* (2) was described by Baker and Bailey (7), who also observed an additional mild catalysis by triethylamine and a weaker catalyst, pyridine. (Dimethylaniline was not catalytic.) Triethylamine noticeably catalyzed the reactions of

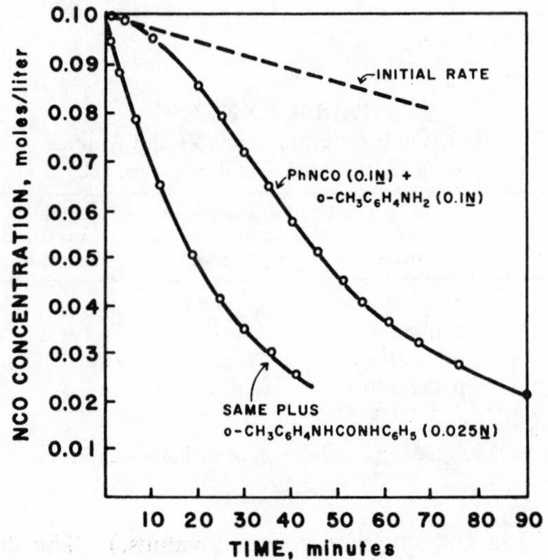

Fig. 11. Urea catalysis of the isocyanate-amine reaction. (Taken from refs. 2,19.)

phenyl and *p*-methoxyphenyl isocyanates with aniline, but had only a slight effect on the reaction of cyclohexyl isocyanate with aniline. The proposed sequence was (22), in which A may be amine, substituted urea, or tertiary amine catalyst. The disubstituted urea formed from

$$\mathrm{ArNCO + A \rightarrow [complex] \xrightarrow{RNH_2} ArNHCONHR + A} \tag{22}$$

the reaction was only slightly soluble in the reaction medium (benzene, at 20°C.), which complicated the results.

A recent paper by Cooper and co-workers (17) reported a fairly strong catalytic effect of an unidentified zinc compound on the reaction of an aromatic isocyanate with 3,3′-dichlorobenzidine. This result is presented as a part of the comparative study of catalytic effects in Section XII at the end of this chapter.

The effects of several catalysts on the reaction between phenyl isocyanate and 3,3′-dichloro-4,4′-diaminodiphenylmethane (MOCA) in toluene at 30°C. was reported by Axelrood and co-workers (3). The isocyanate concentration was 0.01*M*, the diamine was 0.005*M*, and the catalyst was 8.4% by weight of the isocyanate. The reaction was followed by infrared, and the time required for 50% disappearance of NCO was determined. Results are shown in Table XXXIX, along

TABLE XXXIX[a]

Relative Reaction Rates of Phenyl Isocyanate with PPG-2000 and MOCA in Toluene at 30°C.

Catalyst	Time, min., to reach 50% reaction with: MOCA	PPG-2000	MOCA-PPG-2000	PPG-2000 rate/MOCA rate
None	1260	>1600	404	—
Diethylenetriamine	43	100	22	0.43
Dibutyltin dilaurate	600	46	36	13
Stannous octoate	70	5	4	14
Cobalt naphthenate	600	31	24	20
Lead naphthenate	240	6	5	40

[a] Taken from ref. 3.

with similar data for the reaction of phenyl isocyanate with poly(oxypropylene) glycol of molecular weight 2000 (PPG-2000), and an equimolar combination of MOCA and PPG-2000. It is apparent from the "PPG-2000 rate/MOCA rate" column that relative effectiveness of the various catalysts for isocyanate reaction with hydroxyl and with amine is quite different. There appears to be a synergistic effect in the combination of MOCA and PPG-2000, especially in the absence of catalysts.

V. Reactions with Water

As was described in Chapter III, the reaction of isocyanates with water is a complex one and may involve several possible mechanisms. Naegeli and co-workers (44) proposed the possibilities shown in (23),

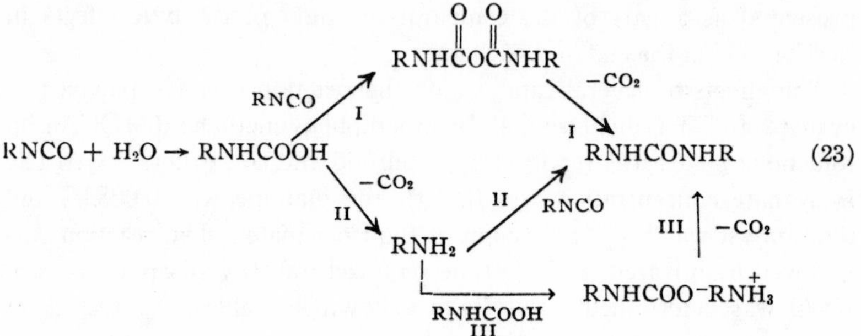

and experience confirms the reasonableness of the proposal. Consecutive reaction of isocyanate with the product, the disubstituted urea, is also a probability, of course.

Reaction sequence I would be favored when the carbamic acid is relatively stable but is fairly reactive toward isocyanate. Sequence II would be favored when the carbamic acid decomposes rapidly and the amine thus liberated reacts quickly with the isocyanate. This sequence is the one most often considered in simplified discussions of isocyanate reactions. Sequence III might increase in significance when the carbamic acid is not stable but the amine and the isocyanate react only at a slow rate, for example when steric hindrance is pronounced.

The effect of substituents on an aromatic isocyanate in its reaction with excess water was studied by Naegeli and co-workers (44). The products of the reaction were analyzed for amine and disubstituted urea. A variety of solvents and temperatures was used in the study, with the same general trends being apparent in all combinations of experimental conditions.

The substituent (X) on XArNCO could obviously affect each step of each of the three reaction sequences proposed. To illustrate, it could affect each of the steps of sequence II separately:

$$\text{XArNCO} + \text{H}_2\text{O} \xrightarrow{k_1} \text{XArNH}_2 + \text{H}_2\text{O}$$

$$\text{XArNCO} + \text{XArNH}_2 \xrightarrow{k_2} \text{XArNHCONHArX}$$

If k_1 were much larger than k_2, then with an excess of water one would expect a high yield of amine, $XArNH_2$. On the other hand, if k_2 were much larger than k_1, a high yield of the substituted urea should be obtained.

With X = H, 4-CH_3O, 4-CH_3, and 3-CH_3O, a high yield of urea was obtained in every case, as would be expected from the effect of these substituents on an aromatic amine, with regard to rate of reaction with an isocyanate. When X = 2-NO_2 and 2,4-$(NO_2)_2$, a high yield of amine was obtained. This behavior was the result in part of reduction of base strength of the amine by the negative substituents, so that k_2 was small. It may also be assumed that these negative substituents resulted in increased values for k_1. The net effect was that k_1 was much greater than k_2 for these reactions.

The effect of substituents on the isocyanate-water reaction is thus in agreement with other isocyanate reactions with active hydrogen compounds. Negative substituents promote the addition of water to the isocyanate, but those same groups on the resulting amine retard the addition of that amine to the isocyanate. In extreme cases, e.g., 2,4-dinitrophenyl isocyanate, the water may add to the isocyanate so fast and the resulting amine may add so slowly that all isocyanate is consumed by water, none by amine, and a high yield of amine is obtained. Electropositive substituents on the isocyanate may retard the addition of water, but the same groups on the resulting amine promote the addition of that amine so that only the disubstituted urea is obtained.

The kinetics of the isocyanate-water reaction appear to be similar to those of the isocyanate-amine and isocyanate-alcohol reactions. Morton and co-workers (42,43) showed that the rate depended on the water concentration, as indicated in Table XL. From these data it

TABLE XL[a]

Reaction of Phenyl Isocyanate with Water
(0.5*M* isocyanate in dioxane)

Water/isocyanate mole ratio	Temp., °C.	$k \times 10^4$, l./mole sec.
4:1	25	1.42
2:1	25	0.77
1:1	25	0.41
1:1	35	0.73
1:1	50	1.53

[a] Taken from refs. 42,43.

was shown that a plot of $(H_2O)/k$ vs. (H_2O) gave a straight line, in agreement with mechanism (24). From the data in Table XL the

$$RNCO + H_2O \underset{k_2}{\overset{k_1}{\rightleftharpoons}} [\text{complex}] \xrightarrow[k_3]{(H_2O)} RNHCONHR + H_2O + CO_2 \quad (24)$$

activation energy for the phenyl isocyanate-water reaction was calculated to be 11.0 kcal./mole.

The reaction between *o*-tolyl isocyanate and water in dioxane at 80°C. was studied by Shkapenko and co-workers (52). The isocyanate concentration was 0.2*M*, and 0.036*M* triethylamine was used as a catalyst. Like Morton and co-workers, Shkapenko *et al.* found the rate of isocyanate disappearance to be dependent on the NCO/H_2O ratio, as was the rate and volume of carbon dioxide evolved. Their results are shown in Figures 12 and 13. The quantity of isocyanate used

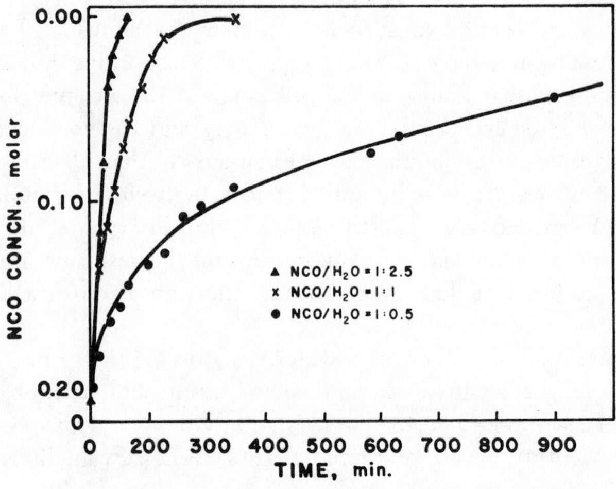

Fig. 12. Rate of isocyanate disappearance as influenced by isocyanate/water ratio. (Taken from ref. 52.)

should have generated approximately 220 ml. of carbon dioxide if 1 mole of this gas had been formed from 2 moles of isocyanate. The gas evolution apparently was complicated by the stability of some intermediate, perhaps the anhydride of the isocyanate and the carbamic acid, RNHCOOCONHR.

When the reaction was run at 100°C., a larger quantity of carbon dioxide was evolved than was obtained at 80°C. Similarly, when the reaction mixture from an 80°C. run was heated to 100°C., an additional quantity of carbon dioxide was evolved. These results indicate that in this system the carbamic anhydride, once formed, decomposed readily at 100°C., and also that the carbamic anhydride may not have been formed in a significant amount when the initial reaction was conducted at 100°C.

This apparent formation of significant amounts of the carbamic anhydride, and its slow rate of decomposition at 80°C. in this system, illustrate the danger of estimating the rate of the isocyanate-water reaction by the rate of carbon dioxide evaluation. The discrepancy

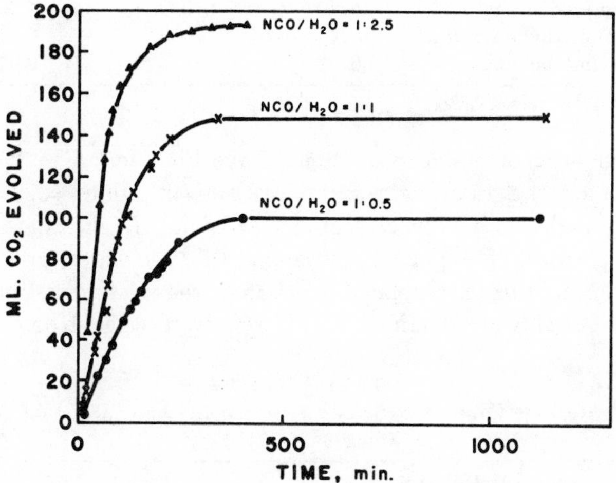

Fig. 13. Rate and extent of carbon dioxide evolution as influenced by isocyanate/water ratio. (Taken from ref. 52.)

between the rate of isocyanate disappearance and the rate of gas evolution also emphasizes the need for a complete analysis of the reaction if valid conclusions are to be drawn concerning rate and mechanism.

Catalysis of the isocyanate-water reaction by tertiary amines is well known, especially from research in the foam industry. Based on the rate of carbon dioxide evolution, the rate of the catalyzed reaction is generally increased as the base strength of the tertiary amine catalyst is increased (1).

As in the case of catalysis of the isocyanate-hydroxyl reaction by triethylenediamine, this amine catalyzes the isocyanate-water reaction much more vigorously than would be predicted from its base strength (Table XLI) (27,28). Again this strong effect may be due to the absence of steric hindrance.

TABLE XLI[a]
Reaction of Phenyl Isocyanate with Water at 23°C.
(0.072*M* isocyanate, 0.036*M* water, 0.0014*M* catalyst)

Catalyst	pK_b	$k \times 10^4$, l./mole sec. In benzene	In dioxane
None	—	0.64	0.016
Triethylamine	3.36	—	0.66
Triethylenediamine	5.40	6.0	1.8
N,N'-Dimethylpiperazine	5.71	—	0.65
N-Ethylmorpholine	6.49	—	0.33

[a] Taken from refs. 27, 28.

Certain organometallic compounds have been found to be strong catalysts for the isocyanate-water reaction in dilute solution and relatively high catalyst concentrations (18,34). In dioxane solution, at 70°C., with 0.25*M* phenyl isocyanate, 0.125*M* water, and catalyst concentration at or extrapolated to 0.025*M*, the relative results shown in Table XLII were obtained. This relatively very strong catalytic

TABLE XLII[a]
Relative Catalyst Activity for Isocyanate-Water Reaction
(dioxane, 70° C.)

Catalyst	Relative rate
None	1.1
N-Methylmorpholine	25
Triethylamine	47
Tetramethylbutanediamine	100
Triethylenediamine	380
Tributyltin acetate	14,000
Dibutyltin diacetate	100,000

[a] Taken from ref. 34.

effect of the tin salts is not apparent in a flexible foam system, where gas evolution is slow with 0.2–0.6 part of tin catalyst per 100 parts of resin, but is fast with 0.1 part of triethylenediamine, for example. The discrepancy may come in the extrapolation of the catalyst effect from the concentration used to 0.025*M* in the work of Cox and Hostettler, or in the different reaction media compared here.

The effect of several typical foam catalysts was studied by Wolfe, using a tetrahydrofuran or tetrahydrofuran-Cellosolve acetate solution at 30°C. (58). The relative catalytic effect was observed, based on the rate of carbon dioxide evolution from a solution of 80:20 tolylene diisocyanate (6.2 g.) and water (0.57 g.), with catalyst concentration

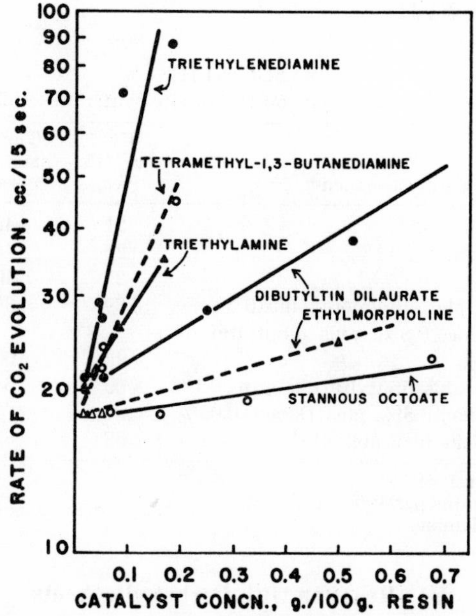

Fig. 14. Effect of catalyst concentration on the isocyanate-water reaction. (Taken from ref. 58.)

expressed in terms familiar to the foam industry, grams per 100 g. of resin used in a foam recipe, which may also be assumed to mean approximately grams of catalyst per 36 g. of tolylene diisocyanate.

The effect of catalyst concentration on the maximum rate of gas evolution is shown in Figure 14 for several catalysts. It may be noted that this range of catalyst concentration (based on isocyanate) is much lower for the tin catalysts than that to which the data of Cox and Hostettler were extrapolated. On the other hand, the data of Wolfe do not compare the catalysts on the basis of molecular concentration.

thus placing the tin catalysts much lower on the scale of relative activity than did Cox and Hostettler.

Using typical catalyst concentrations used in a one-shot polyether foam system, Wolfe found a mild synergistic effect from combining triethylenediamine and tin catalysts. It is not clear whether this effect comes from physical phenomena such as improved solubility or increased rate of migration of the mixed catalysts in the system, or from purely catalytic effects at the site of reaction. His results are shown in Table XLIII.

TABLE XLIII[a]

Effect of Combined Catalysts on Isocyanate-Water Reaction at 30°C.

Catalyst, concn.[b]	CO_2, cc./15 sec.	Time to max. rate, sec.	Order of activity
Ethylmorpholine, 0.5%	21	45	1.0
Dibutyltin dilaurate, 0.1%	25	45	1.2
Dabco,[c] 0.05%	29	40	1.4
Dabco, 0.05% plus ethylmorpholine 0.5%	39	35	1.9
Ethylmorpholine, 0.5%, plus dibutyltin dilaurate, 0.1%	42	60	2.0
Dabco, 0.05%, plus dibutyltin dilaurate, 0.1%	59	65	2.8
Ethylmorpholine, 0.5%, plus Dabco, 0.05%, plus dibutyltin dilaurate, 0.1%	88	55	4.2

[a] Taken from ref. 58.
[b] Weight in grams per 100 g. resin.
[c] Triethylenediamine.

VI. Reaction with Carboxylic Acids

Similar to the reaction of an isocyanate with water, the isocyanate-carboxylic acid reaction may follow one or more of several sequences, as in (25). Thus, the simple rate of disappearance of isocyanate or

$$\mathrm{RNCO} + \mathrm{R'COOH} \longrightarrow \mathrm{RNH\overset{O}{\overset{\|}{C}}O\overset{O}{\overset{\|}{C}}R'} \longrightarrow \mathrm{RNH\overset{O}{\overset{\|}{C}}R'} + \mathrm{CO_2}$$
$$\hookrightarrow \mathrm{RNHCONHR} + \mathrm{(R'CO)_2O} + \mathrm{CO_2}$$
$$\downarrow$$
$$2\,\mathrm{RNHCOR'} + \mathrm{CO_2} \qquad (25)$$

rate of gas evolution would not provide a thorough basis for studying the reaction.

The kinetics of the reaction between isocyanates and carboxylic acids have been studied only briefly. Some rate data compared to rates of reactions with other active hydrogen compounds are given in Section XI of this chapter. In that study the reaction appeared to follow second order kinetics for approximately the first 30% of the reaction.

Hoshino and co-workers (33) reported pseudo first order rate constants for the reaction of phenyl isocyanate in a large excess of acetic acid, based on the rate of carbon dioxide evolution at 100–110°C. Their results are shown in Table XLIV.

TABLE XLIV[a]

Rate of Pseudo First Order Reaction of Phenyl Isocyanate with Acetic Acid

Temp., °C.	k, sec.$^{-1}$	Temp., °C.	k, sec.$^{-1}$
100	0.00068	107	0.0017
105	0.00074	110	0.0091

[a] Taken from ref. 33.

Ozaki and Shimada (48) also followed the rate of the isocyanate-acid reaction by the rate of carbon dioxide evolution. When the carboxylic acid was present in large excess the rate of gas evolution was first order in isocyanate; when isocyanate was in excess the reaction was second order. Aromatic acids were generally less reactive than aliphatic acids, and within a group of aromatic acids the stronger acids reacted more slowly than did the weaker ones. The value for Hammett's (30) constant ρ was —0.16. Catalyst studies showed that triethylamine and potassium acetate were catalytic, dimethylaniline was not; boron fluoride etherate was very mildly catalytic in some cases and had no effect in others. In reactions of aromatic isocyanates with acids the formation of amide, acid anhydride and CO_2 was increased (1) by the addition of electron-attracting groups on the isocyanate, (2) by the introduction of an *ortho* substituent on the isocyanate, (3) by an increase in temperature, (4) when the catalyst concentration was small, and (5) when the acidity of the acid was low.

In a study of the anhydrides of several isocyanate-carboxylic acid combinations, Parker and co-workers (49) showed by infrared that dissociation to the isocyanate occurred in solutions at room temperature. Several anhydrides were prepared at 5°C. without solvent, and the rate of loss of carbon dioxide was observed at several temperatures. This was found to be first order, based on the concentration of mixed anhydride, at least within some temperature limits. Data are given in Table XLV. The anhydride from phenyl isocyanate and cinnamic acid showed a decrease in calculated first order rate constant at 125–145°C.

TABLE XLV[a]
First Order Rates of Carbon Dioxide Evolution from Anhydrides of Phenyl Isocyanate and Carboxylic Acids

Carboxylic acid	Temp., °C.	$k_1 \times 10^4$, sec.$^{-1}$	E_a, kcal.
Mono-*n*-butyl-*cis*-Δ^4tetrahydrophthalic	56.7	1.89	
	79.0	9.19	16.5
Cinnamic	65.4	1.59	
	78.7	2.92	
	97.2	7.02	
	97.6	7.04	11
	125.2	3.61	
	145.2	2.07	
β-Phenylpropionic	56.2	5.62	
	64.2	6.61	
	108.7	12.5	3.7

[a] Taken from ref. 49.

The rate of gas evolution from the anhydride of phenyl isocyanate and β-phenylpropionic acid appeared to follow second order kinetics above 100°C. Data for the limited temperature range studied are shown in Table XLVI.

TABLE XLVI[a]
Second Order Decomposition of Anhydride from β-Phenylpropionic Acid and Phenyl Isocyanate

Temp., °C.	$k \times 10^4$, l./mole sec.	E_a, kcal.
119.7	6.75	—
130.2	15.2	—
136.2	25.3	23.8

[a] Taken from ref. 49.

The products of these decompositions were found to be mixtures of diphenylurea, the corresponding anilide, and the symmetrical carboxylic anhydride, in addition to the carbon dioxide.

The studies reported to date do not permit one to conclude what the exact mechanisms of reactions between isocyanates and carboxylic acids are.

VII. Reactions with Phenols

The effect of catalysts on the rate of reaction of α-naphthyl isocyanate with *o*-cresol was studied by Tarbell and co-workers (56), and may be assumed typical for the isocyanate-phenol reaction in solution. The extent of reaction was determined from the weight of purified product. Results are shown in Table XLVII.

TABLE XLVII[a]
Effect of Catalysts on Reaction of α-Naphthyl Isocyanate with *o*-Cresol
(9.2 mmole of each reactant, catalyst as shown, in 3.0 cc. ligroin, 65°C.)

Catalyst	Cat. concn., mmole	Time to indicated % reaction, min.			
		10%	25%	50%	90%
None	—	~9 days (216 hr.)	—	—	—
CH_3COOH	1.9	250	—	—	—
$ClCH_2COOH$	1.9	175	—	—	—
$(CH_3)_2N—C_6H_5$	1.9	60	175	400	—
Cl_3CCOOH	1.9	40	100	250	—
HCl	1.6	~10	25	60	—
Pyridine	1.6	—	~15	50	—
$(C_2H_5)_2O·BF_3$	0.8	—	—	~15	~40
$(C_2H_5)_3N$	0.13	—	—	—	~10

[a] Taken from ref. 56.

Other compounds which qualitatively showed a catalytic effect were sodium carbonate, sodium acetate, and zinc chloride. As noted in Chapter III, additional catalysts for this reaction include aluminum chloride.

No reaction was observed between α-naphthyl isocyanate and the following phenols, even in the presence of catalyst: 2,4-dinitrophenol, 2,6-dinitro-4-chlorophenol, and picric acid. Thus the reduction of phenol reactivity by negative substituents is similar to that in the aromatic amine series.

The catalytic effect of dimethylaniline may be significant with regard to the mechanism of the isocyanate-phenol reaction. It will be recalled that Baker and Holdsworth (9) found that dimethylaniline was not a catalyst for the isocyanate-alcohol reaction. This lack of catalytic effect was considered evidence that coordination of catalyst with alcohol hydrogen was not a significant part of the reaction mechanism.

Conversely, the catalytic effect of dimethylaniline in the isocyanate-phenol reaction suggests that the sequence (26), (27) may at least be one type of reaction occurring. The greater acidity of the phenolic hydrogen, compared to that of the alcoholic hydrogen, is in agreement with this suggestion.

$$ArOH + ArN(CH_3)_2 \rightleftharpoons Ar\bar{O} + ArN\overset{+}{H}(CH_3)_2 \qquad (26)$$

$$RNCO + Ar\bar{O} \rightleftharpoons \left[\begin{array}{c} RN{=}C{-}O \\ | \\ OAr \end{array}\right]^{-} \xrightarrow{ArN\overset{+}{H}(CH_3)_2} RNHCOOAr + ArN(CH_3)_2 \qquad (27)$$

If such a sequence does obtain, one then is led to the conclusion that the lack of reactivity of 2,4-dinitrophenol in the presence of catalyst means that the 2,4-dinitrophenolate ion is not sufficiently basic to overcome the steric hindrance of its own *o*-nitro group and attack the isocyanate successfully.

In uncatalyzed systems at 20 and 30°, Baker and Gaunt (10) found phenol to be about as reactive as *tert*-butyl alcohol, but in certain catalyzed systems the phenol was as reactive as ethyl alcohol (Table XLVIII).

TABLE XLVIII[a]
Comparison of Phenyl Isocyanate Reactions with Phenol and Alcohols
($0.24M$ reactants in dibutyl ether)

	$k_{exp.} \times 10^4$, l./mole sec., $0.03M$ $(C_2H_5)_3N$			$k_0 \times 10^4$ l./mole sec.
ROH	20°C.	30°C.	E_a, kcal.	20°C.
Phenol	12.0	16.7	5.8	0.01
Ethyl alcohol	12.7	20	7.85	0.30
tert-Butyl alcohol	0.015	0.027	13	0.009

[a] Taken from ref. 10.

VIII. Reaction with Ureas

Because of the relatively high temperatures required and the many side reactions possible at these temperatures, the reaction between an isocyanate and a substituted urea is a difficult one to study kinetically with satisfactory results. Though the initial reaction leads to a biuret, the "active" hydrogens in this compound may be nearly as active as those in the original urea. Dissociation of biuret and other products may occur, followed by reactions between the compounds then available. In spite of these factors, the reaction has been of great interest because of its relation to cross link formation in many urethane polymers, especially water-blown foams and amine-cured elastomers.

Phenyl and *o*-tolyl isocyanates were used by Bennet and co-workers (11,51) as model compounds in a study of this reaction with phenylurea and *sym*-diphenyl urea. A suitable solvent which showed no significant loss of isocyanate in a blank solution stored for the maximum reaction time and temperature was *o*-dichlorobenzene. Thus loss of isocyanate by dimerization and trimerization was not considered likely. The reaction of isocyanate with phenylurea, as followed by dibutylamine titration of unreacted isocyanate, fit second order kinetic calculations over the approximate range of 10 to 60% reaction and with isocyanate-substituted urea molar ratios of 1:1, 2:1, and 1:2. The rate data obtained over the temperature range of 60 to 140°C. did not agree with the Arrhenius rate equation, suggesting a change in the course of the reaction at the higher temperatures. (Other authors have reported Arrhenius activation energies based on a narrower temperature range.) Data are shown in Table XLIX.

TABLE XLIX[a]

Relative Rates of Reactions of Aromatic Isocyanates and Substituted Ureas ($0.01M$ in each reactant, in dichlorobenzene)

Isocyanate	Urea	Temp., °C.	$k \times 10^4$, l./mole sec.
Phenyl	$C_6H_5NHCONH_2$	60	3.7
Phenyl	$C_6H_5NHCONH_2$	100	31.7
Phenyl	$C_6H_5NHCONH_2$	140	47.8
Phenyl	$(C_6H_5NH)_2CO$	100	9.9
Phenyl	$(C_6H_5NH)_2CO$	140	22.7
o-Tolyl	$C_6H_5NHCONH_2$	100	10.8
o-Tolyl	$C_6H_5NHCONH_2$	140	18.4 (21.0[b])
o-Tolyl	$(C_6H_5NH)_2CO$	100	3.6
o-Tolyl	$(C_6H_5NH)_2CO$	140	8.2 (3.8[b])

[a] Taken from refs. 11, 51.
[b] With ethylmorpholine, 10% based on isocyanate concentration.

It is noteworthy that ethylmorpholine, a typical catalyst for the isocyanate-hydroxyl and isocyanate-water reactions, had no significant catalytic effect here.

Typical reaction curves are shown in Figure 15.

The rate of reaction between *sym*-di-*o*-tolylurea and *o*-tolyl isocyanate in dioxane at 80°C. was reported by Shkapenko and co-workers (52). Results are shown in Figure 16. The isocyanate concentration was 0.2*M*, and triethylamine was present at 0.036*M* concentration. The rate for the first 50% of reaction is in fairly close agreement with the data of Bennet and co-workers, but the sudden increase in rate beyond 50% reaction is surprising and not readily explainable. Perhaps some additional reaction such as trimerization became significant at that time.

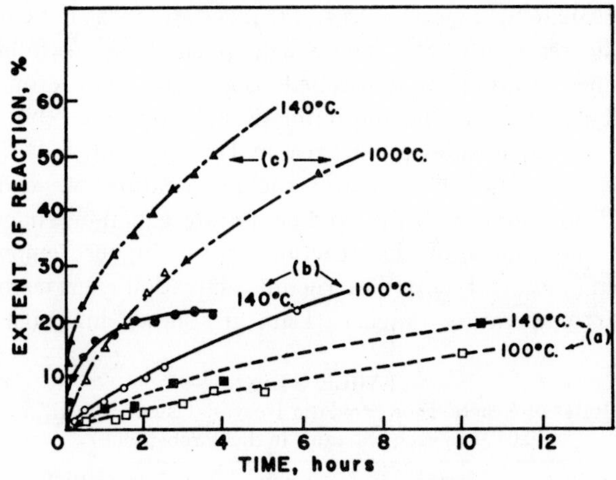

Fig. 15. Reaction of isocyanates with ureas in dichlorobenzene: (a) *o*-Toyl isocyanate and diphenylurea, - - -. (b) Phenyl isocyanate and diphenylurea, —. (c) Phenyl isocyanate and phenylurea, — - —. (Taken from ref. 11.)

Morton and co-workers (42,43) reported a second order rate constant of $1.48 \pm 0.60 \times 10^{-4}$ l./mole sec. for the reaction of phenyl isocyanate with diphenylurea in dioxane at 80°C. This value is in good agreement with the results of Bennet and co-workers (11).

Data concerning the relative effect of several catalysts on the phenyl-isocyanate-*sym*-diphenylurea reaction in dioxane at 70°C. were given by Cox and Hostettler (18,34). In contrast to Bennet, these authors found a moderate catalytic effect from typical tertiary amines. Results are shown in Table L.

Results with the tin catalysts were obtained by extrapolating data obtained at much lower catalyst concentrations, and comparisons were based on the time required to reach 50% reaction. The catalytic

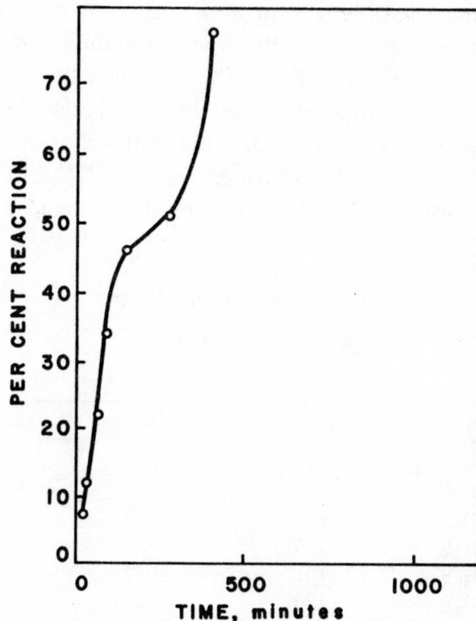

Fig. 16. Disappearance of isocyanate: *o*-tolyl isocyanate, and *sym*-di-*o*-tolylurea in dioxane at 80°C. (Taken from ref. 52.)

effect of the tertiary amines was not in agreement with the observations of Bennet and co-workers (11), who evaluated the catalyst at 140°C. in dichlorobenzene. It is possible that catalysis would be apparent at 70° but not at 140°C.

TABLE L[a]

Relative Reactivity of Phenyl Isocyanate with *sym*-Diphenylurea, with Catalysts (dioxane, 0.25M isocyanate, 0.025M catalyst, 70°C.)

Catalyst	Relative rate
None	2.2
N-Methylmorpholine	10
Triethylamine	4
Tetramethyl-1,3-butanediamine	12
Triethylenediamine	90
Tributyltin acetate	8000
Dibutyltin diacetate	12,000

[a] Taken from ref. 34.

In addition to the rate of biuret formation, the rate of biuret dissociation is of interest with regard to the thermal stability of biuret cross links in urethane polymers. Kogon (37) studied the dissociation of biurets by following the appearance of the NH band at 6750 cm.$^{-1}$, which is characteristic of ureas and urethanes but not of biurets or allophanates. The dissociation in $Cl(CF_2CFCl)_2Cl$ and $Cl(CF_2CFCl)_3Cl$ followed first order kinetics (Table LI). These

TABLE LI[a]
Dissociation of Substituted Biurets

$$C_6H_5NHC(=O)\text{—}N(R)COR'$$

R	R′	Temp., °C.	$k \times 10^4$, sec.$^{-1}$	E_a, kcal./mole
C_6H_5	$N(CH_3)C_6H_5$	131	6.8	—
C_6H_5	$N(CH_3)C_6H_5$	145	15.0	17.8
C_6H_5	$N(C_2H_5)_2$	138	0.9	—
C_6H_5	$N(C_2H_5)_2$	145	1.5	20.0
C_2H_5	$N(C_2H_5)_2$	131	0.2	—
C_2H_5	$N(C_2H_5)_2$	150	1.32	34.2

[a] Taken from ref. 37.

results indicate greater thermal stability for alkyl-substituted than for aryl-substituted biurets; and also show that biuret cross links in a polymer would not have good thermal stability.

IX. Reactions with Urethanes

The study of reactions of isocyanates with urethanes is subject to the same difficulties as is that of isocyanates with ureas, and the reasons for interest are similar. The uncatalyzed isocyanate-urethane reaction is even slower than the isocyanate-urea reaction, so there may be even more possibilities of side reactions in the former case. Hence it is not surprising that some studies of this reaction have resulted in data that did not fit simple kinetic relations.

In conjunction with the study of the isocyanate-urea reaction, Bennet and co-workers (11) observed the reaction between monoisocyanates and model urethanes. The reaction was much slower than the isocyanate-urea reaction, and the data did not give uniform rate constants with any kinetic equation. The calculated second order rate constants became progressively smaller as the reaction proceeded.

For comparison purposes the second order rate constants for approximately the 0–20% reaction range are shown in Table LII.

Morton and co-workers (42,43) reported values of 0.02–0.06 $\times$ 10^{-4} l./mole sec. for the second order rate constant for the phenyl isocyanate-butyl carbanilate reaction in dioxane at 80°C.

The reaction between isocyanate and urethanes with a large excess of isocyanate as solvent was studied by Kogon (38). Calculations were based upon the rate of disappearance of the NH infrared band at 6750 cm.$^{-1}$, which is, characteristic of urethanes and ureas, but not

TABLE LII[a]

Relative Rates of Reactions between Aromatic Isocyanates and Urethanes at 140°C.

(0.035*M* in each reactant, in dichlorobenzene)

Isocyanate	Urethane	$k \times 10^4$, l./mole sec.
Phenyl isocyanate	$C_6H_5NHCOOC_2H_5$	0.2 (0.14[b])
o-Tolyl isocyanate	$C_6H_5NHCOOC_2H_5$	0.1

[a] Taken from ref. 11.
[b] With ethylmorpholine, 10% based on isocyanate.

of isocyanates, allophanates, or biurets. The data fit a second order rate calculation, but the large excess of isocyanate could have obscured deviations from second order. Results are shown in Table LIII. These rate constants were of the same order of magnitude as those reported by Bennet *et al.* In addition, the lack of catalytic effect by methylmorpholine confirmed the similar observation by Bennet *et al.*, who used ethylmorpholine.

The equilibrium data were in agreement with greater stability of the allophanate at lower temperatures, and greater dissociation at higher temperatures. The fact that measurable dissociation occurred at 106°C. shows that an allophanate cross link would be a relatively unstable one.

The reactions in which catalyst was added did not permit equilibrium measurements. As equilibrium was approached an exothermic reaction occurred and the reaction mass solidified, largely due to trimerization of the isocyanate.

Cooper and co-workers (17) showed that urethanes from *p*-phenylene diisocyanate and unsaturated glycols are much more reactive at 100°C. than those from saturated glycols. Conditions of the reactions

TABLE LIII[a]

Rate and Equilibrium Constants for Reactions of Ethyl Carbanilates with Excess Aryl Isocyanate, No Solvent

$$RC_6H_4NCO + R'C_6H_4NHCOOC_2H_5 \rightleftharpoons RC_6H_4NHCON(C_6H_4R')COOC_2H_5$$

R	R′	Temp., °C.	NCO/NH	$K_{equil.}$, l./mole	ΔH, kcal.	ΔS, cal./deg.	$k_{rate} \times 10^4$, l./mole sec.	E_a, kcal.
H	H	137	12.6	0.203		−13.2	0.065	
H	H	137	12.6[b]	—			0.072	
H	H	128	12.6	0.242	−6.7	−13.8	0.042	15.9
H	H	128	12.6[b]	—			0.050	
H	H	128	9.1	0.243		−13.8	0.050	
H	H	106	12.6	0.397	−6.8	−15.9	0.017	16.5
H	H	128	18.0	0.248		−14.0	0.036	
H	*p*-CH_3	128	12.6	0.349			0.036	
H	*o*-CH_3	128	12.6	0.568			0.127	
o-CH_3	*o*-CH_3	143	12.6	0.146			0.070	
o-CH_3	*p*-CH_3	143	12.6	0.094			0.043	

[a] Taken from ref. 38.
[b] Catalyzed by *N*-methylmorpholine.

were not given, and the values for the rate constants appear large compared to other's results, but the comparison is striking (Table LIV).

Cooper and co-workers (17) also observed that an unidentified iron compound was a mild catalyst for the reaction of an aromatic isocyanate with a urethane, as summarized in Section XII at the end of this chapter. More recently, Kogon (40) showed that a number of specific metal compounds are strong catalysts for the reaction of aromatic isocyanates with certain urethanes, even at room temperature. By using infrared to identify the allophanate formed, it was shown that several metal compounds catalyzed the reaction between phenyl isocyanate and

TABLE LIV[a]

Reaction of *p*-Phenylene Diisocyanate with Urethanes at 100°C.

Glycol used for urethane	$k \times 10^4$, l./mole sec.
1,4-Butanediol	0.33
1,4-Butenediol	2.00
1,4-Butynediol	47.00

[a] Taken from ref. 17.

ethyl carbanilate at room temperature, without solvent. The results are given in Table LV.

The reaction did not proceed in two weeks at room temperature without a catalyst. Even with a catalyst, the reaction did not proceed when ethyl carbanilate or phenyl isocyanate was replaced by ethyl carbamate or ethyl isocyanate, respectively.

Some of these catalysts were also strongly effective in trimerizing phenyl isocyanate at room temperature, without solvent, as shown in

TABLE LV[a]

Metal Carboxylate Catalysis of Allophanate Formation at Room Temperature

Catalyst	Metal concn., moles/l., × 10^5	Time, hr.	Allophanate yield, %
Lead naphthenate	7.7	4	96
Lead 2-ethylhexanoate	5.2	5	95
Lead linoresinate	5.4	5	96
Cobalt naphthenate	6.1	6	96
Cobalt 2-ethylhexanoate	6.2	7	97
Cobalt linoresinate	6.1	7	96
Zinc 2-ethylhexanoate	5.2	5	95
Zinc linoresinate	10.1	88	12
Copper naphthenate	11.2	88	69
Copper linoresinate	12.2	88	50
Manganese naphthenate	6.0	88	69
Manganese 2-ethylhexanoate	7.1	88	10
Manganese linoresinate	7.3	88	45
Iron naphthenate	6.9	88	36
Iron linoresinate	5.2	90	42
Cadmium naphthenate	6.0	88	10
Vanadium naphthenate	5.5	88	10

[a] Taken from ref. 40.

Table LVI. As the reaction times and yields in the previous Tables LV and LVI indicate, the trimerization was generally slower than was the allophanate formation. To confirm this, equimolar quantities of phenyl isocyanate and ethyl carbanilate were reacted at room temperature in the presence of cobalt 2-ethylhexanoate. A 95.5% yield of the allophanate and a 0.84% yield of phenyl isocyanate trimer were obtained. Thus under these conditions trimerization did not compete significantly with allophanate formation.

The rate of dissociation of allophanates was observed by Kogon (37) by following the appearance of the NH absorption at 6750 cm.$^{-1}$.

TABLE LVI[a]

Catalysis of Phenyl Isocyanate Trimerization at Room Temperature

Catalyst	Metal concn., moles/l., $\times 10^5$	Trimer yield, % after 48 hr.
Lead naphthenate	7.7	100
Cobalt naphthenate	6.1	100
Iron naphthenate	4.6	10
Manganese naphthenate	3.9	5
Copper naphthenate	7.5	5
Vanadium naphthenate	5.5	10
Cadmium naphthenate	6.0	50
Zinc naphthenate	5.5	0

[a] Taken from ref. 40.

The reaction in $Cl(CF_2CFCl)_2Cl$ and $Cl(CF_2CFCl)_3Cl$ was first order (Table LVII).

TABLE LVII[a]

Rate of Dissociation of N,N′-Diphenyl Ethyl Allophanate

Temp., °C.	$k \times 10^4$, sec.$^{-1}$	E_a, kcal.
132	0.39	
150	1.65	26.2

[a] Taken from ref. 37.

X. Reactions with Thiols

Reactions of monoisocyanates with thiols have been studied quantitatively by Dyer and co-workers using dilatometric methods (23,24). Somewhat like the reactions of phenols with isocyanates, the reactions of thiols (mercaptans) with isocyanates was found to be very slow in the absence of catalysts, but subject to strong catalysis by bases.

In the initial study the rate constant for the uncatalyzed reaction between phenyl isocyanate (0.6*M*) and 1-butanethiol (1*M*) in toluene at 25°C. was found to be approximately 5×10^{-7} l./mole sec. Product catalysis (by thiol carbanilate) was observed in the absence of tertiary amine catalyst, or more strongly in the presence of triethylamine. In the reaction of phenyl isocyanate with *tert*-butanethiol no catalysis by the product was observed, however, even when tertiary amine catalyst was present. The apparent second order rate constant for the phenyl isocyanate-1-butanethiol reaction was shown to increase somewhat as the SH/NCO ratio increased, and was directly proportional to the concentration of amine catalyst. No reaction was observed between phenyl isocyanate and thiolcarbanilate under the conditions of the kinetic experiments, although a very slow reaction of unidentified nature was observed at very high triethylamine concentrations. Typical data for catalyzed reactions are shown in Table LVIII (23).

TABLE LVIII[a]
Second Order Rate Constants for Phenyl Isocyanate-Thiol Reactions at 25°C. (reactants 1:1 ratio, 0.25*M*)

Thiol	Catalyst concn.	Solvent	$k \times 10^{-4}$ l./mole sec.
1-Butane	0.0006*M*	Toluene	8.0
1-Dodecane	0.0006*M*	Toluene	6.4
tert-Butane	0.02*M*	Xylene	2.7

[a] Taken from ref. 23.

In a more detailed study (24) the reaction between phenyl isocyanate and thiols was reported to be in agreement with the following combination of reactions:

(1) *Spontaneous reaction:*

$$\text{ArNCO} + \text{RSH} \rightarrow \text{ArNHCOSR}$$

(2) *Base-catalyzed reaction:*

$$\text{ArNCO} + \text{R}'_3\text{N}: \rightleftharpoons \left[\begin{array}{c}\text{ArN=C—O}\\ \uparrow \\ \text{NR}'_3\end{array}\right] \xrightarrow{\text{RSH}} \text{ArNHCOSR} + \text{R}'_3\text{N}$$

(complex 1)

(3) *Product-catalyzed reaction:*

$$\text{ArNCO} + \text{ArNHCOSR} \rightleftharpoons \left[\begin{array}{c}\text{ArN=C—O} \rightarrow \text{H—NAr}\\ | \\ \text{COSR}\end{array}\right] \xrightarrow{\text{RSH}} 2\text{ArNHCOSR}$$

(complex 2)

(4) *Combined base-product catalyzed reaction:*

$$\left[\begin{array}{c}\text{ArN=C—O}\\ | \\ \text{NR}'_3\end{array}\right] + \text{ArNHCOSR} \rightleftharpoons \left[\begin{array}{c}\text{ArN—C—O} \rightarrow \text{H—NAr}\\ \uparrow \qquad\qquad | \\ \text{NR}'_3 \qquad \text{COSR}\end{array}\right] \xrightarrow{\text{RSH}} 2\text{ArNHCOSR} + \text{R}'_3\text{N}$$

(complex 1) (complex 3)

This combination of reactions corresponds to Baker's proposal for the isocyanate-alcohol reaction, with the addition of the combined catalysis by base and product and with the product serving as an acid catalyst in the Dyer sequence. From these four equations the experimentally observed second order rate constant should be made up of four terms:

$$k_e = k_0 + k_c(\text{basic catalyst}) + k_p(\text{product}) + k_{cp}(\text{base})(\text{product})$$

Data were shown which were in agreement with this mechanism and rate equation. The only product of the phenyl isocyanate-1-butanethiol reaction identified was the thiolcarbanilate.

Catalytic rate constants (k_c) were determined for a number of tertiary amines from the slope of the plot of k_e against amine concentration. Selected data are shown in Table LIX; values of k_c were obtained from these and other data at different catalyst concentrations.

TABLE LIX[a]

Effect of Catalysts on Phenyl Isocyanate-Thiol Reaction in Toluene at 25°C.

Catalyst	pK_b	Catalyst concn. (M)	$k_e \times 10^4$, l./mole sec.	k_c
1-Butanethiol (0.075M isocyanate, 0.16M thiol)				
1,2,2,6,6-Pentamethylpiperidine	2.75	0.0032	12.6	0.37
Tri-*n*-butylamine	3.11	0.00733	16.6	0.22
Triethylamine	3.26	0.001855	19.2	1.03
Tri-*n*-propylamine	3.35	0.00878	16.4	0.19
1-Ethylpiperidine	3.60	0.00241	16.0	0.65
1-Methylpiperidine	3.87	0.00247	15.2	0.55
Benzyldimethylamine	5.07	0.00512	18.3	0.37
Triethylenediamine	5.80	0.00079	17.5	2.17
N-Ethylmorpholine	6.30	0.1310	19.1	0.0147
Diethylaniline	7.44	0.5075	(too slow)	0
Pyridine	8.85	0.5374	0.9	0.00016
2-Butanethiol (0.20M isocyanate and thiol)				
Tri-*n*-butylamine	3.11	0.0433	9.4	0.028
Triethylamine	3.26	0.00736	9.5	0.13
Pyridine	8.85	0.50	0.28	0.000051

[a] Taken from ref. 24.

From the data in Table LIX it is apparent that the effectiveness of a catalyst is a function of both its base strength and the steric hindrance. This behavior is emphasized by plotting log k_c against pK_b as in Figure 17. As in the case of the phenyl isocyanate-methyl alcohol reaction (9), dialkylanilines did not appear to be catalysts for the isocyanate-thiol reaction. This dependence of the catalyst strength on steric

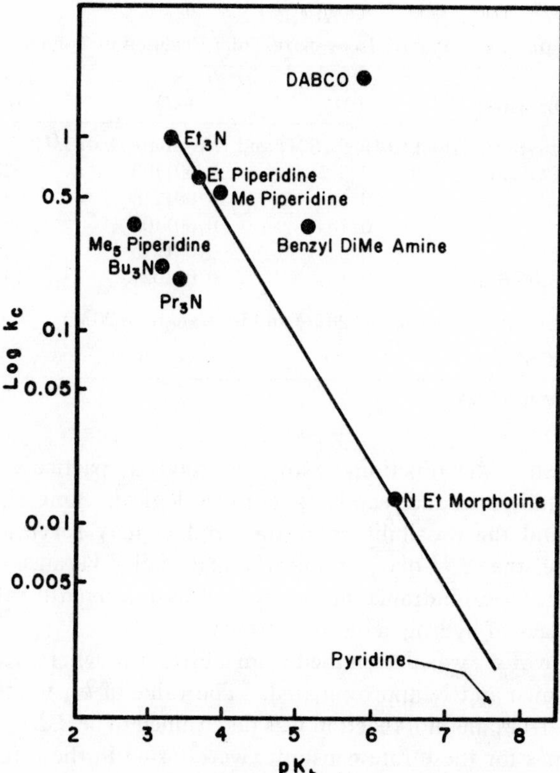

Fig. 17. Relation between base strength and catalyst strength for the NCO-SH reaction. (Taken from ref. 24.)

hindrance (deviation from the Brønsted law), seems to rule out the possibility that the catalyst could function primarily by promoting ionization of the thiol.

Product catalysis was demonstrated by the data in Table LX. Values for k_p were obtained by plotting k_e values at constant triethylamine concentrations against product concentration. The value for k_p was found to be approximately 10^{-3}, for the reaction with 1-butanethiol, but varied with the amine concentration.

The *N,N*-disubstituted thiolcarbanilate was not catalytic. It was suggested that this observation showed the necessity for the NH group for product catalysis, and the product was shown as functioning as an

TABLE LX[a]

Product Catalysis of Phenyl Isocyanate-Thiol Reaction in Toluene at 25°C.

Thiolcarbanilate	Concn. (M)	$(C_2H_5)_3N$ concn. (M)	$k_e \times 10^4$, l./mole sec.
1-Butanethiol (0.15–0.16M) and isocyanate (0.075M)			
$C_6H_5NHCOSBu$-*n*	0.075	0.001109	13.5
	0.11	0.001116	16.4
	0.15	0.001102	16.3
	0.22	0.001115	19.4
$(C_6H_5)_2NCOSBu$-*n*	0.15	0.00102	11.1
2-Butanethiol (0.20M) and isocyanate (0.20M)			
$C_6H_5NHCOSBu$-*sec*	0.20	0.00150	2.2

[a] Taken from ref. 24.

acid catalyst. The function as an acid catalyst, particularly in the combined amine-product catalysis, appears logical. One should also keep in mind the possibility that the product may serve as a basic catalyst, and the *N,N*-diaryl thiolcarbanilate failed because of a combination of steric hindrance and very low base strength, rather than because of lack of hydrogen on the nitrogen.

The value of k_{cp} was determined from a given run wherein k_e, k_0, and k_c were known and k_p approximated. The value of k_{cp} for the phenyl isocyanate-1-butanethiol reaction was determined to be 2.2.

The values for these rate constants were tested in the rate equation by calculating k_e from the summary equation and comparing it to the observed value for k_e for the initial reaction. This was done in twenty-eight runs with a variety of amine concentrations, NCO/SH ratios, with and without added thiolcarbanilate. While k_e ranged from 3.5×10^{-4} to 16.1×10^{-4} l./mole sec., the average deviation of calculated k_e from observed k_e was only 0.3 unit. These results substantiated the proposed mechanism quite well.

Additional experiments showed an effect of solvent which was often opposite to that observed for the isocyanate-hydroxyl reaction reported by Ephraim *et al.* (26). Results are shown in Table LXI.

When the amine-catalyzed reaction was run in dimethylformamide or in dimethyl sulfoxide the rate was too fast to measure. Even in the absence of amine catalyst the rate in these solvents was very fast. When tested as basic catalysts dimethylformamide and dimethyl sulfoxide showed little effect, but this is not unreasonable because of the

TABLE LXI[a]
Rates of Amine-Catalyzed Phenyl Isocyanate-1-Butanethiol Reactions in Different Solvents at 25°C.
(0.075M isocyanate, 0.16M thiol)

Solvent	Amine concn. (M)	$k_e \times 10^4$, l./mole sec.
Toluene	0.001855	19.2
Butyl acetate	0.00181	44.3
Nitrobenzene	0.0001042	216.0
Acetonitrile	0.002286	0.05

[a] Taken from ref. 24.

much lower concentration when used as catalyst instead of as a solvent. In this reaction the solvents which might appear to promote ionization of the thiol gave a faster rate of reaction. A study of catalysts in a solvent such as nitrobenzene compared to the study in toluene would be of interest to see if catalysts obey the Brønsted law in ionizing solvents more closely than they do in solvents of low ionizing power.

In addition, energies and entropies of activation were calculated from data at 20 and 25°C. (Table LXII). Since this temperature range is so narrow the data should be considered as only approximate.

TABLE LXII[a]
Energies and Entropies of Activation of Catalyzed Phenyl Isocyanate-Thiol Reaction in Toluene
(0.20M isocyanate, 0.20M thiol)

$[Et_3N]$	Thiol	$k_e \times 10^4$, l./mole sec.		Act. energy, kcal./mole	Act. entropy, e.u.
		20°C.	25°C.		
6.26×10^{-4}	1-Butanethiol	7.0	7.9	3.93	−63.8
62.6×10^{-4}	2-Butanethiol	7.6	8.7	4.55	−58.1

[a] Taken from ref. 24.

Iwakura and Okada (35) recently published a study of the amine-catalyzed reaction of isocyanates with thiols which was very similar to that of Dyer, Glenn, and Lendrat (24). The results of Iwakura and Okada confirmed the effect of catalyst structure on activity, the effect of solvent on the reaction, and the activation energy of the catalyzed reaction. Several additional points of interest were established. The relative rate of reaction with phenyl isocyanate decreased in the order phenylmethane thiol > 1,4-butanethiol > 1-butanethiol ~ 1-dodecane-thiol. Thiophenol reacted too slowly at 30°C. to provide a reaction rate constant, even in the presence of triethylamine. At comparable catalyst concentrations, phenyl isocyanate reacted with 1-butanethiol approximately eighty times as fast as ethyl isocyanate.

An interesting study of the reaction of phenyl isocyanate with monothioethylene glycol illustrated the differences between the behavior of the thiol and hydroxy groups (54). When equimolar quantities of reactants were used, without a catalyst, the product was the mercaptourethane:

$$ArNCO + HOCH_2CH_2SH \rightarrow ArNHCOOCH_2CH_2SH$$

The unusually strong effect of tertiary amines on the reactivity of the thiol group was demonstrated by the reaction in the presence of a tertiary amine. In this case the product was the hydroxythiourethane:

$$ArNCO + HOCH_2CH_2SH \xrightarrow{R_3N} RNHCOSCH_2CH_2OH$$

XI. Summary of Relative Rates of Reactions with Active Hydrogen Compounds

Sufficient data are available to permit reasonably good comparisons of the relative reactivity of model compounds representing the more important active hydrogen groups which may react with isocyanates. Whenever possible, comparisons are based on series of data from a single laboratory, with constant solvent and catalyst.

TABLE LXIII[a]
Relative Rates of Reactions of Phenyl Isocyanate with Active Hydrogen Compounds at 80°C.
(dioxane, 1:1 reactant ratio)

Active hydrogen compd.	$k \times 10^4$ l./mole sec.	Relative rate
n-Butyl carbanilate	0.06	1
Acetanilide	0.99	16
n-Butyric acid	1.56	26
Diphenylurea	4.78	80
Water	5.89	98
n-Butanol	27.5	460

[a] Taken from ref. 42.

Fortunately the rates of reactions of isocyanates with active hydrogen compounds are sufficiently different that one can usually suppress the subsequent reactions with the initial products, if desired. Thus, amines react readily even at 0°C., while alcohols, water, and some carboxylic acids react at moderate rates at 25–50°C. Reactions with other carboxylic acids, ureas, amides and urethanes may become important at about 100°C. and above, with the relative reactivity usually decreasing approximately in the order given.

Recent data on the relative reactivities of a series of active hydrogen compounds as given by Morton and Diesz (42) are shown in Table LXIII.

A later publication by Morton and co-workers (43) gave a somewhat different summary of relative rates of reactions, as shown in Table LXIV. These data seem preferable to those of Table LXIII in that water is now shown as being more reactive than the substituted urea.

TABLE LXIV[a]
Revised Relative Rates of Reactions of Phenyl Isocyanate with Active Hydrogen Compounds at 80°C.
(dioxane, 1:1 reactant ratio)

Active hydrogen compd.	$k \times 10^4$ l./mole sec.	Relative rate
n-Butyl carbanilate	0.02 ± 0.02	1
n-Butyranilide	0.28 ± 0.05	14
Diphenylurea	1.48 ± 0.60	74
n-Butyric acid	1.56 ± 0.33	78
Water	5.89[b]	295[b]
n-Butanol	27.5[b]	1375[b]

[a] Taken from ref. 43.
[b] Calculated from rate data obtained at lower temperatures.

The rates of reactions of several familiar isocyanates with typical active hydrogen compounds were reported by Cooper, Pearson, and Darke (17). The solvent and reactant concentration were not reported; it is assumed that no catalyst was used. The method of calculating rate constants was not indicated, but all constants were shown as second order rate constants. Data are given in Table LXV.

This is a particularly interesting comparison with regard to control of polymer cross linking by biuret or allophanate formation. For example, 1,5-naphthalene diisocyanate shows the greatest tendency toward allophanate formation, and hexamethylene diisocyanate the least.

Similarly, in foam formation, the 2,6-tolylene diisocyanate would be expected to form biuret cross links much faster than would the 2,4-

TABLE LXV[a]
Reactions of Isocyanates with Active Hydrogen Compounds at 100°C.

Isocyanate	Reactive grouping				
	Hydroxyl[b]	Water	Urea[c]	Amine[d]	Urethane[e]
p-Phenylene diisocyanate					
k, l./mole sec., × 10^4	36.0	7.8	13.0	17.0	1.8 at 130°C.
E_a, kcal./mole	11.0	17.0	15.0	7.9	
2-Chloro-1,4-phenylene diisocyanate					
k, l./mole sec., × 10^4	38.0	3.6	13.0	23.0	
E_a, kcal./mole	7.5	6.4	15.0	3.4	
2,4-Tolylene diisocyanate					
k, l./mole sec., × 10^4	21.0	5.8	2.2	36.0	0.7 at 130°C.
E_a, kcal./mole	7.9	10.0	17.0	9.5	
2,6-Tolylene diisocyanate					
k, l./mole sec., × 10^4	7.4	4.2	6.3	6.9	
E_a, kcal./mole	10.0	24.0	11.8	9.0	
1,5-Naphthalene diisocyanate					
k, l./mole sec., × 10^4	4.0	0.7	8.7	7.1	0.6
E_a, kcal./mole	12.0	7.7	13.0	12.0	
Hexamethylene diisocyanate					
k, l./mole sec., × 10^4	8.3	0.5	1.1	2.4	2 × 10^{-5} at 130°C.
E_a, kcal./mole	11.0	9.2	17.0	17.0	

[a] Taken from ref. 17.
[b] Poly(ethylene adipate).
[c] Diphenylurea.
[d] 3,3′-Dichlorobenzidine.
[e] *p*-Phenylenedibutylurethane.

tolylene diisocyanate. Thus an 80:20 ratio of 2,4- and 2,6-isomers would be more reactive toward hydroxyl and water than would a 65:35 ratio, but the 65:35 ratio should give more biuret cross linking.

The rate constants for the reactions of hexamethylene diisocyanate at least with hydroxyl appear large in relation to those for the aromatic isocyanate. Others have found the aliphatic isocyanates consistently less reactive than unhindered aromatic isocyanates. The wide variation in the reported rates of the other reactions, not always consistent with the structure of the reactants, and variations in activation energies in any given series are unexpected. Several of these data are not in agreement with what would be expected from other published results.

More information concerning the experimental data would be necessary in order to interpret these results satisfactorily.

The effect of temperature on the reactions of *p*-phenylene diisocyanate with the model active hydrogen compounds of Table LXV is shown in Figure 18 (17). It is readily apparent from Figure 18 that

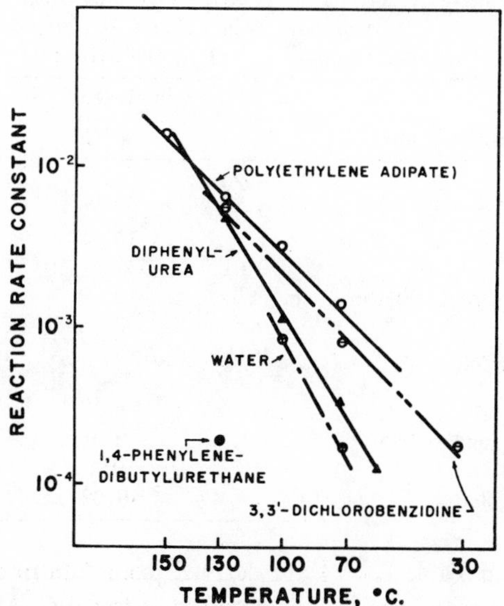

Fig. 18. Effect of temperature on reactivity of *p*-phenylene diisocyanate with model compounds. (Taken from ref. 17.)

all of the uncatalyzed reactions except allophanate formation should reach a similar rate constant at about 130–150°C.

In addition to the comparisons of reactivity within data from a single laboratory, it is possible to give an approximate comparison based on data from different laboratories. As has been apparent throughout this chapter, the effects of structure of reactants, solvent, temperature, and catalysts are not accurately known for a wide range of variations. The reactions are not simple second order, but are complex, with possibilities of catalysis by a reactant and a product, and with strong solvent effects. In most cases temperature effects have been evaluated over only a narrow range, often only at two temperatures. Thus calculated activation energies are often only approximate and in many cases data have not been adequate to show a constant mechanism of reaction throughout a significant temperature range. With these many limitations the data in Table LXVI are presented as an approximation of relative reactivities in uncatalyzed systems at 25 and 80°C.

TABLE LXVI
Approximate Relative Reactivity of Phenyl Isocyanate with Active Hydrogen Compounds in Toluene
(assumed reactants at 1:1 equivalent ratio)

Active hydrogen compd.	$k \times 10^4$, l./mole sec. 25°C.	$k \times 10^4$, l./mole sec. 80°C.	Act. energy, kcal./mole
Aniline	10–20	—	—
1-Butanol	2–4	30	8–9
2-Butanol	1	15	10
tert-Butanol	0.01	—	—
Diethylene glycol adipate	0.5	5	10
Water	0.4	6	11
1-Butanethiol	0.005	—	—
Phenol	0.01	—	—
Diphenylurea	—	2	—
n-Butyric acid	—	2	—
n-Butyranilide	—	0.3	—
Ethyl carbanilate	—	0.02	16.5

The values in Table LXVI are derived from data in earlier parts of this chapter. The solvent is considered to be toluene. Where possible, values are averages of selected data from different laboratories. Selections were based on the reasonable appearance of the data from an over-all point of view, based on the general pattern of structure, solvent, temperature, and catalyst effects given in this chapter. For simplicity the comparison is made for phenyl isocyanate. Data for other isocyanates could be predicted based on electronic structure (see Tables V and VI) and steric hindrance.

XII. Summary of Catalytic Effects

Although the choice of temperature, isocyanate, and active hydrogen compound permits one to control isocyanate reactions to a large extent, the choice of catalyst often gives much broader control. Furthermore, the catalytic effect may be so powerful in many cases that it overrides the influence of changes in isocyanate structure or reaction medium. For these reasons many commercial uses of isocyanates include catalysts to give the desired reaction control. Although Section XI was a useful guide to relative reactivities in uncatalyzed systems, it would be very misleading for such commercial operations as flexible foam systems. This section summarizes relative reactivities in catalyzed systems and the selective activity of different catalysts.

As shown earlier in this chapter, steric hindrance in either reactant or catalyst may reduce the effect of a catalyst. A most notable example is the failure of dialkylanilines to catalyze the reaction with alcohols. As an example of the effect of steric hindrance in a reactant, triethylamine catalyzes the reaction of phenyl isocyanate with *tert*-butyl alcohol much less than that with *n*-butyl alcohol.

Catalyst effects may be expected to be much more pronounced at low than at high temperatures. The activation energy for the triethylamine-catalyzed isocyanate-primary hydroxyl reaction is about 3–4 kcal./mole compared to about 10 kcal. for the uncatalyzed reaction. Thus, the temperature coefficient for the uncatalyzed reaction is greater, and as temperature is increased the ratio of rates for the catalyzed and uncatalyzed reactions will approach one.

As a guide to urethane foam systems, Cox and Hostettler (18,34) compared the effects of several types of catalysts on the reaction of phenyl isocyanate with an alcohol, water, and a urea. Reactions were run in dioxane at 70°C., with 0.25*M* isocyanate, and an equivalent amount of active hydrogen compound. Catalyst effects were extrapolated to 0.025*M* concentration and compared based on the time to reach 50% reaction. Data are shown in Table LXVII.

TABLE LXVII[a]
Effects of Catalysts on Relative Reactivities of Phenyl Isocyanate with Active Hydrogen Compounds
(dioxane, 70°C., 10 mole per cent catalyst)

Catalyst	Relative reactivity with:		
	n-Butanol	Water	Diphenylurea
None	1.0	1.1	2.2
N-Methylmorpholine	40	25	10
Triethylamine	86	47	4
Tetramethyl-1,3-butanediamine	260	100	12
Triethylenediamine	1200	380	90
Tributyltin acetate	80,000	14,000	8000
Dibutyltin diacetate	600,000	100,000	12,000

[a] Taken from ref. 34.

Thus, in a system in which alcohol, water, and substituted urea may all react at about the same rate in the absence of a catalyst, the use of dibutyltin diacetate may give a relative reactivity of approximately 50:8:1.

The use of other metal compounds as catalysts may also permit selective control of certain reactions. The effects of metal catalysts identified only by the metal ion were reported by Cooper and co-workers (17). Although this description of the catalysts is inadequate and the isocyanate was not specified, the results in Table LXVIII are interesting guides. Catalyst concentration was $10^{-3}M$. The value for the uncatalyzed reaction with ureas in Table LXVIII appears high compared to others' data.

TABLE LXVIII[a]

Effects of Metal Catalysts on Isocyanate Reactions with Active Hydrogen Compounds

($k \times 10^4$ l./mole sec.)

Catalyst type	Active hydrogen group and temp. Hydroxyl (100°C.)	Water (100°C.)	Amine (130°C.)	Urethane (130°C.)	Urea (100°C.)
None	36	8	45	30	51
Zn	53	20	230	—	190
Mn	64	—	—	—	—
Ce	110	—	—	—	—
Fe	300	—	—	80	—
V	400	—	—	—	—

[a] Taken from ref. 17.

The effects of several catalysts on three types of reactions which are commercially important were reported by Bailey and co-workers (5). The rise time of a prepolymer foam system was used as a guide to the rate of the isocyanate-water reaction. The curing of a castor oil prepolymer coating was observed: this was primarily a measure of the rate of the isocyanate-water reaction, but in the use of the cobalt naphthenate catalyst other reactions such as allophanate formation, trimerization, and free radical type of reactions characteristic of a drying oil cure may have contributed. Prepolymer gelation was also observed: gelation could result from isocyanate dimerization or trimerization, allophanate formation, or biuret formation if some water had been used in the prepolymer formation. Results are shown in Table LXIX.

TABLE LXIX[a]
Relative Catalyst Activity

Catalyst	Foam, max.[b] rise time, sec.	Film dry[c] time, min.	Gelation[d] time, days
Triethylamine	255	76	7.5
Diethylcyclohexylamine	315	90	12
Dimethylethanolamine	570	105	27
Methylmorpholine	930	245	30
Cobalt naphthenate	3600	35	0.67

[a] Taken from ref. 5.
[b] Castor oil–TDI prepolymer foam system.
[c] Castor oil–MDI prepolymer solution, 0.001 mole catalyst/10 g. prepolymer, poured on mercury, let air dry.
[d] Castor oil–MDI prepolymer (10 g.) in benzene (5 g.), 0.002 mole catalyst.

From data reported in this and preceding sections of this chapter, as well as those in Chapter III, a summary of approximate catalytic effects may be compiled, as in Table LXX. An attempt is made to list those catalysts which have been shown to promote each type of reaction.

It is readily apparent from Table LXX that many catalysts are effective for more than one of the isocyanate reactions. This fact makes it highly desirable to analyze the products of a catalyzed reaction completely in order to be sure of the extent of all reactions that may have taken place. It is unfortunate that most rate studies have been based on the rate of disappearance of one reactant or on the rate of formation of one product. Many more thorough studies are required to provide a satisfactory knowledge and understanding of the rates and mechanisms of isocyanate reactions.

XIII. Catalysis in the Control of Polymer Formation

The successful preparation of urethane polymers requires the proper choice of reactants to give the desired polymer structure, and adequate control of the reactions occurring. It is obvious from Chapter III that many reactions are possible, even in relatively simple systems. Some control of the reactions may be obtained from the structure of the reactants, ratios of reactants, and temperature of reaction. Often even greater control may be realized by the proper choice of catalysts. In some cases the desired control requires the neutralization of a catalyst which is already present. Several examples of catalyst neutralization and catalyst choice will be indicated. Additional examples familiar to

TABLE LXX

Summary of Catalysts Promoting Different Isocyanate Reactions

Catalysts that promote reaction with the active hydrogen compound shown								
Amines	Alcohols	Water	Carboxylic acids	Ureas	Urethanes	Phenols	Trimerization	Dimerization[a]
Dabco	Bi cpds.	Dabco	Co cpds.	Sn cpds.	Pb cpds.	Tert. amines	Strong bases and basic salts	Phosphines
Pb cpds.	Pb cpds.	Tert. amines	Fe cpds.	Dabco	Co cpds.	$ZnCl_2$	Pb cpds.	Tert. amines (in high concn.)
Sn cpds.	Sn cpds.	Sn cpds.	Mn cpds.	Zn cpds.	Zn cpds.	Basic salts	Co cpds.	—
Co cpds.	Dabco		Dabco		Cu cpds.	$AlCl_3$	Fe cpds.	
Zn cpds.	Ti cpds.		Tert. amines		Mn cpds.	Acids	Cd cpds.	
Ureas	Fe cpds.		KO_2CCH_3		Fe cpds.	—	V cpds.	
Tert. amines	Sb cpds.				Cd cpds.		Tert. amine plus alcohol	
Carboxylic acids	U cpds.				V cpds.			
	Cd cpds.				—			
	Co cpds.							
	Th cpds.							
	Al cpds.							
	Hg cpds.							
	Zn cpds.							
	Ni cpds.							
	Tert. amines							
	V cpds.							
	Ce cpds.							
	MgO							
	BaO							
	Pyrones							
	Lactams							
	Acids							

[a] For aromatic isocyanates only.

the foam industry are found in Chapter V, and others will be apparent in subsequent chapters.

Since bases and many soluble heavy metal compounds are very strong catalysts, while acids are generally weak catalysts for only some of the isocyanate reactions, acids may often be used to stabilize isocyanate systems. In reality the acid must serve to neutralize a base or render inactive a metal which may be present, for example as a polyether polymerization catalyst or esterification catalyst. Thus, it was shown by Heiss and co-workers (32) that prepolymer readily gelled when made with an excess of diisocyanate and using a polyether glycol that was basic with potassium phosphate. Since both reactants were difunctional, gelation must have resulted from one or more of three reactions: trimerization of isocyanate groups, allophanate formation, or possibly biuret formation (coming ultimately from the small water content of the polyether). On the other hand, no gelation occurred when the reaction was conducted using acidified polyether glycol. As expected, because of weak acid catalysis of the isocyanate-hydroxyl reaction, some increase in the rate of urethane formation was noted at high acid levels.

The general relation between catalysis by inorganic bases, acid catalysis, and acid retardation or stabilization is shown in Figure 19, based on the work of Heiss and co-workers (32). The effects are shown for the isocyanate-hydroxyl, isocyanate-urethane, isocyanate-urea, and isocyanate trimerization reactions, since these were the most likely reactions in the prepolymer system studied.

A similar study of only the acid side of Figure 19 was reported by Cooper and co-workers (Fig. 20) (17). In their work *p*-nitrobenzoyl chloride was used as a retarder. The acid chlorides may be assumed to function as a source of hydrogen chloride, which would then neutralize a base. As shown in Figure 20, no acid catalysis was noted in the range tested for the isocyanate-urethane reaction and little, if any, for the isocyanate-hydroxyl reaction. The isocyanate-water reaction showed distinct acid catalysis, whereas the isocyanate-urea reaction showed retardation. This result suggests the presence of some catalyst initially in the isocyanate-urea system, which was progressively neutralized by the acid chloride.

Whereas simple acids such as hydrogen chloride are usually the best neutralizers of basic catalysts, heavy metal catalysts are often neutral-

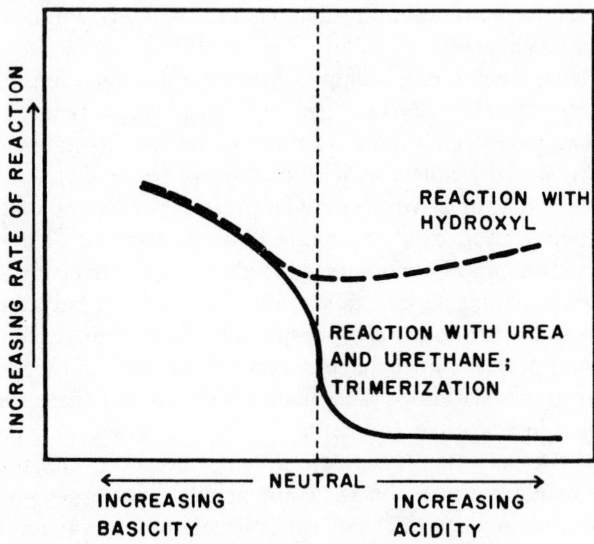

Fig. 19. General catalytic effects of strong acids and bases. (Taken from ref. 32.)

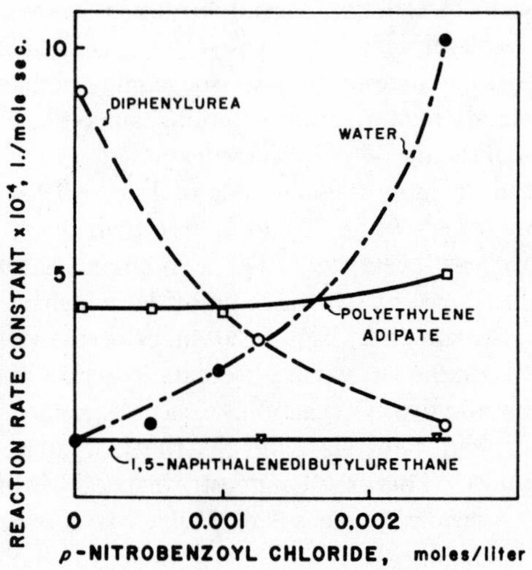

Fig. 20. Effect of an acidic retarder on the reaction between *p*-phenylene diisocyanate and model compounds. (Taken from ref. 17.)

ized best by acidic compounds which may also function as chelating agents, e.g., citric acid. Relatively little has been published on neutralization of heavy metal catalysts, but it is generally known that hydrogen chloride or acid chlorides will often, though not always, neutralize a metal catalyst.

By the proper choice of temperature and catalyst one can often force reactions in the desired direction. For example, in the preparation of linear polymers one should choose difunctional reactants, a low temperature so that biuret, allophanate, or trimerization reactions are not favored, and a catalyst that will promote only the chain-lengthening reaction. Thus, Heiss (31) found that magnesium oxide gave a fast polymerization of diisocyanate and dihydroxy compound to a linear polymer. In contrast, sodium phenolate catalysts gave fast polymerization but with branching.

Another typical case is that in which the resin contains a basic catalyst that could promote allophanate, biuret, or trimer formation. In this case the base should be neutralized with hydrogen chloride and the isocyanate-hydroxyl reaction can then be catalyzed with tertiary amine.

When a cross-linked polymer is desired it is usually obtained with best control by using a trifunctional reactant such as a triol, and catalyzing only the isocyanate-hydroxyl reaction. An added advantage of this technique is that the cross link thus obtained has better thermal stability than does a biuret or allophanate cross link.

References

1. Alzner, B. G., and K. C. Frisch, *Ind. Eng. Chem.* **51,** 715 (1959).
2. Arnold, R. G., J. A. Nelson, and J. J. Verbanc, *Chem. Revs.* **57,** 47 (1957).
3. Axelrood, S. L., C. W. Hamilton, and K. C. Frisch, *Ind. Eng. Chem.* **53,** 889 (1961).
4. Bailey, M. E., V. Kirss, and R. G. Spaunburgh, *Ind. Eng. Chem.* **48,** 794 (1956).
5. Bailey, M. E., A. Khawam, and G. C. Toone, paper presented at the American Chemical Society Meeting, Atlantic City, Sept., 1956.
6. Bailey, M. E., C. E. McGinn, and R. G. Spaunburgh, paper presented at the American Chemical Society Meeting, Atlantic City, Sept., 1956.
7. Baker, J. W., and D. N. Bailey, *J. Chem. Soc.* **1957,** 4649, 4652, 4663.
8. Baker, J. W., M. M. Davies, and J. Gaunt, *J. Chem. Soc.* **1949,** 24.
9. Baker, J. W., and J. B. Holdsworth, *J. Chem. Soc.* **1947,** 713.
10. Baker, J. W., and J. Gaunt, *J. Chem. Soc.* **1949,** 9, 19, 27.

11. Bennet, W. B., J. H. Saunders, and E. E. Hardy, paper presented at the Alabama Academy of Sciences, Tuscaloosa, Ala., April, 1954.
12. Britain, J. W., and P. G. Gemeinhardt, *J. Appl. Polymer Sci.* **4,** 207 (1960).
13. Brock, F. H., *J. Org. Chem.* **24,** 1802 (1959).
14. Burkus, J., and C. F. Eckert, *J. Am. Chem. Soc.* **80,** 5948 (1958).
15. Carwin Chem. Co. Bulletin, "Carwin Diisocyanates," March 15, 1955.
16. Case, L. C., *J. Chem. Eng. Data* **5,** 347 (1960).
17. Cooper, W., R. W. Pearson, and S. Darke, *Ind. Chemist* **36,** 121, 1960.
18. Cox, E. F., and F. Hostettler, paper presented at the American Chemical Society Meeting, Boston, April, 1959.
19. Craven, R. L., paper presented at the American Chemical Society Meeting, Atlantic City, September, 1956.
20. Cunningham, R. E., and T. G. Mastin, *J. Org. Chem.* **24,** 1585 (1959).
21. Davis, T. L., and F. Ebersole, *J. Am. Chem. Soc.* **56,** 885 (1934).
22. Davis, T. L., and J. M. Farnum, *J. Am. Chem Soc.* **56,** 883 (1934).
23. Dyer, E., and J. F. Glenn *J. Am. Chem. Soc.* **79,** 366 (1957).
24. Dyer, E., J. F. Glenn, and E. G. Lendrat, *J. Org. Chem.* **26,** 2919 (1961).
25. Dyer, E., H. A. Taylor, S. J. Mason, and J. Sampson, *J. Am. Chem. Soc.* **71,** 4106 (1949).
26. Ephraim, S., A. E. Woodward, and R. B. Mesrobian, *J. Am. Chem. Soc.* **80,** 1326 (1958).
27. Farkas, A., and K. G. Flynn, *J. Am. Chem. Soc.* **82,** 642 (1960).
28. Farkas, A., G. A. Mills, W. E. Erner, and J. B. Maerker, *Ind. Eng. Chem.* **51,** 1299 (1959).
29. Ferstandig, L. L., and R. A. Scherrer, *J. Am. Chem. Soc.* **81,** 4838 (1959).
30. Hammett, L. P., *Physical Organic Chemistry,* McGraw-Hill Co., New York, 1940, p. 184.
31. Heiss, H. L., *Rubber Age* **88,** 89 (1960).
32. Heiss, H. L., F. P. Combs, P. G. Gemeinhardt, J. H. Saunders and E. E. Hardy, *Ind. Eng. Chem.* **51,** 929 (1959).
33. Hoshino, T., T. Muyaiyama, and H. Hoshino, *J. Am. Chem. Soc.* **74,** 3097 (1952).
34. Hostettler, F., and E. F. Cox, *Ind. Eng. Chem.* **52,** 609 (1960).
35. Iwakura, Y., and H. Okada, *Can. J. Chem.* **38,** 2418 (1960).
36. Kaplan, M., *J. Chem. Eng. Data* **6,** 272 (1961).
37. Kogon, I. C., *J. Org. Chem.* **23,** 1594 (1958).
38. Kogon, I. C., *J. Org. Chem.* **24,** 83 (1959).
39. Kogon, I. C., *J. Org. Chem.* **24,** 438 (1959).
40. Kogon, I. C., *J. Org. Chem* **26,** 3004 (1961).
41. McGinn, C. E., and R. G. Spaunburgh, paper presented at the American Chemical Society Meeting, Atlantic City, Sept., 1956.
42. Morton, M., and M. A. Deisz, paper presented at the American Chemical Society Meeting, Atlantic City, Sept., 1956.
43. Morton, M., M. A. Deisz, and M. Ohta, "Degradation Studies on Condensation Polymers," U. S. Dept. of Commerce Report PB-131795, March 31, 1957.

44. Naegeli, C., A. Tyabji, L. Conrad, and F. Litwan, *Helv. Chim. Acta* **21,** 1100 (1938).
45. Naegeli, C., A. Tyabji, and L. Conrad, *Helv. Chim. Acta* **21,** 1127 (1938).
46. O'Brien, J. L., and A. S. Pagano, paper presented at the Delaware Regional Meeting of the American Chemical Society, February 5, 1958.
47. Ozaki, S., and T. Hoshino, *Nippon Kagaku Zasshi* **80,** 664 (1959); *Chem. Abstracts* **55,** 4398*a* (1961).
48. Ozaki, S., and S. Shimada, *Nippon Kagaku Zasshi* **80,** 430, 434, 506 (1959); *Chem. Abstracts* **55,** 4396*i* (1961).
49. Parker, J. A., J. J. Thomas, C. L. Zeise, E. A. Peterson, and R. P. Dryden, paper presented at the American Chemical Society Meeting, September, 1957.
50. Sato, M., *J. Am. Chem. Soc.* **82,** 3893 (1960).
51. Saunders, J. H., *Rubber Chem. and Technol.* **32,** 337 (1959).
52. Shkapenko, G., G. T. Gmitter, and E. E. Gruber, *Ind. Eng. Chem* **52,** 605 (1960).
53. Simons, D. M., and R. G. Arnold, *J. Am. Chem. Soc.* **78,** 1658 (1956).
54. Smith, J. F., and E. C. Friedrich, *J. Am. Chem. Soc.* **81,** 161 (1959).
55. Sorenson, W. R., *J. Org. Chem.* **24,** 978 (1959).
56. Tarbell, D. S., E. C. Mallatt, and J. W. Wilson, *J. Am. Chem. Soc.* **64,** 2229 (1942).
57. Tazuma, J. J., and H. K. Latourette, paper presented at the American Chemical Society Meeting, Atlantic City, Sept., 1956.
58. Wolf, H. W., Jr., Foam Bulletin, "Catalyst Activity in One-Shot Urethane Foam," E. I. du Pont de Nemours and Co., Mar. 16, 1960.

V. FORMATION OF URETHANE FOAMS

I. Introduction

Urethane foams of the rigid type were developed in Germany prior to 1945, and reported by O. Bayer in 1947 (9). This type of foam sparked the principal interest in isocyanates and polyurethanes in the period 1945–1952. Further research in the laboratories of Farbenfabriken Bayer led to the development of a flexible urethane foam system which was announced in 1952 by Höchtlen (22). It was the development of this system that insured the commercial success of the polyurethane industry.

The formation of urethane foam is a much more complex phenomenon than any of the other urethane applications. In addition to the chemical and physical aspects of a polymerization system, foam formation adds the peculiarities of a colloidal system. For these reasons relatively little is known in a quantitative sense about the formation of urethane foam. Nevertheless, the commercial importance of foams has led to considerable research, which helps provide a fairly reliable picture of the simpler relationships.

An understanding of the formation of urethane foams involves consideration of the organic chemistry of the reactions leading to gas formation and molecular growth, the colloid chemistry of nucleation and bubble stability, and the rheology of the polymer system as it cures. A recent review by one of the authors (32) attempted to present such a picture. This chapter brings that review up to date.

Another recent review, by Buist and co-workers (12), of foam production, properties, and applications gave considerable interesting data and observations on factors influencing foam formation, supporting some of the observations reported by Saunders (32).

This chapter has as its object the provision of an understanding of the formation of foam. The technological details of foam production, properties, and applications are reserved for a later chapter. In attempting to provide this desired understanding, a distinction is made between experimentally observed data and reasonable speculation. It is natural to assume that explanations drawn from so many widely scattered facts will be modified and extended as research continues.

II. The Chemistry of Foam Formation and Cure

1. *Reactions of Isocyanates*

The reactions of isocyanates with a variety of model compounds have been reviewed in Chapters III and IV. The reactions that are particularly important for foam formation will be indicated.

The reactive ingredients of a foam system are usually an isocyanate, a hydroxyl-terminated resin, and water. The reaction with a hydroxyl compound produces a urethane:

$$RNCO + R'OH \rightarrow RNH\overset{\overset{\displaystyle O}{\|}}{C}OR' \tag{1}$$

while that with water produces a urea, via an amine intermediate:

$$RNCO + H_2O \rightarrow (RNHCOOH) \rightarrow RNH_2 + CO_2 \tag{2}$$

$$RNCO + RNH_2 \rightarrow RNHCONHR \tag{3}$$

In uncatalyzed systems, the reaction with the amine is relatively quite fast, so much so that mixing an isocyanate with a large excess of water gives a high yield of the disubstituted urea. Although the water reaction is somewhat more complicated than these equations indicate (see Chapter III), the foam density is very near that calculated, assuming equations (2) and (3) to be correct, at least in some systems (29,30).

The isocyanate may also react with the urea and with the urethane, to give a biuret and an allophanate, respectively:

$$RNCO + RNH\overset{\overset{\displaystyle O}{\|}}{C}NHR \rightarrow RN\overset{\overset{\displaystyle O}{\|}}{C}NHR \quad \text{(N-CONHR) (biuret)} \tag{4}$$

$$RNCO + RNH\overset{\overset{\displaystyle O}{\|}}{C}OR' \rightarrow RN\overset{\overset{\displaystyle O}{\|}}{C}OR' \quad \text{(N-CONHR) (allophanate)} \tag{5}$$

Reactions (4) and (5) may be reversed slowly by heating to temperatures of approximately 110–130°C. and faster at higher temperatures.

Another indication of the relatively poor stability of the biuret and allophanate groups is the ease with which they are attacked by amines at elevated temperatures (4):

$$\mathrm{RN(CONHR)\overset{O}{\overset{\|}{C}}NHR + RNH_2 \rightarrow 2RNH\overset{O}{\overset{\|}{C}}NHR} \quad (6)$$

$$\mathrm{RN(CONHR)\overset{O}{\overset{\|}{C}}OR' + RNH_2 \rightarrow RNH\overset{O}{\overset{\|}{C}}OR' + RNH\overset{O}{\overset{\|}{C}}NHR} \quad (7)$$

The approximate relative rates of these isocyanate reactions in uncatalyzed, dilute systems are indicated in Table I (32). The relative

TABLE I[a]

Relative Rates of Isocyanate Reactions with Active Hydrogen Compounds

Active hydrogen compd.	Rel. rate uncatalyzed	Effect of catalysts (11,19,20)		
		Tert. amine	Alkali	Tin
Urethane	1	None	Strong?	None?
Urea	100	None	Strong?	Weak
Water	400[b]	Strong	Strong	Weak
Alcohol	400	Strong	Strong	Very strong

[a] Taken from ref. 31.

[b] One reference indicates that diphenylurea has a relative reactivity of 80, water 98, and *n*-butanol 460 (27). Numerous observations in our laboratory and in those of Farbenfabriken Bayer indicate that water and primary alcohols react at about the same rate; see also Chapter IV.

effect of several types of catalyst is also indicated qualitatively. An exception to the general behavior of the tertiary amines is found in the case of triethylenediamine, Dabco, which has been shown to catalyze the gelation of prepolymers (32). This result means that this catalyst promotes one or more of the following reactions: dimerization, trimerization, or allophanate formation. The "alkali" group in Table I refers to compounds such as sodium hydroxide and sodium alkoxides. The "tin" group refers to stannous octoate and dibutyltin dioctoate. The use of a question mark indicates that the results shown are qualitative only and have not been confirmed by detailed kinetic studies.

The rates of the reactions are influenced by the electronic structure of the reactants and by steric hindrance, as outlined in Chapter IV.

As an example of the latter, primary alcohols react faster than do secondary alcohols. A more striking example is seen in a comparison of the reactions of two isocyanates with two amines, as shown in Table II (3,13). A comparison of the uncatalyzed reaction between

TABLE II[a]
Effect of Steric Hindrance on Isocyanate-Amine Reactions (dioxane solution, 31°C.)

Isocyanate	Amine	Time to 50% reaction, min.
$H_3C-C_6H_4-NCO$ (para)	$C_6H_5-NH_2$	25–30
$C_6H_4(CH_3)-NCO$ (ortho)	$C_6H_5-NH_2$	202
$C_6H_4(CH_3)-NCO$ (ortho)	$C_6H_4(CH_3)-NH_2$ (ortho)	>1000

[a] Taken from refs. 3, 13.

o-tolyl isocyanate and *o*-toluidine with other reactions suggests that it is slower than the initial uncatalyzed reaction between tolylene diisocyanate and hydroxyl groups or water. Thus the time required to reach 50% reaction between 80:20 tolylene diisocyanate and the polyester from diethylene glycol and adipic acid at 28°C. in benzene has been reported to be about 700 min., while that for 60/40 TDI and 2-ethylhexanol was about 200 min. (6). As indicated in Table I, alcoholic hydroxyls and water have approximately the same degree of reactivity. Furthermore, the isocyanate-hydroxyl and isocyanate-water reactions can be catalyzed very strongly, whereas no more than very mild catalysis of the isocyanate-amine reaction is usually observed (13). Axelrood and co-workers (5) showed that the tin catalysts normally used in making foam catalyze the isocyanate-polyether glycol reaction much more than that of the reaction of isocyanate with a specific aromatic amine. Dabco was exceptional in that it catalyzed the reaction with amine about as much as that with glycol.

The reaction between an isocyanate with an *ortho* substituent and an amine with an *ortho* substituent may well be one of the reactions of prime importance in the last stages of cure of foams based on tolylene diisocyanate. The slow rate of this reaction is considered to be very significant, and will be referred to later in connection with a proposed mechanism of final cure.

One should bear in mind the possibility that relative rate data obtained in dilute solution may not be a reliable guide to rates in nonsolvent systems in which the reaction medium changes markedly, as in foam formation. Furthermore, the choice of the specific catalysts in the foam system may alter the relative rates. With these limitations, however, the reactions between model compounds provide a starting point from which to build an understanding of foam chemistry.

Other reactions of isocyanates are possible in a foam system, but do not appear of major importance at this time. A discussion of reaction with carboxyl groups may be omitted since carboxyl groups are relatively rare in foam resins. Dimerization, trimerization, and carbodiimide formation are all possibilities, but no significant indications of their participation in foaming have come to the authors' attention.

2. *Function of the Isocyanate in Foaming*

The isocyanate used in foaming, usually an 80:20 mixture of 2,4- (Structure I) and 2,6-tolylene diisocyanate (Structure II), serves

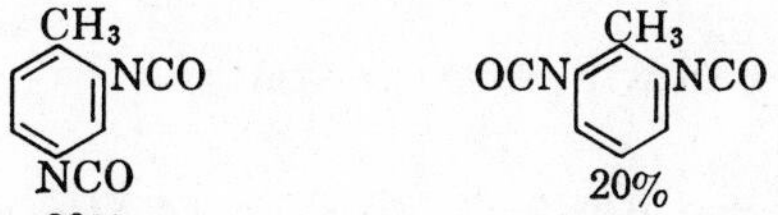

CH_3 / NCO / NCO — 80% (I)

OCN / CH_3 / NCO — 20% (II)

several purposes. It may react with water to form carbon dioxide, a suitable gas for foaming. (In some systems a low boiling gas such as trichlorofluoromethane may be added to provide part or all of the foaming.) The diisocyanate also reacts with the functional groups in the resin, insuring that the resin is built into the final polymer molecules. The stoichiometry of the system is such that in the latter stages of polymerization the polymer end groups are largely the very reactive isocyanate group. This high reactivity helps greatly in insuring that a maximum number of chain ends will be joined to other chain ends, thus providing a relatively close approach to a theoretical network structure.

A linear resin or a slightly branched one is normally used for flexible foams, and a more highly branched one for rigid foam. The chemistry of foam formation is similar in either case, except that the rigid foam is much more cross linked than the flexible. For convenience, this discussion will be directed primarily toward the formation of flexible foams.

Two types of processes are generally used for producing foam. In the "one-shot" process the diisocyanate, resin, and water are all mixed simultaneously, along with suitable catalysts, stabilizers, cell size control agents, and additional blowing agent if desired. The reactions begin immediately, with foam rise starting about ten seconds after mixing and being complete within one or two minutes. The foam continues to cure for several hours to a day. The reactions involved are the same as in the prepolymer method, but may be more readily illustrated in the description of that process as indicated below.

The second general type of process is the "prepolymer" process, In this method the reaction with the resin is completed first:

$$2R(NCO)_2 + HO \sim\!\sim OH \rightarrow \underbrace{OCN{-}R{-}NH\overset{O}{\overset{\|}{C}}O \sim\!\sim O\overset{O}{\overset{\|}{C}}NH{-}R{-}NCO}_{\text{"Prepolymer"}} \quad (8)$$

The prepolymer may later be foamed by reaction with water, with simultaneous growth of molecular structure:

$$nOCN{-}R{-}NH\overset{O}{\overset{\|}{C}}O \sim\!\sim O\overset{O}{\overset{\|}{C}}NH{-}R{-}NCO + nH_2O \rightarrow \left[{-}NH\overset{O}{\overset{\|}{C}}NH{-}R{-}NH\overset{O}{\overset{\|}{C}}O \sim\!\sim O\overset{O}{\overset{\|}{C}}NH{-}R{-}\right]_n + nCO_2 \quad (9)$$

An inert blowing agent may also be used in small amounts to augment the foaming.

For low density foams the molecular ratio of diisocyanate to resin is usually higher than 2:1, so that much more urea structure is built into the polymer chain (Structure III).

$$\left[{-}(NH\overset{O}{\overset{\|}{C}}NH{-}R{-})_xNH\overset{O}{\overset{\|}{C}}O \sim\!\sim O\overset{O}{\overset{\|}{C}}NH{-}R{-}\right]_n$$

(III)

Cross linking is most successfully introduced into the polymer by the use of branched resins, so that an idealized structure may be illustrated by Structure IV when a trifunctional resin is used. The average weight for each such unit, i.e., average weight per branch point, has been shown to be in the order of 400 to 700 for "rigid" foams and 2500 to 20,000 or more for "flexible" foams (10). "Semi-flexible" and "semi-rigid" foams bridge the gap from about 2500 to 700 weight per branch point.

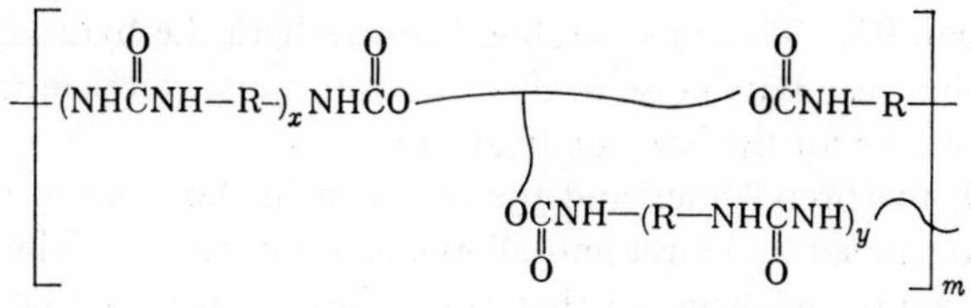

$$\left[\begin{array}{l} \text{—(NH}\overset{\text{O}}{\overset{\|}{\text{C}}}\text{NH—R—)}_x\text{NH}\overset{\text{O}}{\overset{\|}{\text{C}}}\text{O}\frown\!\!\frown\!\!\frown\text{O}\overset{\text{O}}{\overset{\|}{\text{C}}}\text{NH—R—} \\ \qquad\qquad\qquad\qquad \text{O}\underset{\text{O}}{\underset{\|}{\text{C}}}\text{NH—(R—NH}\underset{\text{O}}{\underset{\|}{\text{C}}}\text{NH)}_y\frown \end{array}\right]_m$$

IV

Branching in the prepolymer may also be developed by forcing allophanate or biuret formation by heating the prepolymer. (A little water is included in the polyether if biuret formation is desired.) Such branch points are not preferred because of their limited thermal stability.

A hybird method, the "semi-prepolymer" process, is also used in some cases. In this process a part of the resin is mixed with all of the isocyanate to give a prepolymer containing a large excess of unreacted isocyanate. This prepolymer is then foamed by reaction with the remainder of the resin, which may contain water, catalyst, and silicone oil. This process is particularly useful for rigid foams. Many rigid foams are produced commercially by this process using trichlorofluoromethane as the only blowing agent; i.e., without water.

The stoichiometry of the system is normally such that the ratio of total isocyanate equivalents to total active hydrogen equivalents in the reactants is close to one. In the prepolymer process, in which the resin is first reacted completely, the final ratio of NCO/H_2O may be as low as 1.6:1, or 80% of theoretical. Such a ratio may not seriously affect molecular weight because of the kinetics of the reactions involved. The first step in the water reaction is normally the slow step (eq. 10), whereas step (11) is normally much faster:

$$\sim\!\!\text{R—NCO} + \text{H}_2\text{O} \rightarrow [\sim\!\!\text{RNHCOOH}] \rightarrow \sim\!\!\text{RNH}_2 + \text{CO}_2 \qquad (10)$$

$$\sim\!\!\text{RNCO} + \sim\!\!\text{RNH}_2 \rightarrow \sim\!\!\text{RNH}\underset{\text{O}}{\underset{\|}{\text{C}}}\text{NHR}\sim \qquad (11)$$

In such a sequence a moderate excess of water increases the rate ot foaming but any effect on molecular growth is not sufficient to influence the foam properties.

The one-shot process may be expected to be less efficient in reaction of the hydroxyl groups of the resin than is the prepolymer process. Hence in the one-shot process the "index number" or percentage of stoichiometric isocyanate requirement is usually closer to 100, normally no less than 95. This is desirable, because here the hydroxyls of the resin, with a reactivity close to that of water, must compete with water and with amine for the isocyanate groups.

In both the prepolymer and the one-shot methods some isocyanate may be consumed by biuret and allophanate formation. The reactions of model compounds suggest that biuret formation would be preferred over allophanate formation, but that neither should occur to an appreciable extent unless excess isocyanate (index number over 100) is present. This apparently is true at least in one tertiary amine-catalyzed system (30). Thus, Sandridge and co-workers showed that one-shot foams prepared from tolylene diisocyanate, a polyether triol of molecular weight 3000, and tetra(hydroxylpropyl)ethylenediamine, with dimethylpiperazine catalyst, at 90–100 index were only slightly attacked by aniline at 140°C. for five minutes. Similar foams prepared at 120 index were attacked much more extensively (30), indicating a significant amount of biuret and, less likely, allophanate groups (4).

The indicated reactions will occur as long as the reactant groups are sufficiently mobile to collide with each other with a reasonable frequency. Toward the end of the foam formation, however, chain ends will be relatively immobile so that the rate of collision of end groups with a reactive site will become progressively slower. One may expect the time to come when diffusion of water molecules, present as an excess in the foam system or from the atmosphere, will provide an opportunity for the few remaining isocyanate end groups to react. In this case some will doubtless be converted to amine end groups and will not have the opportunity to collide with an isocyanate group. Thus one should expect the foam to contain some terminal amine groups. Furthermore, because of the slow rate of reaction of isocyanate and amine groups when each is shielded by an *ortho* methyl group, compared to the isocyanate-water reaction, the water reaction may be preferred at similar effective concentrations of water and amine end groups. The balance in favor of the water reaction will actually be even stronger because of the presence of catalysts which promote the isocyanate-water reaction much more than the isocyanate-amine reaction (13). (The role of catalysts will be discussed more fully in the next section.) The presence of aromatic amine end groups has been shown semiquantitatively by colorimetric methods, even when an excess of isocyanate over the stoichiometric requirement was used. The amine group concentration increased as the water content of the foam system was increased from 80 to 120% of the stoichiometric requirement (32).

Foams prepared by the prepolymer process should not contain terminal hydroxyl groups, since these were all consumed in the formation of the prepolymer. In one-shot processes, or in semi-prepolymer processes where some resin is added to the mixture just before foaming, one should expect to find hydroxyl end groups in very low concentrations.

The greater efficiency of the prepolymer process with regard to converting all resin branch points into foam cross links, i.e., greater efficiency of reacting all chain ends, is illustrated by the data in Table III (32). Both foams were of 2.0 lb./cu. ft. density. Thus, the

TABLE III[a]

Comparison of Prepolymer and One-Shot Foams

Foam process	Polyether resins	Foam vol. swell in dimethyl-acetamide, %	Soluble fraction, %
Prepolymer (amine catalyst)	3000 mol. wt. triol (40) 2000 mol. wt. glycol (60)	440	7.5
One-shot (tin and amine catalysts)	3000 mol. wt. triol (100)	480	15.5

[a] Taken from ref. 32.

prepolymer foam, prepared from resins having a greater average weight per branch point (7500), was perhaps slightly more cross-linked than was the one-shot foam, which was prepared from a resin having a much lower average weight per branch point (3000). Obviously the one-shot foam must have had more free end groups than did the prepolymer foam. In addition, the one-shot foam contained a higher per cent of soluble polymer.

3. *Role of Catalysts in Foam Systems*

In addition to the major reactants a foam system usually contains one or more catalysts which have a major effect on the chemistry of the system. The catalyst serves to drive the reactions between prepolymer and water, or between isocyanate, resin, and water at such rates that the foam rises and cures sufficiently fast to prevent collapse of the foam. In any foam system several different reactions are involved, for example, those of the isocyanate groups in the 2- and 4-positions of tolylene diisocyanate; therefore the catalyst type and concentration must be carefully chosen to provide a suitable balance of reactions. The gas evolution and the polymer growth must be matched so that the gas is trapped efficiently and the polymer has the right strength at the end of the gas evolution to maintain its volume without collapse or gross shrinkage. The significant aspects of the development of polymer strength will be discussed in a later section on the rheology of the foams.

The catalysts most commonly used are tertiary amines and tin compounds such as stannous octoate, stannous oleate, dibutyltin dioctoate, and dibutyltin dilaurate. Alkaline or metal impurities which may sometimes be present in the resins may also contribute to the catalytic effects. Acidic impurities in the resins or isocyanate might serve to neutralize a portion of the catalyst, thus reducing the catalytic effect slightly.

A. THE TERTIARY AMINE CATALYSTS

The tertiary amines, being catalysts for both the water reaction and the hydroxyl reaction, have been used with much success. In fact, these compounds are the only catalysts necessary for the preparation of flexible foams in the "one-shot" process using polyesters terminating in primary hydroxyl groups, and in the prepolymer process using either polyesters or polyethers. Rigid foam systems, because of their greater degree of cross linking, build gel strength so rapidly that tertiary amines are adequate catalysts for one-shot or prepolymer systems using polyesters or polyethers.

The structure of the tertiary amine has a considerable influence on its catalytic effect and also on its usefulness for foam production (2,18). Factors generally considered are catalytic strength, odor, vapor pressure, solubility, and cost. The catalytic strength generally increases as the basicity of the amine increases and as steric shielding of the amino nitrogen decreases (7). Dialkyl aryl amines generally are not catalytic for the foaming reaction (21) because of steric effects (7). Thus, relatively low molecular weight dimethyl alkyl amines are strong catalysts, are water soluble, and have a high vapor pressure; their odor therefore leaves the foam quickly. Being strong catalysts, they are used in low concentration; e.g., 0.1–0.4% of the weight of resin. It is often observed that foams made using only these catalysts have poor compression set or may cure only slowly to a state having low compression set. This behavior may be the result of the low initial catalyst concentration and the high vapor pressure. In other words, the catalyst may not stay in the foam long enough to catalyze adequately the cure required for good compression set.

Higher molecular weight amines, e.g., dimethylcetylamine, are not such strong catalysts for the early reactions, e.g., during foam rise, hence may be used in concentrations of 1 to 2% of the resin weight. With this concentration and the inherent low vapor pressure, this type of catalyst will remain in the foam a long time, helping insure good compression set but leaving an amine odor in the foam for a long time.

A catalyst of intermediate molecular weight and effect, ethylmorpholine (21), has been popular in spite of its odor, thus attesting to its value. Of moderate activity, it is often used in concentration of about 0.5 to 1% of the resin weight. Its catalytic strength provides a desirable balance of reactions, while its concentration and vapor pressure are such that it generally insures good compression set, yet its odor does not linger in the foam as long as does that of dimethylcetylamine.

The tertiary amine catalysts provide satisfactory foaming with either the one-shot polyester or the polyether prepolymer systems, both of which are relatively high in initial viscosity. Furthermore, the polyesters used have primary hydroxyl groups, which are more reactive toward isocyanates than are secondary hydroxyl groups. The tertiary amine catalysts generally are not adequate catalysts for one-shot systems for polyether flexible foams, largely because of the low viscosity of the polyethers used (about 300 cps. at 25°C., compared to 10,000–20,000 cps. for the polyesters) but also in part because the majority of the commercially available polyethers most suitable for foam have secondary hydroxyl groups. (Even the polyethers with an increased percentage of primary hydroxyl groups have not given good one-shot foam with amine catalysts, probably because of their low viscosity.) Thus, with a tertiary amine-catalyzed polyether one-shot system the gas evolution occurs before the polymer viscosity is adequate to trap and hold the gas. One tertiary amine, triethylenediamine (Dabco) (V), is strong enough in its catalytic effect that one-

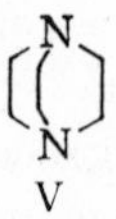

shot polyether foam can be made with it (15,16), but the difficulties of processing have been too great for satisfactory commercial production. This deficiency of the tertiary amine catalysts, combined with the attractive economic possibilities of a one-shot polyether system, led to the development of the tin catalysts.

B. THE TIN CATALYSTS

Using different methods of evaluating the effects of catalysts, the team of Britain and Gemeinhardt (11) and the team of Hostettler and Cox (20) independently observed the remarkably strong catalytic effect of many metal compounds. Many previous references to metal catalysts were known but the remarkable effect of the tin catalysts was not thoroughly identified and put into commercial use until late in 1958 (1).

Tin catalysts such as dibutyltin dioctoate, dibutyltin dilaurate, stannous oleate, and stannous octoate are many times more powerful for the isocyanate-hydroxyl reaction than are the tertiary amines, but apparently are not strong catalysts for the isocyanate-water reaction in a foam system. Thus the tin catalysts can be used to force the reaction between isocyanate and polyether at such a rate that viscosity is rapidly increased and the gas is trapped and held satisfactorily.

Unlike many of the tertiary amines, which evaporate from the foam, the tin catalysts remain in the foam permanently, although they may undergo some change chemically with time; e.g., oxidation of stannous tin to stannic tin, or hydrolysis. One must then choose a catalyst system that will have no adverse effect on the foam during its use. Extensive testing showed that the tin catalysts in use did not promote the hydrolysis of the foams (32). The normal oxidation tests as used for foam rubber failed to show any adverse effect on oxidation resistance. When oxidation conditions were made much more vigorous, e.g., 24 hours at 140°C., it was found that the dibutyltin salts of carboxylic acids promoted an oxidative degradation. Stannous salts such as stannous octoate and stannous oleate had no deleterious effect on properly formulated foam, even at 140°C. (32).

Experiments showed that the tin-catalyzed degradation did not occur in a high vacuum or in a nitrogen atmosphere and was retarded by many antioxidants; so, clearly, it may be assumed to be oxidative in nature. Furthermore, since polyester foams prepared with dibutyltin dioctoate did not show the degradation, it must be associated with the polyether portion of the molecule; probably the tertiary hydrogen adjacent to the ether oxygen is directly involved. Typical data on 2 lb./cu. ft. one-shot foams prepared from a 3000 molecular weight triol are listed in Table IV, where an amine-catalyzed polyether prepolymer foam was used as a control. (For comparison, latex foam rubber became unusable after 2 to 4 hours at 140°C.) The catalyst concentration, based on 100 parts of resin, is shown (32).

TABLE IV[a]

Air Oxidation of Flexible Urethane Foams at 140°C.

Foam system	Catalyst	Retention of load bearing after 24 hr. at 140°C., %[b]
Polyether, prepolymer	Amine (2%)	82
Polyether, one-shot	Dibutyltin salt (0.2%)	0
Polyether, one-shot	Dibutyltin salt (0.15%) plus antioxidant (0.05%)	96
Polyether, one-shot	Stannous octoate (0.5%)	100
Polyester, one-shot	Dibutyltin salt (0.2%)	100

[a] Taken from ref. 32.

[b] Foams were measured for RMA indent, at 25% indent with 1 min. rest, using 15 × 15 × 4 in. samples. The effect is often less pronounced with thinner samples.

The testing of a host of catalysts showed that most but not all tin compounds with alkyl groups attached directly to tin that promoted foam formation also promoted thermal degradation (32). It is suggested that the alkyl radicals initiate the oxidative degradation process.

The thermal degradation at 140°C. has doubtful significance with regard to service life, since the degradation occurs at temperatures so far above the normal use temperature. There is real significance for foam production, where the center of the foam blocks may reach 120–140°C., and may be maintained for many hours in that range if the foam blocks are stacked while hot. Under such circumstances serious foam degradation could occur. For this reason only stabilized catalyst systems are commercially attractive; i.e., stannous tin type or dialkyltin salt plus stabilizer.

A similar review of the use of tin catalysts was published recently by Mack (25).

C. MIXED CATALYSTS SYSTEMS

Commercial systems for one-shot polyether foam generally utilize a mixed catalyst system, e.g., a tin catalyst and one or more tertiary amine catalysts. These are chosen to provide a suitable balance between the isocyanate-hydroxyl and isocyanate-water reactions. The tin catalyst offers primary control of the former, whereas the amine catalyst provides control of the latter. The amine catalyst again helps significantly in insuring a rapid development of complete polymer properties, including low compression set.

The mixed catalyst system provides an excellent opportunity to eliminate such difficulties as foam shrinkage and voids, which may be the result of an improper balance of gas evolution and polymer properties at the time of maximum gas evolution. This aspect of foam control is discussed in Section IV of this chapter.

4. The Final Cure of Urethane Foams

The development of cure to the final level of mechanical properties should be related to changes in molecular weight, degree of cross linking, elasticity, and viscosity of the polymer. Of the properties most commonly measured on foam, the compression set is normally the last to reach its ultimate value. An example is shown in Table V, in which a 2.3 lb./cu. ft. polyether prepolymer foam (Mondur PG-50) catalyzed by Mobay Catalyst C-16, a tertiary amine, was tested after the several curing intervals listed (32).

Properties such as tensile modulus, elongation and softness are influenced by changes in the degree of cross linking, whereas in the weight per branch point range of about 1500–15000 compression set appears to be independent of cross linking (10,30). The experiments described herein show added evidence that compression set is independent of changes in cross linking, as long as at least a moderate number of cross links are present.

Using a polyether prepolymer, foam was tested after varying curing intervals for compression set (70°C., 22 hours, 50% deflection, based on deflection) and swelling in acetone. As shown in Table VI, the solvent swelling did not change significantly after 15 to 30 minutes,

TABLE V[a]

Effect of Cure Time on Prepolymer Foam Properties

Oven aging period, 120°C., hr.	2	2	2	5
Aging period at room temp., days	2	3	9	2
Tensile strength, p.s.i.	21.2	20.6	19.8	21.4
Elongation, %	320	310	320	360
Compression set, %[b]	51	48	9.4	7.3
Compression-deflection, p.s.i. at				
25% deflection	0.35	0.35	0.37	0.36
50% deflection	0.51	0.52	0.55	0.51
75% deflection	1.39	1.45	1.65	1.41

[a] Taken from ref. 32.
[b] Compressed 3 hr. at 90% deflection, 70°C.

but a much longer time was required for the compression set to reach a low level (32).

It is suggested that the rate at which low compression set is reached is dependent primarily upon the rate of disappearance of terminal isocyanate groups. The high compression set of fresh foams may be the result of reaction of these isocyanate groups during the period of the test (22 hours at 70°C.), while the foam is in the compressed state. In such a case the bonds formed during this test period would be in equilibrium with the compressed state. These bonds would then provide a restraining force tending to prevent complete recovery of the foam when released from compression. The extent of the restraining force, and hence degree of set, would be proportional to the free isocyanate groups at the beginning of the test period.

The mode of disappearance of the remaining terminal isocyanate groups during cure then becomes of interest. Reactions (12) to (14) appear worthy of consideration.

TABLE VI[a]

Relation between Swell Index, Cure, and Compression Set (system: Mondur F-76, 2.24 parts water)

Catalyst(s)	Cure: Time, hr.	Cure: Temp., °C.	Compression set, %	Acetone swell, vol. %
Ethylmorpholine and Catalyst 16	0.5	25	50	135
	16	72	9.7	135
Catalyst 16	0.25	25	50	172
	16	72	<10	170

[a] Taken from ref. 32.

$$\sim\mathrm{NCO} + \mathrm{H_2O} \rightarrow \sim\mathrm{NH_2} + \mathrm{CO_2} \tag{12}$$

$$\sim\mathrm{NCO} + \sim\mathrm{NH_2} \rightarrow \sim\mathrm{NHCONH}\sim \tag{13}$$

$$\sim\mathrm{NCO} + \sim\mathrm{NHCONH}\sim \rightarrow \sim\underset{\substack{|\\ \mathrm{CONH}\sim}}{\mathrm{N}}\mathrm{CONH}\sim \tag{14}$$

Reaction (12) could involve water from the atmosphere or excess water from the foam recipe. This reaction would change the nature of the terminal group but not the molecular weight, degree of cross linking, or per cent gel in the polymer.

Reaction (13) should be important for a time but become progressively slower for reasons of increasing chain immobility and steric hindrance, as cited previously. This reaction should reduce the soluble polymer content and increase the effective cross links somewhat by joining chain ends; i.e., by improving the efficiency of converting branch points in the raw materials into cross links in the foam.

Reaction (14) should be relatively slow because of the inherently slow rate of the reaction and the absence of strongly accelerating catalysts. This reaction should reduce the soluble portion of the polymer and increase the degree of cross linking.

The fact that the solvent swelling did not decrease in a time interval when the compression set changed markedly suggests that reaction (12) is the most important reaction in the final stage of cure. This proposal is in agreement with the familiar observation that a steam treatment during cure will shorten the cure period required to develop low compression set.

As a practical method of reducing compression set, the steam cure obviously should be used only after the foam has been given the opportunity to cure as far as possible via reaction (13) above, since that reaction will develop a higher molecular weight and more nearly perfect network structure than will reaction (12). A possible relationship is illustrated in Figure 1 (32).

If one were to cure the foam with heat alone it might be necessary to reach point *C,* with essentially no remaining isocyanate groups, to have good compression set. It would be reasonable to expect that one could apply steam at time *B,* when reaction (13) would have reached a negligible rate, to destroy the few isocyanate groups, thus getting

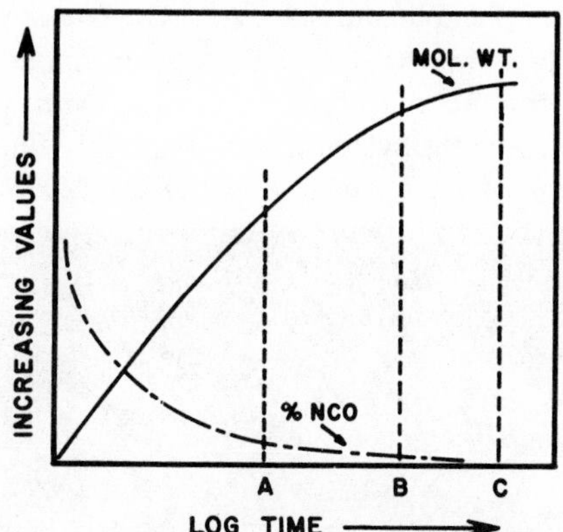

Fig. 1. Relative change of molecular weight and per cent NCO in foam with time. (Taken from ref. 32.)

low set, but without affecting molecular weight greatly. On the other hand, one clearly should not use steam at time *A*, while reaction (13) is still proceeding, since at that time disappearance of all isocyanate groups by reaction (12) would seriously limit the molecular weight.

The beneficial effect of a high temperature cure is doubtless partly to promote the disappearance of isocyanate groups by increasing the rate constants for reactions (12), (13), and (14) described above. An even greater beneficial effect, however, may be to maintain some adequate degree of mobility of chain ends after the polymer has gelled, thus providing a maximum opportunity for reaction (13) to occur.

III. Colloid Chemistry of Foam Formation

The preparation of a urethane foam involves the formation of gas bubbles in a liquid system which is polymerizing, and the growth and stabilization of those bubbles as the polymer forms and cures. Hence the colloidal aspects of bubble nucleation, growth, and stability are of prime importance to the foam chemist. The usual treatments of liquid-gas colloids provide only good indications of the physical behavior in a urethane foam system. The rapid and extensive changes in the system as the foam forms and cures limit the reliability of data from the liquid-gas colloid systems in which the nature of the liquid phase changes relatively little during an experimental interval. One may explain many foam phenomena, however, if it is assumed that normal colloid relations are important and reasonably applicable to the first short interval of time in the preparation of a foam, perhaps the first 10 to 30 seconds, while the system is still relatively fluid. As the foam

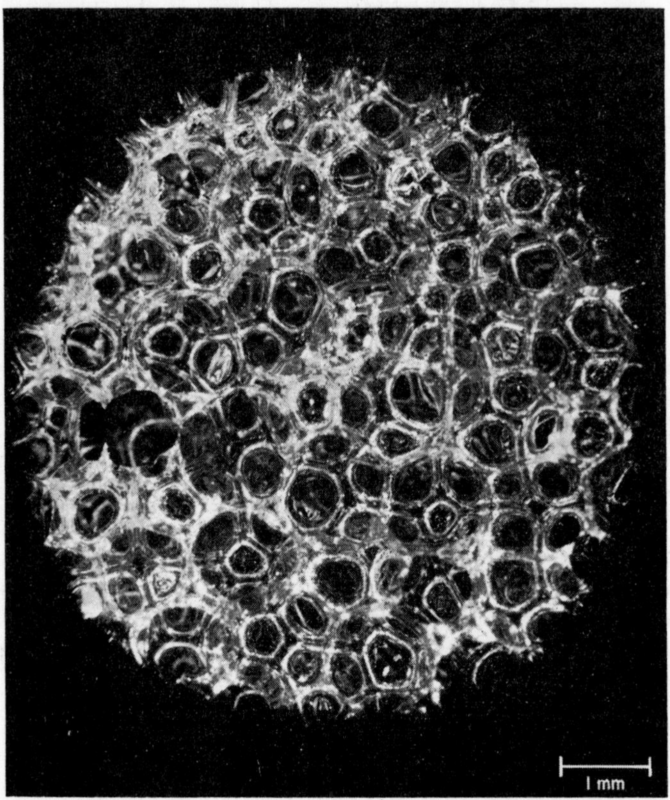

Fig. 2. Photomicrograph of flexible polyester-urethane foam. (Taken from ref. 32.)

producer knows all too well, the first 30 seconds after the mixing of components often make the difference between obtaining a foam or not, or less drastically, between obtaining the desired cell size or not.

The formation of a foam proceeds through several stages. In the first, the blowing agent, whatever it may be, generates a gas in solution in the liquid phase, with the gas reaching its saturation limit in solution, then becoming supersaturated, and finally coming out of solution in the form of a bubble. This formation of a bubble is called "nucleation," and is assisted by the presence of a second, finely divided phase such as a finely divided solid or an irregular solid surface. Such a second phase, which assists the formation of bubble is called a "nucleating agent." A familiar example in the "boiling chip," added to a distillation to insure a steady, even flow of small gas bubbles during distillation.

When the bubble is first formed it is a sphere surrounded by a relatively thick liquid phase. As more gas is generated by the blowing agent the new gas may form new bubbles and it may also diffuse from the liquid phase into existing bubbles, causing them to become larger. As more bubbles form and as the bubbles grow the foam volume increases, with the result that the polymerizing liquid phase becomes ever thinner. The bubbles lose their spherical shape as the liquid phase becomes thinner, with the bubbles finally assuming a structure bounded by several flat planes or membranes of polymerizing liquid. Where membranes join each other a rib or stalk is seen that is thick compared to the membranes (14). A magnified cross section of a flexible polyester-urethane foam is shown in Figure 2 (32), in which the straight ribs and five- and six-sided cells may readily be seen. Thus in the final foam most of the polymer is in the ribs, relatively little in the membranes.

A cross section of a rigid polyester-urethane foam (carbon dioxide blown) is shown in Figure 3 (32). The structure appears to be very much the same as that of a flexible foam.

The different stages of bubble formation and growth are considered in more detail in the following sections. These sections explain, at least to some degree, the role of the components in a foam system other than the reactants and catalysts, e.g., the surface tension depressants (silicone oils or emulsifiers) and cell size regulating agents.

1. Bubble Nucleation

The first key to the preparation of a foam is the formation of a gas bubble in the liquid system. The gas may be carbon dioxide, generated by the reaction of isocyanate and water. In some cases the gas may be the vapor state of a low boiling liquid which was initially dissolved in the reactants. In any case, the gas must come out of solution, quickly forming a tremendous number of tiny bubbles in the

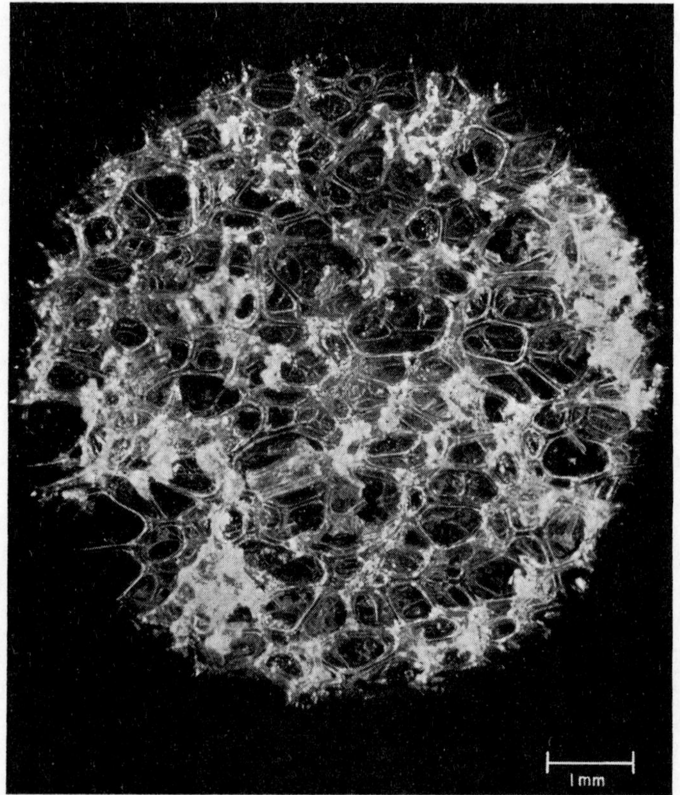

Fig. 3. Photomicrograph of rigid polyester-urethane foam. (Taken from ref. 32.)

liquid mass. These bubbles must be stabilized while the liquid medium polymerizes; i.e., while viscosity is increasing very rapidly.

The process of forming bubbles in a gas-liquid solution is often called nucleation. A very enlightening description by LaMer of the nucleation of sulfur solutions (24) may be applied to the nucleation of other materials such as gases. Figure 4 shows the general relationships that may be expected.

Figure 4 may be applied to urethane foam as follows (32), assuming first that no added nucleating agent is present. In the time interval of Zone I the gas concentration in solution exceeds the equilibrium saturation concentration (the solution becomes supersaturated) and, with rapid gas generation, reaches the concentration where self-nucleation begins. Sufficiently rapid gas generation may be achieved by catalysis of the isocyanate-water reaction, or by a sharp increase in the vapor pressure of an added lowboiling solvent, the increase being due to an increase in the temperature of the system. Such an increase in temperature is a rapid result of the catalyzed isocyanate-hydroxyl reaction in one-shot systems.

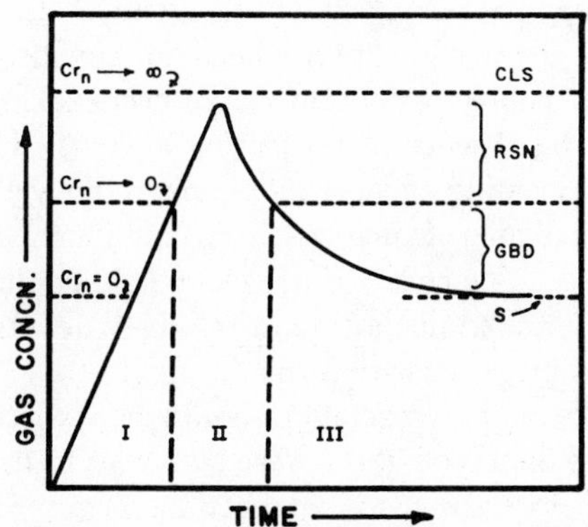

Fig. 4. Relation between changes in gas concentration in solution and nucleation and growth of foam cells. Legend: Cr_n = nucleation rate; CLS = critical limiting supersaturation; RSN = rapid self-nucleation, partial relief of supersaturation; GBD = growth by diffusion; S = saturation. (Taken from ref. 32.)

Self-nucleation will occur (Zone II) as long as the gas concentration is in the indicated range. As soon as nucleation relieves the gas concentration sufficiently, no more bubbles are formed, but the concentration of gas in solution is further reduced by diffusion into the bubbles that already exist (Zone III). Finally, no more gas is generated and the equilibrium saturation concentration of gas in solution is reached. From this time on, bubbles can grow only by diffusion of gas from small bubbles into larger bubbles, by coalescence, or because of exothermic expansion of the gas in the bubbles.

The beginning of Zone II corresponds approximately to the development of a creamy appearance in the reaction mixture. Thus the time interval of Zone I is approximately the time often called the "cream time" of a foam system. This interval may be approximately 10 seconds.

Thus far the duration of Zone II has not been clearly established, but may be assumed to be less than the time required to reach maximum foam volume ("rise time"), hence must be less than approximately 60–120 seconds for most systems. A reasonable approximation might be closer to 10–20 seconds. The time interval of Zone III should be terminated approximately when the foam rise is completed.

In most foam systems added nucleating agents may be present. It is possible that finely dispersed silicone oils, especially the dimethyl siloxane type, may serve as nucleating agents. In the presence of nucleating agents one would expect a behavior similar to that described above except that bubble formation would occur at lower gas concentrations than in the absence of nucleating agents. The function of a silicone oil as a nucleating agent would explain the well-known relation in polyether prepolymer foam systems: an increase in silicone oil concentration favors fine cells. Fine cells would be the result of faster nucleation and continued nucleation at relatively low degrees of supersaturation, so that more cells are formed.

Dissolved gases in the reactants should be expected to influence foaming. Thus if dissolved gases were sufficient to have the reactants near saturation before the foaming reactions begin, one might expect faster nucleation and finer cells. Several related observations are well known to the industry. For example, feeding limited amounts of air into the mixhead of the foam machine aids in producing fine cells. Similarly, using a large orifice opening on the mixhead, thus reducing pressure in the mixhead and probably increasing air leakage into the mixhead, favors fine cells (32).

A very striking illustration of the effect of dissolved gases has been demonstrated with polyether prepolymer systems (32). Vacuum degassing of several commercial prepolymers (Mondur PG-48, PG-50, PG-56) resulted in prepolymers which could not be made to foam with standard recipes. Regardless of the silicone oil concentration, the degassed prepolymers "boiled" when foaming was attempted; i.e., carbon dioxide was lost in huge bubbles so that no foam was formed. Addition of carbon dioxide, air, nitrogen, butane, or finely divided solids such as silica to the prepolymers prior to foaming permitted normal foaming. All of these additives could be expected to assist in the nucleation of the foam.

The relations shown in Figure 4 would also explain why catalysts which are strong promoters of the isocyanate-water reaction, e.g., tetramethyl-1,3-butanediamine, favor fine-cell formation in polyether prepolymer foams, compared to milder catalysts such as ethylmorpholine (32). The faster catalyst would force the gas concentration higher into the self-nucleation zone, thus giving faster nucleation and more cells, therefore finer cells.

The lowering of surface tension by silicone oil or other additives should also be important in that it would permit self-nucleation at lower gas concentrations than if the surface tension were not reduced.

2. *Bubble Stability*

When a bubble has been formed in a urethane foam system it may be expected to follow behavior patterns similar to those of bubbles in soap-water systems. Obviously, such an analogy would not be expected to exist for long in the life of the foam bubble because of the rapid growth of viscosity and elasticity of the polymer phase.

The stability of aqueous foams has been reviewed by deVries (14). The general principles are summarized briefly here, and the applicability to urethane foams is indicated.

To disperse a given volume of gas in a unit volume of liquid one must increase the free energy of the system by an amount of energy (ΔF) as indicated by the equation:

$$\Delta F = \gamma \cdot A$$

in which γ is the surface tension and A is the total interfacial area. Therefore, in a liquid foam system there is always a tendency to reduce the interfacial area. This relation means that a greater increase in free energy of the system will be required to produce fine cells than to produce large cells; further, that coalescence of cells and foam collapse will be favored energetically unless other factors prevent, i.e., curing of the foam before collapse can occur. It is also apparent that lowering the surface tension of the liquid, e.g., by the addition of silicone oil, will reduce the free energy increase associated with the dispersion of gas, and will aid in the development of fine cells, which correspond to a large value for A.

The size of the foam cell changes with time because of diffusion of gas from the liquid phase into the cell, and also by coalescence of cells. According to classical theory, the gas pressure in a spherical bubble is larger than the pressure in the surrounding liquid by a difference (ΔP) given by the equation:

$$\Delta P = 2\gamma/R$$

in which R is the radius of the bubble. Therefore, the gas pressure in a small bubble is larger than that in a large bubble. The difference in pressure (ΔP_1^2) for two bubbles of radii R_1 and R_2 is given by the equation:

$$\Delta P_1^2 = 2\gamma[(1/R_1) - (1/R_2)]$$

Consequently in a liquid system there is diffusion of gas from the small bubbles into the large bubbles. Hence the small bubbles tend to disappear and the large bubbles to grow. As a result the average bubble size in a polydisperse system increases with time.

It is also noteworthy that low values of γ favor low pressure differences between bubbles of different size, hence better bubble stability and small average cell size.

Film rupture is important in urethane foam formation until the polymer is almost completely cured. While the polymer phase is still a liquid the following relations may be expected to hold, at least approximately.

Pure liquids will not give a stable foam, regardless of the surface tension. To have a relatively stable foam one must have at least two components, one preferentially adsorbed at the surface. The surface tension is determined by the type and amount of adsorbed solute (Gibbs' theorem):

$$d\gamma = -\Sigma\Gamma d\mu$$

in which Γ is the surface excess of a component of chemical potential μ. With limited amounts of the solute an increase in surface area decreases Γ, thereby raising γ, tending to counteract further extension of the surface. This relationship combats an increase in area or a thinning of the cell membrane. Since it is readily recognized that membranes are more likely to rupture the thinner they are, this resistance to thinning helps stabilize the cell.

Another factor influencing cell stability is temperature. An increase in temperature reduces the surface tension, thus promoting thinning of the cell membranes, hence promoting rupture.

An additional feature affecting bubble stability is the drainage of the liquid in the bubble walls due to capillary action. A cross section of a portion of a cell is indicated in Figure 5. The theory of LaPlace and Young states that the pressure at points *1* and *2* is lower than that in the bubble wall, *3*. Consequently, there is a tendency to flow from

3 toward *1,* in opposition to gravity, and toward *2,* reinforcing flow due to gravity. Drainage is proportional to the square of the distance (L) and both forms of drainage will be retarded by an increase in viscosity. This stabilizing effect of viscosity increases is of prime importance in urethane foams.

The rupture of a film requires a very small activation energy due to an initial increase in area at the initiation of the rupture ($\Delta F = \gamma \cdot A$). Once rupture has occurred, however, the growth of the rupture is exceedingly fast.

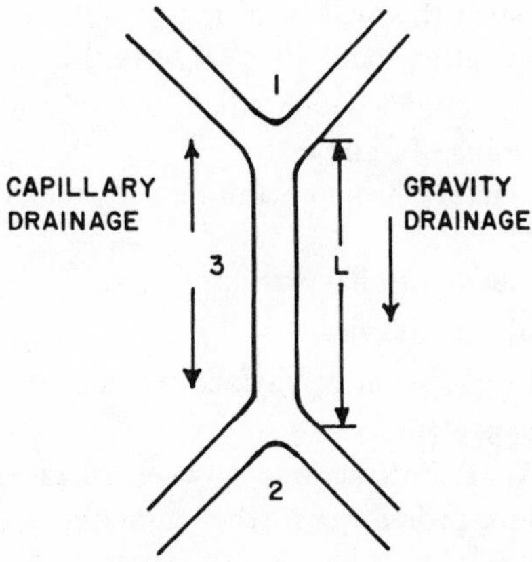

Fig. 5. Cross section of a portion of foam cell related to thinning of a membrane by drainage. (Taken from ref. 32.)

A relationship that is probably of small importance in urethane foams is the "electrical double layer" effect. If there is an accumulation of electrical charge on each surface of the film, e.g., as a result of orientation of an ionic emulsifier on each surface, then repulsion of the electrical charges as the two surfaces approach each other will help limit the thinning of the film. This effect is generally less important in organic liquids of low dielectric constant than in aqueous systems.

An influence which may offset the electric repulsions of film surfaces is the van der Waals attraction between the surfaces of a very thin film. When a film becomes so thin that van der Waals' forces at one surface can attract molecules at the other surface, then this attraction will hasten the further thinning of the film.

In summary, the following factors resist the formation of very thin films and/or the subsequent thinning of those films, hence are stabilizing influences:

(*a*) An increase in surface area requires an increase in free energy, $\Delta F = \gamma \Delta A$.

(*b*) A reduction in the surface excess of the adsorbed component as a film becomes thinner increases the surface tension, $d\gamma = -\Sigma \Gamma d\mu$, thus increasing still further the free energy required to give the increase in area, hence tending to prevent thinning and rupture.

(*c*) An increase in viscosity retards thinning of membranes. In a urethane foam system this will be of major importance, and doubtless dominates all others after about 40 to 60 seconds.

(*d*) The electric double layer effect exerts a small retarding influence on the thinning of films.

The following factors promote thinning of membranes, hence promote film rupture:

(*a*) Drainage due to capillary action.

(*b*) Drainage due to gravity.

(*c*) Any local depression of surface tension, e.g., due to local hot spots or antifoam agents.

(*d*) Van der Waals' attractions between surfaces may become significant in thin films, promoting further thinning.

In urethane foams one may expect the effects indicated below (32):

(*a*) A surface tension depressant, e.g., silicone oil or emulsifier, should help give fine cells, $\Delta F = \gamma A$, and should help stabilize cells toward gas diffusion, $\Delta P = 2\gamma[(1/R_1 - 1/R_2)]$.

(*b*) A rapid build of viscosity should reduce thinning of the cell walls, hence stabilize the foam.

(*c*) An attempt to prepare too fine cells may lead to collapse because rupture is more likely to occur in very thin cell walls. What may be even more important, in very fine cells the ribs of the cells are very thin and may not be strong enough to stop the rupture that has started in a membrane. Thus, the rupture will continue indefinitely and the foam will collapse.

(*d*) Foreign matter which can reduce the surface tension locally, such as wax particles, may cause local collapse, "holes," by the local depression of the surface tension.

3. *Urethane Foam Systems*

In light of the preceding discussion the role of silicone oils and other such surface tension depressants in urethane foams becomes fairly clear (32). The surface tension of a polyether prepolymer is depressed from approximately 36 dynes/cm. to a minimum of 26–27 dynes/cm. by 0.1% of dimethyl siloxane (50 cts. viscosity) (32), similar to the effect on a polyether itself (17). However, approximately 0.5–1.7% of silicone is normally required to stabilize the foaming of the prepolymer. It may be assumed that the higher concentration of the silicone oil is needed during foaming because of the tremendously greater surface area during foaming, hence greater dispersion of the silicone oil.

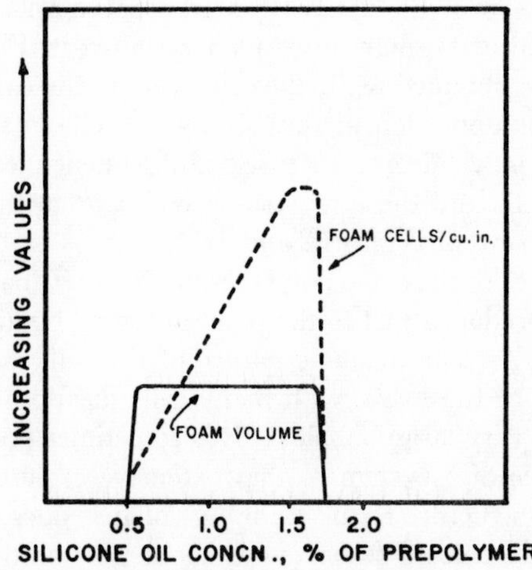

Fig. 6. Typical relation between silicone oil concentration and foam stability and cell size in a polyether prepolymer foam. (Taken from ref. 32.)

A typical relation between silicone oil concentration and foam behavior in a polyether prepolymer system is shown in Figure 6 (32). Thus, approximately 0.5% of oil was needed to stabilize a specific foam during rise. With less oil very large bubbles were formed, were not stable, but coalesced and the foam failed to rise; i.e., "boiled." With from 0.5 to 1.7% of oil the foam was stable, but the cell size varied. With low oil concentrations the cells were large, whereas with high oil concentrations the cells were fine, perhaps due to combined surface tension and nucleation effects. With still more oil the foam reached its full height but then collapsed. Collapse may have been caused by early rupture of the very fine cells, when the very thin cell ribs were too weak to stop the growth of the rupture. It is this relation between fine-cell structure and foam collapse which results in the familiar difficulty of consistently producing the finest cell foam, compared to the ease of producing a medium or coarse cell foam.

The development of cell structure and the growth of cells in a normal, properly balanced polyether prepolymer flexible foam system is illustrated in Figure 7. A series of high speed photographs was taken as the foam rose in a mold having a transparent plastic side (26). Pictures obtained at regular intervals are shown in Figure 7. Clear pictures were not obtained while the cells were in the earliest, spherical structure, but the upper left picture shows the cells in the early stages of developing a polyhedron structure. Subsequent pictures show the growth of the cells and the final structure similar to that of the polyester-urethane foams of Figures 2 and 3.

Similar pictures of the same polyether prepolymer foam systems, but with silicone oil reduced just to the point of foam "boiling," are shown in Figure 8 (26). The unstable nature of the cells is apparent very early in the life of the foam, with many cells disappearing by coalescence into a few very large bubbles. It is sometimes possible to obtain a delicate balance of a system so that extensive coalescence occurs to give a "sponge" structure to the foam but collapse does not occur. An example would be a foam stabilized at about the point represented by the third photograph in Figure 8. Such systems are popular for the production of artificial sponges but are difficult to achieve. The usual behavior of a foam that exhibits the extent of coalescence shown in Figure 8 is to continue coalescence to the point at which only a few very large bubbles remain, and these break, losing their gas before polymerization stabilizes the system.

The stabilization of a foam system is greatly influenced by the initial viscosity of the system, although the formation of the bubbles may be influenced very little, if at all, by the viscosity (23). This beneficial effect of viscosity is illustrated in several ways in the urethane foam systems. Thus in systems of relatively high initial viscosity such as one-shot polyester foams in which the polyesters have viscosities of 10,000–20,000 cps. at room temperature (e.g., with Multron R-18 and R-68), no silicone oil is needed for foam stability, but may be added to

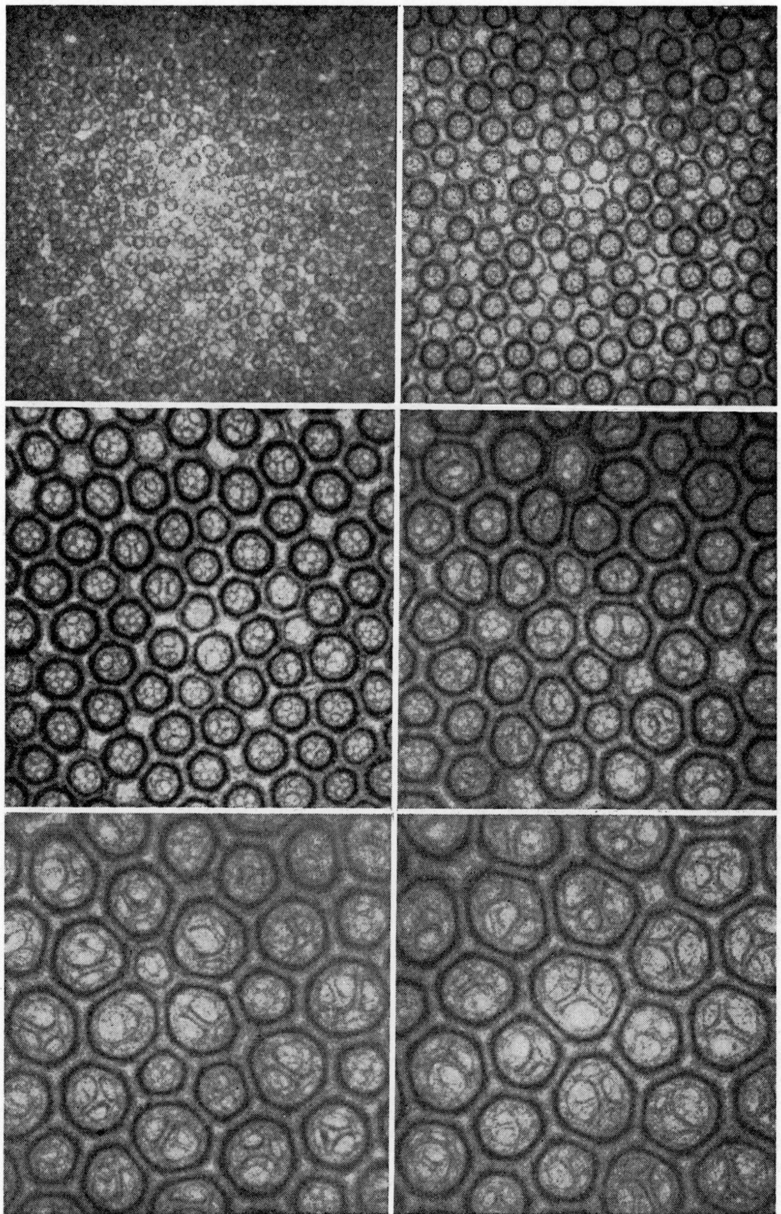

Fig. 7. Stages of cell growth in a normally balanced polyether prepolymer foam system. The time of foaming increases from the top left toward the bottom right picture; 8 power magnification.

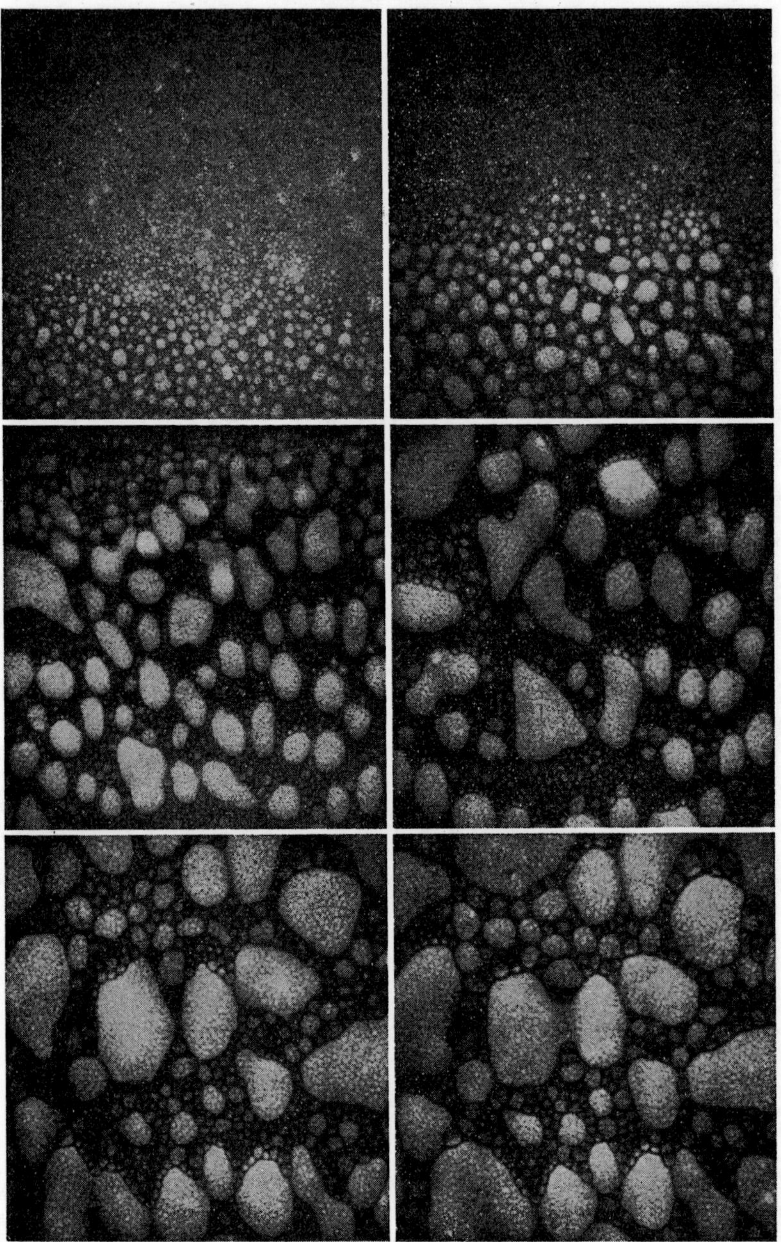

Fig. 8. Stages of cell growth and coalescence in a polyether prepolymer foam system deficient in silicone oil. The time of foaming increases from the top left toward the bottom right picture; 2.4 power magnification.

control cell size. Similarly with polyether prepolymers of 20,000–30,000 cps. viscosity at room temperature (e.g., with Mondur PG-42 and PG-44) no silicone oil is necessary for foaming. With polyether prepolymers having viscosities of 8000–12,000 cps. at room temperature (e.g., Mondur PG-56), however, silicone oil is necessary as a foam stabilizer.

The effect of viscosity was most pronounced in the early effort to prepare one-shot polyether foams using polyethers of 300 cps. viscosity. The dimethyl siloxane silicone oils which are suitable for polyether prepolymer foams were completely inadequate stabilizers, even when the very powerful tin catalysts were used. The stabilizing effect of the alkylsilane-polyoxyalkylene copolymer (e.g., Silicone L-520) is truly remarkable, and must be given equal or greater credit than the tin catalysts for making possible the one-shot polyether foams.

IV. Viscoelastic Changes in Foaming

In addition to the chemical reactions occurring during the preparation of a foam and the colloidal aspects of developing a dispersion of a gas in a polymerizing medium, a complete understanding of foam formation requires a consideration of the viscoelastic changes which occur. In the preparation of a flexible foam one observes the change from a liquid system first to a plastic gel and then to a highly elastic polymer. In the rigid foam systems one similarly observes the change from liquid reactants to a plastic gel and finally to a thermoset, rigid, elastic polymer. These changes taking place in a flexible foam system will be considered first.

1. Effect on Cell Structure, Voids, and Foam Collapse

In considering the chemistry of the flexible foams it was noted that gas evolution caused an increase in foam volume, and, at the same time, the polymer molecular weight increased greatly. The curing of the polymer developed a cross-linked structure. From a general knowledge of polymer properties one would predict that the growing polymer would change progressively from its initial liquid state into a thermoplastic, soluble, highly viscous polymer of moderate molecular weight; then as some branching developed into cross links the polymer would become insoluble and take on some elastic properties. Finally, when the molecular weight reached very high values and the polymer was cross linked into a network structure with moderately long chain segments between cross links the polymer should be highly elastic. Such a network structure should in an ideal case have no viscous character, and hence its dynamic viscosity should be essentially zero.

These changes are shown graphically in Figure 9, along with certain other features of the foam system which may be related, the natural opening of the foam cells (i.e., not due to mechanical crushing of the

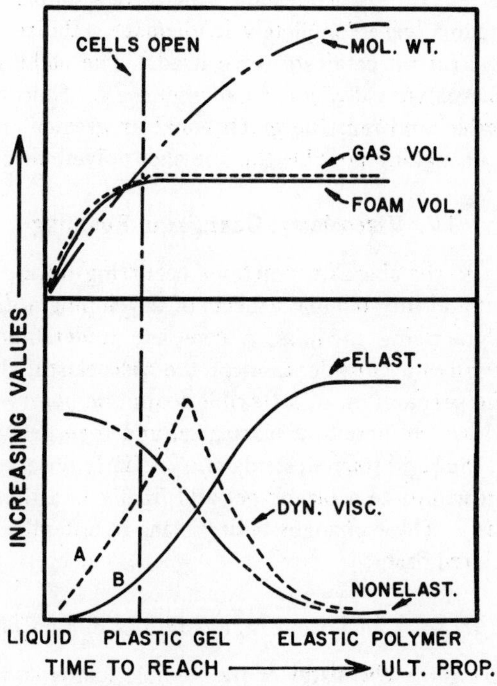

Fig. 9. Typical changes in a flexible foam with time. (Taken from ref. 32.)

foam) and the development of the ultimate physical properties (32). The curves for gas volume and foam volume have been observed experimentally with commercial polyether prepolymer foam systems (32).

By using an oscillating "resonance elastometer" the viscosity curve and the elasticity curve have been demonstrated approximately for a polyether prepolymer system (28), although with a time scale somewhat different from that of a commercial foam system. In the resonance elastomer the heat losses and surface/volume ratio were such that maximum foam rise was obtained in approximately 7 minutes, rather than approximately 2 minutes, as in flexible foam production. The viscosity maximum was reached in approximately 10 minutes, then decreased, and the elasticity maximum was reached in approximately 100 minutes.

The curves for molecular weight, per cent elastic portion of the polymer, and per cent viscous portion of the polymer are assumptions which seem reasonable.

The opening of the cells in a flexible foam, commercially a very significant and desirable step, occurs to a large extent just as the foam reaches its maximum height. Experimentally, an apparent break in the rate of gas evolution as measured by the displacement of water, along with the increase in foam volume, has been observed several times, as shown in Figure 9 (32). It is proposed that the cells open at the time when the last surge of gas is observed. Further, it is suggested that the membranes of the cells at this time have reached a state of high viscosity, but still have very low elasticity. The high viscosity does not permit the membrane to flow fast enough to expand and relieve the pressure of the gas that is still being generated. At the same time, the elasticity is too low to permit reversible stretching of the membranes. The combination of failure of the cell to expand, a steadily increasing gas pressure, and low mechanical strength of the thin membrane results in rupture of the membrane; i.e., an opening of the cells.

If at this time of maximum gas evolution the membrane ruptures and the stalk or rib of the cell does not have sufficient mechanical strength to stop the rupture, then the rupture will spread. If the rupture stops within several inches one has a "split" or a "void" in the foam. If the rupture does not stop, the foam collapses. The rib may be expected to rupture if the cells are so small that the rib is little thicker than the membrane, or if the polymer cure has not progressed far enough for the rib to have the strength to stop the rupture. The two effects would be expected to be interrelated.

On the other hand, if at the time of maximum gas evolution the cell membranes do not rupture, the cells are closed, and when the foam cools the cells of a flexible foam will contract due to the reduced internal pressure of the cooling gas. Failure of the membranes to rupture could be expected to result from too low a viscosity, so that the membrane could flow as the gas volume increased, thus relieving pressure as it developed. Failure to rupture could also be expected to occur if the membrane were so elastic that it could stretch reversibly to accommodate the last increase in gas volume. In the former case the polymer cure would not have progressed far enough at the time of maximum gas evolution, and in the latter case the cure would have progressed too far.

This hypothesis concerning the natural opening of the cell walls is in agreement with many observations of foam systems (32). For example, with one-shot polyether foams one can regulate the isocyanate-water reaction (gas evolution plus polymer growth) with an amine catalyst and the isocyanate-hydroxyl reaction (polymer growth) with a tin catalyst. One can often reduce closed cells by reducing the tin catalyst; i.e., reducing polymer growth and, doubtless, elasticity at the time of maximum gas evolution. Similarly, one can often eliminate voids or splits by increasing the tin catalysts or reducing the amine catalyst, both of which should increase polymer (cell rib) strength at the time of maximum gas evolution (cells opening).

An example of closed cell formation apparently due to too low a viscosity at the critical time has also been observed. In some cases very low tin catalyst concentrations have given closed cells, whereas a small increase in tin catalyst would provide open cells. (A still further increase in tin catalyst would again give closed cells, apparently due to too high elasticity at the critical time.)

Sandridge and co-workers observed the relation between stannous octoate (T-9) catalyst concentration and foam characteristics related to open cell character as shown in Figure 10 for a typical one-shot foam based on a 3000 molecular weight polyether triol (29). With the amine catalyst held constant, an increase in the T-9 catalyst gave a progressive change from voids to good foam to closed cells. Foam having large cells gave open cells with a narrower catalyst concentration range than did foam with fine cells. This is to be expected, since the very thin membranes of the fine cells should rupture at a higher degree of cure than would the thicker membranes of the larger cells.

Another type of observation supporting the hypothesis concerning closed-cell formation is the relation between degree of branching of the resin reactant and rate of polymerization. Based simply on the statistical probability of reaction of end groups, at a given rate of isocyanate-hydroxyl reaction one would expect to develop a network structure and hence elasticity faster with a moderately branched resin than with a less branched one. Thus, with other factors remaining constant, one could expect that progressively increasing the branching of the resin component should lead to a high percentage of closed cells in a foam. One should also expect that reducing the reactivity of the diisocyanate should compensate somewhat for increases in branching. Conversely, with the resin remaining constant, increasing the reactivity of the diisocyanate should lead to a higher percentage of closed cells in the foam.

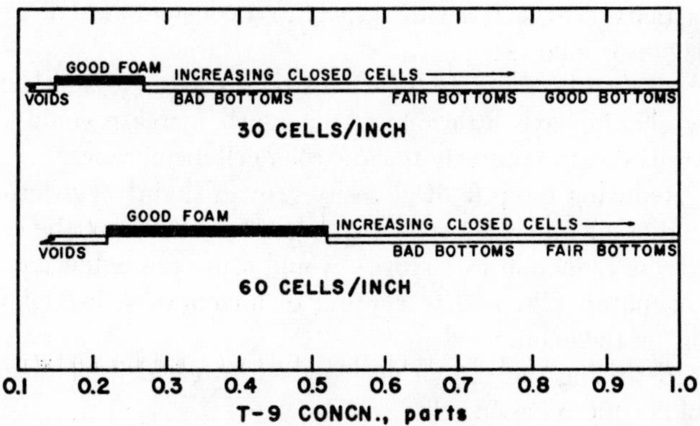

Fig. 10. Relation between T-9 catalyst concentration and foam characteristics related to open cell character in a one-shot polyether flexible foam. (Taken from ref. 29.)

The shrinkage of semiflexible foams because of a high percentage of closed cells is a familiar commercial problem. This is to be expected because of the increased branching of the resins used for semiflexible foams, hence relatively fast growth of elasticity in the cell membranes.

Another commercial example may be taken from the early history of urethane foam development in the United States (32). The initial Bayer system was based on a combination of a 65:35 ratio of 2,4- and 2,6-tolylene diisocyanate and a polyester with a certain degree of branching (Multron R-18). For commercial reasons the 80:20 ratio of 2,4- and 2,6-isomers was preferred in the U. S. Unfortunately, with the same polyester, catalyst, and emulsifier system used with the 65:35 ratio, the 80:20 ratio gave severe foam shrinkage due to closed cells. A change to a somewhat less branched polyester (Multron R-68) gave foam without shrinkage when using 80:20 TDI. One may assume that the 80:20 ratio, having a higher concentration of the more reactive 2,4-isomer, developed elasticity faster with Multron R-18 than did the 65:35 ratio, hence gave closed cells. The reduced branching of the Multron R-68 compensated for the increased reactivity of the 80:20 ratio.

Reference again to Figure 9 may be made in summarizing viscoelastic effects on closed cells, voids, and collapse in flexible foams (32). If we assume a properly balanced foam system as a reference point, the isolated effects of altering the rate of growth of viscosity (curve *A*) and elasticity (curve *B*) with respect to a constant rate of gas evolution may be as follows:

(*a*) Increasing the rate of viscosity growth (raising curve *A*) slightly should have little effect; too much increase could result in closed cells due to relatively thick, strong cell membranes.

(*b*) Reducing the rate of viscosity growth slightly (lowering curve *A*) could result in closed cells due to continued flow of the cell walls. An extreme reduction in viscosity would cause too extensive thinning of all membranes, too early rupture of membranes, loss of gas, and "boiling" of the foam.

(*c*) Increasing the rate of development of elasticity (raising curve *B*) could result in closed cells.

(*d*) Reducing the rate of development of elasticity (lowering curve *B*) could result in voids or collapse because of failure of the cell ribs to stop the ruptures which initiate in the cell membranes.

Results somewhat similar to those indicated in Figure 9 may be expected for rigid foams, except that the rigid foam polymer will be largely elastic, but will also retain a significant internal viscosity at room temperature, since it will be at least partially in the glassy state at room temperature. Such curves for elastic modulus and viscosity have been demonstrated qualitatively for a rigid polyester foam using the resonance elastomer (28).

In most rigid foams closed cells are desired. In these cases the system is so balanced that the cell membranes do not rupture at the peak of gas evolution, very likely because of the presence of adequate elasticity to permit stretching without rupture.

In rigid foams a new problem is introduced by the closed-cell character. The polymer must develop adequate strength to maintain its shape before the gas in the cells is cooled, or shrinkage will occur because of contraction of the gas on cooling. Furthermore, in carbon dioxide-blown foams, the carbon dioxide can diffuse out of the cells faster than air can diffuse in (17), thus reducing the pressure in the cells still further. This loss of pressure due to diffusion can cause a very slow shrinkage of the foam. For these reasons a highly crosslinked structure is needed to provide adequate strength in the cell membranes to resist shrinkage, giving dimensionally stable rigid foams. An added advantage of the fluorocarbon-blown rigid foams is the extremely slow rate of fluorocarbon diffusion out of the foam and hence less likelihood of foam shrinkage (8).

2. *Relations between Cell Structure and Properties*

One might expect that the intimate cell geometry of a urethane foam should affect the mechanical properties of the foam. For example, a change in the percentage of the polymer in the cell membranes compared to that in the cell ribs should have an effect. More obviously, the percentage of closed cells should influence several properties. Certain relations are observed between the percentage of open cells in a rigid foam and the water absorption, gas permeability (8), and, in fluorocarbon-blown foams, the thermal conductivity and dimensional stability at elevated temperatures. Thus a higher percentage of closed cells naturally gives a lower degree of water absorption and gas permeability, better retention of fluorocarbon and, hence, better retention of low thermal conductivity, and reduced dimensional stability when hot (due to increased fluorocarbon pressure in the cells).

Similarly, the percentage of open cells, and the degree of "openness" of cells in a flexible foam are related to resiliency. Cells having completely ruptured membranes, i.e., with large holes in the membranes, obviously can permit faster air flow through the foam than cells having some intact membranes or membranes which are merely split, even though the latter would be classed as "open" cells.

In addition to the effect on air flow a structural difference could exist. In a properly formulated open-cell foam the cell membranes should break naturally at a time when all or most of the polymer in the membrane would flow back into the ribs. Such a foam would have essentially all of the polymer in the ribs. In contrast, closed-cell foam which had open cells as result of crushing would have a significant portion of the polymer in the ruptured membranes. These ruptured membranes likely would contribute relatively little to strength of the foam and would reduce the flexibility of the ribs. Thus, such a foam should be somewhat weaker and less resilient than a naturally open-cell foam. Both extremes of structure have been seen in the industry, although foams between the two extremes of structure are most common.

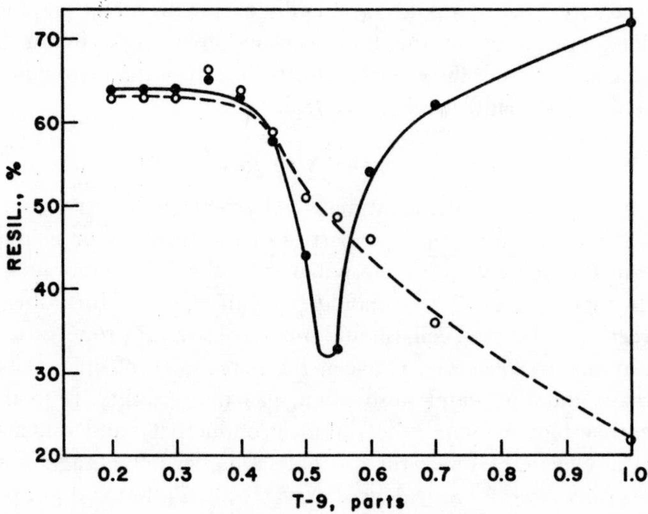

Fig. 11. Resiliency of one-shot polyether foam as affected by catalyst concentration and hence open-cell structure. Key: ● = 60 cells/inch, uncrushed; ○ = 60 cells/inch, crushed. (Taken from ref. 29.)

The data of Sandridge and co-workers are in agreement with these expectations (29). Comparison of Figure 11 with Figure 10 shows that the falling ball resiliency of the one-shot polyether foam (Fig. 11) was high, with or without crushing, when the catalyst concentration (Fig. 10) was such as to give an open-cell foam. As the percentage of closed cells increased the resiliency of the uncrushed foam was reduced. This effect may have been due to the comparatively unyielding nature of a cell face which has an intact membrane as opposed to the flexible structure inherent in the rod-like character of the cell ribs in an open-cell foam. When the number of intact cell membranes became sufficiently large that many cells were completely closed, a pneumatic effect appeared to dominate the resiliency, so that resiliency increased.

Crushing the foam having a few closed cells regained some of the resiliency lost as a result of intact cell membranes. This effect may be assumed to be the result of breaking the membranes. Those foams having high resiliency because of a pneumatic effect had low resiliency after crushing because of the rupture of membranes, and consequent loss of the pneumatic effect. Such crushing, however, very likely did

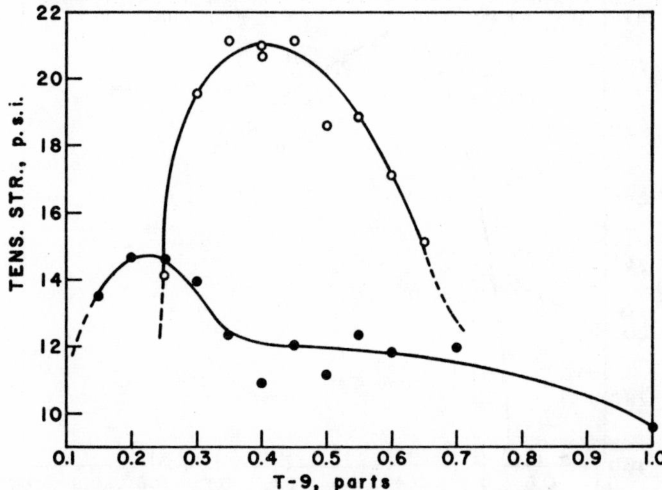

Fig. 12. Effect of open-cell structure, as determined by catalyst concentration, on the tensile strength of fine- and large-cell one-shot polyether foams. Key: ● = 30 cells/inch; ○ = 60 cells/inch. (Taken from ref. 29.)

not remove the membranes completely and hence did not provide a structure as flexible and resilient as the one in which cells opened naturally and in which polymer largely flowed from the ruptured membranes into the cell ribs.

Similarly, the tensile strength and elongation of naturally open-cell foam were higher than those of closed-cell foam, as shown in Figures 12 and 13. The significantly higher tensile strength of a fine-cell foam compared to a large-cell foam is also apparent from Figure 12. Figure 14 shows that the load-bearing capacity of the open-cell foam is somewhat greater than that of a crushed foam which initially had closed cells. All of these factors at medium to high catalyst concentration may be attributed to the greater percentage of polymer in the ribs of the naturally open-cell foam. At very low catalyst concentrations the foam was weak, perhaps because of excess drainage of polymer in the cell ribs, so that some ribs may have been broken and many others may have been very thin in the centers of the ribs. As was noted in Figure 10, voids occurred at these very low catalyst concentrations, supporting the assumption of thin, weak ribs.

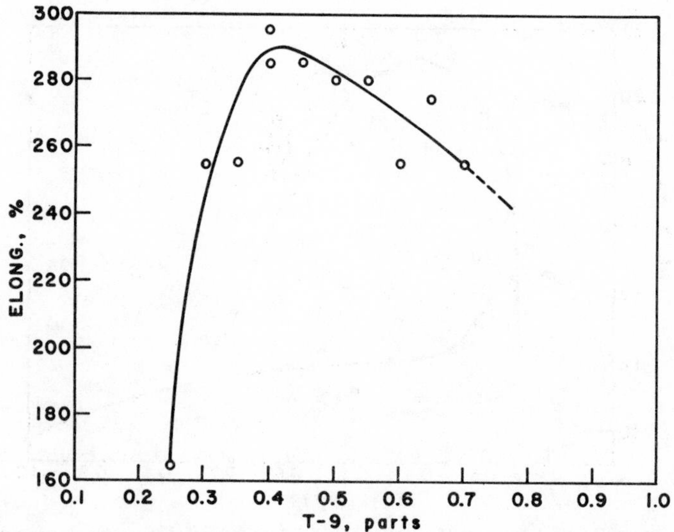

Fig. 13. Elongation of one-shot polyether foam as affected by catalyst concentration and hence open-cell structure. Key: o = 60 cells/inch. (Taken from ref. 29.)

Solvent swelling studies on these foams indicated no significant variation in degree of cross linking, supporting the belief that foam property changes were due primarily to changes in cell geometry. Microscopic examination of the foams was in agreement with the above discussion of cell structure.

In addition to the data of Sandridge and co-workers, it has been known generally that fine-cell structure in one-shot polyester and prepolymer polyether foams favor high tensile strength and elongation, compared to large-cell foam (32). Perhaps the size of the flaws in the foam structure contribute to this relation: the fine-cell foam could be expected to have smaller flaws than the large-cell foam.

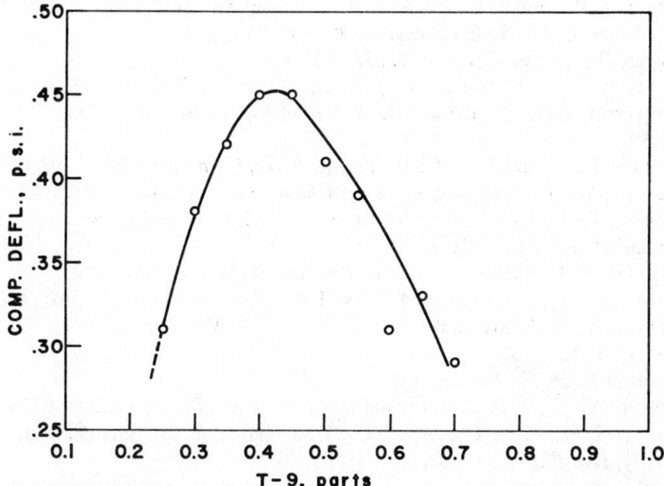

Fig. 14. Compressive strength at 25% deflection of a one-shot polyether foam as affected by catalyst concentration and hence open-cell structure. Key ○ = 60 cells/inch. (Taken from ref. 29.)

3. Structural Factors Affecting Stress Relaxation and Creep in Flexible Foams

In addition to factors influencing compression set in fresh foam, certain structural features may influence the set, stress relaxation, and creep of fully cured foam (32). These features include the type of cross links present, the number and type of polymer end groups, and the hydrogen bonding of the polymer. Since these factors may be equally important for urethane elastomers, the discussion of this subject has been reserved for Chapter VI.

References

1. Anon., *Chem. and Eng. News* **37**, No. 48, 48 (1958).
2. Alzner, B. G., and K. C. Frisch, *Ind. Eng. Chem.* **51**, 715 (1959).
3. Arnold, R. G., J. A. Nelson, and J. J. Verbanc, *Chem Revs.* **57**, 47 (1957).
4. Arnold, R. G., J. A. Nelson, and J. J. Verbanc, paper presented at the American Chemical Society Rubber Division Meeting, May 16–18, 1956.
5. Axelrood, S. L., C. W. Hamilton, and K. C. Frisch, *Ind. Eng. Chem.* **53**, 889 (1961).
6. Bailey, M. E., V. Kirss, and R. G. Spaunburgh, *Ind. Eng. Chem.* **48**, 794 (1946).

7. Baker, J. W., and J. B. Holdsworth, *J. Chem. Soc.* **1947,** 713.
8. Barringer, C. M., *SPE Journal* **15,** 961 (1959).
9. Bayer, O., *Angew. Chem.* **A59,** 257 (1947).
10. Bolin, R. E., J. F. Szabat, R. J. Cote, E. Peters, P. G. Gemeinhardt, A. S. Morecroft, E. E. Hardy, and J. H. Saunders, *J. Chem. and Eng. Data* **4,** 261 (1959).
11. Britain, J. W., and P. G. Gemeinhardt, *J. Appl. Polymer Sci.* **4,** 207 (1960).
12. Buist, J. M., R. Hurd, and A. Lowe, *Chem. & Ind. (London)* **51,** 1544 (1960).
13. Craven, R. L., paper presented at the American Chemical Society Meeting, Atlantic City, Sept., 1956.
14. deVries, A. J., *Rubber Chem. and Technol.* **31,** 1142 (1958).
15. Erner, W. E., A. Farkas, and P. W. Hill, *Modern Plastics* **37,** 107 (1960).
16. Farkas, A., G. A. Mills, W. E. Erner, and J. B. Maerker, *Ind. Eng. Chem.* **51,** 1299 (1959).
17. Frensdorff, H. K., *Rubber Age* **83,** 812 (1958).
18. Gmitter, G. T., E. E. Gruber, and R. D. Joseph, *SPE Journal* **15,** 957 (1959).
19. Heiss, H. L., F. P. Combs, P. G. Gemeinhardt, J. H. Saunders, and E. E. Hardy, *Ind. Eng. Chem.* **51,** 929 (1959).
20. Hostettler, F., and E. F. Cox, *Ind. Eng. Chem.* **52,** 609 (1960).
21. Heiss, H. L., J. H. Saunders, M. R. Morris, B. R. Davis, and E. E. Hardy, *Ind. Eng. Chem.* **46,** 1498 (1954).
22. Höchtlen, A., *Kunststoffe* **42,** 303 (1952).
23. King, E. J., *J. Phys. Chem.* **48,** 141 (1944).
24. LaMer, V. K., *Ind. Eng. Chem.* **44,** 1270 (1952).
25. Mack, G. P., *Fibres Plastics* **21,** 342 (1960); *Chem. Abstracts* **55,** 10950*b* (1961).
26. Mobay Chemical Company, unpublished data.
27. Morton, M., and M. A. Deitz, paper presented at the American Chemical Society Meeting, Sept., 1956.
28. Parks, J. R., L. Cooper (Monsanto Chemical Company), and G. F. Baumann (Mobay Chemical Co.), unpublished data.
29. Sandridge, R. L., P. G. Gemeinhardt, and J. H. Saunders, paper presented at the American Chemical Society Meeting, Sept., 1961.
30. Sandridge, R. L., A. S. Morecroft, E. E. Hardy, and J. H. Saunders, *J. Chem. Eng. Data,* **5,** 495 (1960).
31. Saunders, J. H., *Rubber Chem. and Technol.* **32,** 337 (1959).
32. Saunders, J. H., *Rubber Chem. and Technol.* **33,** 1293 (1960).

VI. RELATIONSHIPS BETWEEN POLYMER STRUCTURE AND PROPERTIES IN URETHANES

I. Introduction

The field of urethane polymers is rapidly growing in commercial importance, especially in foam and elastomer applications. This group of polymers includes a very broad spectrum of structures and "monomer" units. Although all contain repeating urethane groups (hence the name), other groups such as urea, ester, ether, and aromatic may be included. In many cases the urethane groups are even fewer in number than other functional groups. Such a diversity of structures makes possible a very wide range of polymer properties, and adds additional interest and challenge to studies of relations between polymer structure and properties.

The urethanes are relative newcomers to the status of commercial importance, so it is not surprising that relatively little has been published concerning structure-property relationships. Within the last four years, information of value has become available and data have been obtained which permit some semiquantitative relationships to be established. A recent review by one of the authors (56) summarized the more important literature, published through approximately 1959, relating properties to structure, primarily in the fields of elastomers and foams. The data were also interpreted in terms of component structural features and their effects on a typical modulus-temperature curve. This chapter brings that review up to date.

To help clarify the discussions, the general outlines of preparations of major classes of polymers are given. The experimental details of preparing the various forms of urethane polymers are assumed to be familiar to the reader. Details can usually be found in the original references and in the second volume of this series, and will not be discussed unless they influence the interpretation of the polymer structure obtained.

A considerable number of publications dealing primarily with the properties of urethane polymers, but contributing little to an understanding of the relation between those properties and the corresponding polymer structure, has been omitted from this survey. Such publications will be covered in detail in appropriate sections of the second volume of this series.

II. General Considerations

The generalities of structure-property relationships in polymers, when interpreted with the proper emphasis required by the specific species, may be applied to the urethane polymers. These generalities have been reviewed in many excellent books (see references 22,25,32).

A very brief outline of the most significant structural features influencing polymer properties may serve as a useful introduction to the more specific treatment of urethane polymers. Application of these general principles will be more apparent in the later discussion of urethane elastomers, foams, and other polymer forms.

1. Molecular Weight

Most mechanical properties change with molecular weight up to a limiting value, then do not change as the molecular weight increases further. For example, the tensile strength of a vinyl chloride (86%)-vinyl acetate (14%) copolymer increases rapidly as the molecular weight approaches the 10,000 to 14,000 range, but increases very little as the molecular weight is extended beyond approximately 15,000 (33). Other properties that show a similar relation include melting point, elongation, elasticity, and glass transition temperature. On the other hand, solubility, and often brittleness, decrease as the molecular weight approaches a limiting value. In the following discussion of urethanes it is assumed, unless noted otherwise, that all urethane polymers considered are of sufficiently high molecular weight that moderate changes in that feature will not affect properties.

2. Intermolecular Forces

Intermolecular forces, sometimes called "secondary chemical bonds," are the result of hydrogen bonding, dipole moments, polarizability and dispersion effects (van der Waals attractions). These intermolecular attractive forces tend to hold polymer chains together in a manner similar to that of primary chemical bonds, but are much weaker and are more readily affected by increases in temperature or stress (resulting in creep).

The effectiveness of intermolecular forces is reduced by factors such as the repulsion of like charges and anything which keeps mutually attractive groups apart; e.g., plasticizers, bulky neighboring groups such as side chains, and poor geometric "fit" of the groups. Poor "fit" may be the result of irregular spacing of the attractive groups or stereoisomerism.

The presence of strong intermolecular forces combined with good fit favors crystallization of linear polymers, and in branched polymers favors high modulus, ultimate tensile strength, tear strength, density, hardness and glass transition temperature, and relatively low swelling by solvents. Potentially strong intermolecular forces cannot operate to their fullest in moderate to highly cross-linked polymers because the branch points reduce the "fit" of the chains, thus keeping many of the attracting groups too far apart to realize their maximum effectiveness.

3. *Stiffness of Chain Units*

Chain units having very limited rotational or configurational possibilities tend to stiffen polymer chains. Such units are best typified by aromatic rings, where the ring itself is a rigid unit. Such a stiffening effect favors high melting point, glass transition temperature, hardness, strength, and reduced elasticity and solubility. On the other hand, groups which impart a high order of flexibility because of unusual ease of rotation favor softness, flexibility, elasticity, low melting point, and low glass transition temperature. An example of a very flexible group is the ether group.

4. *Crystallization*

Crystallization in polymers is promoted by linearity, close and regular "fit" of polymer chains, strong intermolecular forces, and stiff units in the chain which restrict rotation. In many ways the effects of crystallization are similar to those of cross linking: reduction of solubility, flexibility, elasticity, and elongation, and increase of hardness, tensile strength and melting point. The bonding of one chain to another by crystalline forces is different from that by true cross linking in that the crystalline portion of the polymer may be disrupted reversibly by heat (melting).

5. *Ease of Rotation of Chain Segments*

The ease of rotation of chain segments has a great influence on the properties of a polymer, and is a function of temperature and polymer structure. The "glass transition temperature" (T_g) of a polymer is that temperature at which molecular segments begin to rotate. An ideal noncrystalline polymer is a glass below T_g and is an elastomer at temperatures above T_g. Thus, plastics normally have T_g values above the use temperature, whereas elastomers have T_g values below the use temperature.

The glass transition temperature is normally increased, corresponding to reduced ease of rotation, by increases in cross linking, intermolecular forces, molecular weight (to a limiting value), substituent groups bulky enough to hinder rotation, and stiff groups of limited rotational possibilities. T_g is usually decreased (greater ease of rotation) by reduction in cross linking, intermolecular forces, and molecular weight (in limits), by increases in the number of flexible groups, by substituent groups of the right size and stereo relationship to keep chains apart yet not large enough to hinder rotation by their own bulk, and by plasticizers.

6. *Cross Linking*

The cross linking of polymer chains is of primary importance in controlling many polymer properties. Large increases in the degree of cross linking make amorphous polymers more rigid and cause them to have higher softening points and higher modulus, reduce elongation and swelling by solvents, and raise the glass transition temperatures. Polymers which are largely crystalline may be affected differently by small increases in cross linking. The introduction of a few cross links may first reduce the crystallization by reducing the possibility of chain orientation, thus may change the polymer from a high melting, hard, dense crystalline polymer to a more elastic, softer amorphous polymer. Further increases in cross linking may then have the effects noted first for amorphous polymers.

Many discussions of the effects of cross linking have appeared, and many terms have been used, with some resulting confusion. In this chapter the terms will be used in accordance with the following definitions:

Linear polymer. A polymer consisting of unbranched polymer chains. Such a polymer will be soluble in some appropriate nonreactive solvent.

Branched polymer. A polymer consisting of linear chains with one or more pendant chains attached to each linear chain, which is still soluble in some appropriate nonreactive solvent. A branched polymer may have a configuration such as I, II, or III.

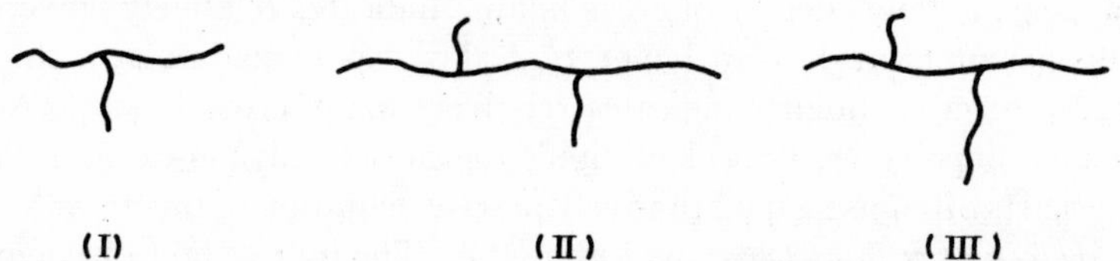

(I) (II) (III)

Cross-linked polymer. A polymer consisting of a series of chains, enough of which are connected by each end to other chains that the resulting polymer is not truly soluble in any nonreactive solvent. These connections are by primary chemical bonds. Thus, the distinction between the branched polymer and the cross-linked polymer is the criterion of solubility. The branched polymer will dissolve, the cross-linked polymer will only swell, in a nonreactive solvent. Of course, a cross-linked polymer may "dissolve" (irreversibly) in a reactive solvent; e.g., a cross-linked polyurethane may dissolve in alcoholic alkali because of hydrolysis.

The cross-linked polymer, actually a three-dimensional network, may be represented by IV. The points of junction of chain segments

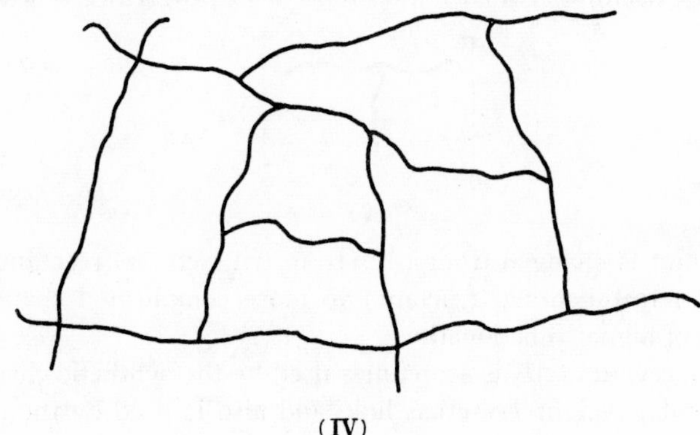

(IV)

are called interchangeably "cross links," "cross link sites," "branch points," and other similarly descriptive terms.

Sol. In a polymer mixture, that portion that is soluble in some appropriate nonreactive solvent; i.e., the linear and branched polymer molecules.

Gel. In a polymer mixture, that portion that is not soluble in some appropriate nonreactive solvent; i.e., the cross-linked polymer molecules.

Degree of cross linking. This term is used in a semiquantitative way, e.g., a "low" degree of cross linking indicates relatively few cross links per unit weight of polymer, typical of elastic materials; a "high" degree of cross linking indicates relatively many cross links per unit weight of polymer, typical of rigid, thermoset polymers. (Polymer physicists often use a quantitatively precise definition of this term.)

Molecular weight per cross link (M_c). The unit weight of polymer divided by the number of cross link junctions or branch points in the unit weight of polymer. For example, if a polyurethane were prepared from 1000 grams of reactants, using a stoichiometric ratio of reactants and 0.25 mole of triol in the 1000 grams, all other reactants being difunctional, the hypothetical molecular weight per cross link, assuming complete reaction of all end groups, would be 1000/0.25 or 4000. Such a value is probably a limiting low value—in many cases not quite all end groups will react as intended. This method of expressing the degree of cross linking is perhaps the most convenient and hence most widely used term by the synthetic polymer chemist. This value represents the molecular weight of the repeating T-shaped unit in the cross-linked polymer derived from a trifunctional monomer (V). The usefulness of such a term becomes progressively less as the

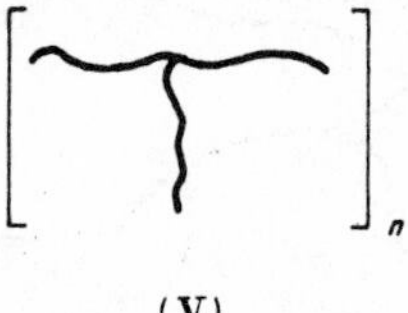

(V)

branch point is changed from a T (from trifunctional reactant) to an X (from tetrafunctional reactant) to more complicated shapes from reactants of higher functionality.

The abbreviation M_c is sometimes used by the synthetic chemist for the molecular weight *per* cross link, and also is used by the polymer physicist for the molecular weight *between* cross links (see the following discussion). Since this discussion is primarily for the synthetic polymer chemist, unless otherwise noted the abbreviation M_c will be used for the molecular weight per cross link, and numerical values will be expressed on that basis.

Molecular weight between cross links. The average molecular weight of chains connecting two cross link sites or branch points. Thus, in the polymer (VI) indicated, the segment l is a chain connecting two branch points or cross link sites, and the molecular weight between cross links is the average molecular weight of all such segments (VI). It is readily seen that this H-shaped repeating structure

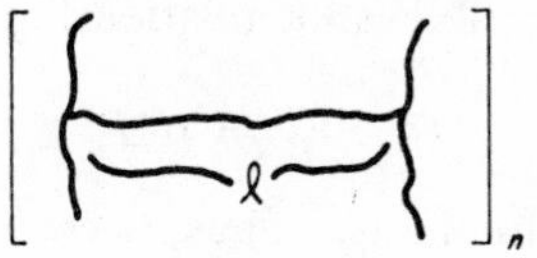

(VI)

is a combination of two T-shaped structures, and for these configurations of branch points the molecular weight *between* cross links is two-thirds of the M_c value. The usefulness of the term molecular weight between cross links also becomes obscure when the branch point is quite complicated, as in a polymer cross linked with sorbitol.

Effective chains per unit volume (ν_e/V). Perhaps the most precise term used by the polymer physicist, this expresses the number of moles of "effective" chains, i.e., chain segments connected at each end to other chains, per unit volume. This term is usually abbreviated ν_e/V, and often is expressed as moles of effective chains per milliliter or moles per 1000 grams of polymer.

Free ends. Polymer segments connected at only one end to another chain of the polymer. Free ends will result from the presence of monofunctional reactants or from the failure of a functional group to react in such a way that it builds into the polymer chain. Branched polymers have free ends, and free ends are essentially always present as imperfections in cross-linked polymers.

7. *Theory of Rubber Elasticity*

Elastic polymers, primarily hydrocarbon in nature, have been studied in great detail by many investigators. Several extremely useful relationships have been found. The "kinetic theory of rubber-like elasticity" (25,62,64) predicts that the tensile stress-strain curve is given by the equation:

$$S = (\nu_e/V)RT(\alpha - 1/\alpha^2) \qquad (1)$$

in which S is the stress based on the original cross sectional area of a tensile specimen, ν_e/V is the moles of effective chains per unit volume, R is the gas constant, T is the absolute temperature, and α is the principal extension ratio. (The quantity α is $(\gamma + 1)$, in which γ is the nominal strain, equal to $(\Delta l/l_0)$, Δl being the increase in length and l_0 the original length.)

The kinetic theory also shows the relationship:

$$G = (\nu_e/V)RT \qquad (2)$$

in which G is the shear modulus. Thus, G equals the slope of a plot of S against $(\alpha - 1/\alpha^2)$. Young's modulus, E, is equal to $3G$ for elastomers, and is equal to the initial slope of a plot of S against γ.

The kinetic theory expression of equation (1) usually does not represent quantitatively an experimental stress-strain curve. For most elastomers, however, a plot of αS against γ gives a straight line for elongations up to about 100%, and the slope equals E. This value of E is quite close to $3G$, in which G is obtained from the slope of a plot of S against $(\alpha - 1/\alpha^2)$.

The degree of cross linking affects the swelling by a solvent in a way analogous to its effect on the modulus. The following equation thus relates the degree of swelling to the equilibrium modulus of a trifunctional cross-linked material (25):

$$(-EV_1/3gRT)(\nu_2^{1/3}g^{2/3} - 2/3\nu_2) - \nu_2 - \ln(1 - \nu_2) = \chi_1\nu_2^2 \qquad (3)$$

in which E is the Young's modulus at absolute temperature T, V_1 is the molar volume of the solvent, g is the volume fraction of gel in the elastomer before swelling, ν_2 equals $1/q_m$ (q_m is the swelling ratio, V/V_o, where V is the volume of the swollen sample and V_o is the volume of the unswollen sample after the sol is removed), and χ_1 is the polymer-solvent interaction parameter. The value of χ_1 may change as the structure of the polymer chain and as the solvent change. When a satisfactory value for χ_1 is obtained the value of ν_e/V may be derived from equilibrium swelling data.

The present theory of rubber elasticity was derived for elastomers that are primarily hydrocarbon in nature, contain relatively few stiff units in the chain, and have relatively low van der Waals forces. It seems likely that significant modifications will be necessary in order to understand the polyurethanes satisfactorily.

Relatively few polymer physicists have turned their attention to polyurethanes thus far, but several papers in this field have recently appeared. The reader's attention is directed in particular to a series by Smith and Magnusson (62,63), who have combined the approach of the polymer physicist, the essential knowledge of the synthetic polymer chemist, and a clear style of reporting.

III. Influence of Component Group Structures in Urethanes

As noted earlier, urethane polymers may contain a variety of groups in the polymer chain, including hydrocarbon, urethane, urea, ester, ether, and aromatic. The ether groups are relatively flexible and the aromatic groups are rigid, while the aromatic and ester groups contribute moderate intermolecular forces and the urea and urethane groups contribute very strong intermolecular forces.

TABLE I[a]
Molar Cohesive Energy of Organic Groups

Group	Cohesive energy, kcal./mole
—CH_2— (Hydrocarbon)	0.68
—O— (Ether)	1.00
—COO— (Ester)	2.90
—C_6H_4— (Aromatic)	3.90
—CONH— (Amide)	8.50
—OCONH— (Urethane)	8.74

[a] Taken from ref. 14.

The relative contribution of the various groups to intermolecular forces may be illustrated by the "molar cohesive energy" of the different groups in small molecules (14). High values indicate strong attractions (Table I). Many other estimates of molar cohesive energies have been given, but the trends are similar in all. The urea group may safely be assumed to have an even greater molar cohesive energy than the urethane group.

The effects of the molar cohesion of groups on the properties of fibers have been summarized (e.g., see references 14 and 31). The relation between melting point and the number of chain atoms in a repeating unit is shown in Figure 1 for polyureas, polyamides, poly-

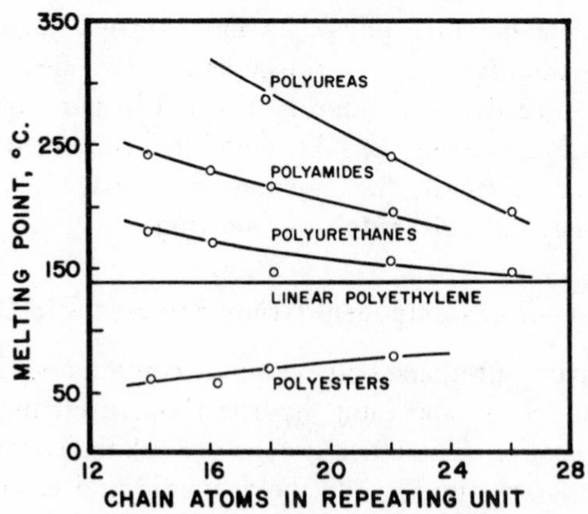

Fig. 1. Trend of melting points in homologous series of polymers. (Taken from ref. 31.)

urethanes, hydrocarbons, and polyesters (31). These data illustrate the greater molar cohesive energy of urea groups compared to urethane and amide groups.

In the systems polyureas, polyamides, and polyurethanes the melting points decrease as the content of strongly attracting groups decreases; i.e., as degree of molar cohesion decreases. In contrast, the content of ester groups has little effect on the melting point. This behavior is considered evidence for the flexible character of the C—O—C group in the ester, which tends to offset the moderately strong cohesive energy of the ester group. The flexibility of this C—O—C linkage also accounts for the lower melting point of a urethane compared to a polyamide of equivalent structure.

Although ester group concentration has relatively little effect on the melting point of polyesters, a somewhat different result may be expected in polyester-urethanes or polyester-ureas. In these mixed polymers containing strong hydrogen donor groups, the ester group may be expected to participate much more in hydrogen bonding than in pure polyesters. As will be shown later in the section on elastomers, an increase in ester group concentration in polyester-urethanes may be expected to have a net increase in the strength of the polymer aggregate.

The flexible effect of the C—O—C group is also shown in the melting point of poly(oxethylenes). Although the molar cohesive energy of this group is higher (1.00) than that of the methylene group (0.68), the melting point of the polyether is only 55–70°C. compared to 110°C. (31) or higher for polyethylene. This flexible effect is the result of reduced hindrance to rotation about the C—O bond compared to that of the C—C bond. In ethane the restriction to rotation about the C—C bond is of the order of 3000 cal./mole because of mutual repulsion of the hydrogens in one methyl group for those in the other methyl group. When these methyl groups are separated by an ether oxygen the hydrogens of one methyl group are sufficiently far from the hydrogens of the other that rotation is much easier.

The flexible ether and thioether groups produce a similar effect on the melting points of urethanes as shown by Bayer (7). Data are given in Table II.

TABLE II[a]

Influence of Ether Groups on Urethane Melting Points (urethanes from hexamethylene diisocyanate)

Glycol	Urethane m.p., °C.
$HO(CH_2)_5OH$	151
$HO(CH_2)_2O(CH_2)_2OH$	120
$HO(CH_2)_2S(CH_2)_2OH$	129–134
$HO(CH_2)_9OH$	147
$HO(CH_2)_4O(CH_2)_4OH$	124
$HO(CH_2)_4S(CH_2)_4OH$	120–125

[a] Taken from ref. 7.

The influence of rigid aromatic rings on polymer properties is generally opposite to that of the ether groups, as illustrated by the influence on melting points (Table III).

The geometric fit of polymer molecules limits the effectiveness of strongly attracting groups. This has been illustrated classically by the familiar "zig-zag" effect of structure on melting point. Thus, in polyurethanes of structure (VII) Bayer (7) showed by molecular

$$-\left[\overset{\overset{\displaystyle O}{\|}}{C}NH(CH_2)_nNH\overset{\overset{\displaystyle O}{\|}}{C}O(CH_2)_{n'}O\right]_x$$

(VII)

TABLE III[a]
Effect of Aromatic Rings on Urethane Melting Points

Urethane components		Urethane m.p., °C.	Ref
Diisocyanate	Glycol		
$OCN(CH_2)_8NCO$	$HOCH_2-C_6H_4-CH_2OH$	168	7
$OCN(CH_2)_8NCO$	$HO(CH_2)_6OH$	153	7
m-$C_6H_4(NCO)_2$	$HO(CH_2)_6OH$	230	15
$OCN(CH_2)_4NCO$	$HO(CH_2)_6OH$	180	7

[a] Taken from ref. 56.

models or space drawings that when n and n' are even the fit of each hydrogen donor group (NH) to each electron donor group (C=O) should be relatively easy, whereas when n or n' is odd the fit should not be perfect. Thus, with an irregular structure (n is odd and fit is poor) not all groups should participate in hydrogen bonding, intermolecular attractions should be weaker, and the melting point should be lower. This effect is illustrated in Figure 2 by melting points of

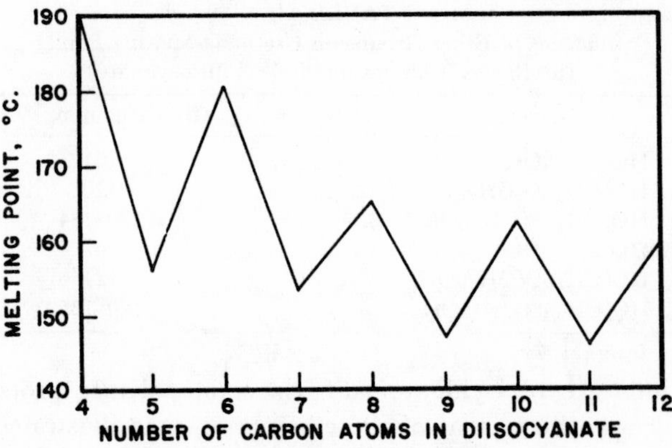

Fig. 2. Melting points of polyurethanes from 1,4-butanediol and aliphatic diisocyanates. (Taken from ref. 7.)

a series of such polymers, which Bayer obtained from 1,4-butanediol and aliphatic diisocyanates (7).

Recent infrared data reported by Trifan and Terenzi (66) indicate less difference in hydrogen bonding between the "even" and "odd" urethanes and polyamides than expected based on melting point behavior. The nonhydrogen-bonded NH absorption band at 2.90 μ indicated about 1% nonbonded NH in both "even" and "odd" urethanes and essentially 0% for polyamides. The effect of temperature on hydrogen bonds was shown for a 6–10 urethane, which had 0.79% nonbonded NH at 23°C., increasing fairly regularly to 4.36% at 125°C., then to 15.96% at 175°C. For comparison, a 6-6 polyamide showed 0% nonbonded NH at 22°C., 1.84% at 150°C., and 3.19% at 200°C. The activation energy for hydrogen bond dissociation was calculated to be 8.36 kcal./mole for a 6-8 urethane, 10.5 for a 6-9 urethane, and 7.3 for a 6-6 polyamide. These data suggest that the mechanical properties of a polymer may be more sensitive to variations in the effective strength of hydrogen bonds than is the infrared absorption. The influences of these component features of urethanes are further illustrated in the following discussions of elastomer and foam properties.

IV. Urethane Elastomers

The urethane elastomers are usually prepared from a long chain diol such as linear polyester or polyether of molecular weight 1000 to 2000, a diisocyanate, and a low molecular weight "chain extender" such as a glycol or diamine. While several reaction sequences may be used, one of the most successful is the "prepolymer" method. In the first step (eq. 4) the diol is caused to react with an excess of

$$R(NCO)_2 + HO\sim\sim OH \rightarrow OCN—R—NHCOO\sim\sim OCONH—R—NCO \quad (4)$$

diisocyanate. The reaction product thus obtained is a moderate molecular weight liquid or low melting solid, and is called a "prepolymer." Terminating in isocyanate groups, it can undergo the usual isocyanate reactions.

The second step (eq. 5) in the process is the addition of a low molecular weight glycol or diamine. The ratio of reactants is usually chosen so that a slight excess of isocyanate groups is present.

$$(n + 1)OCNRNHCOO\sim\sim OCONHRNCO + nHOR'OH \rightarrow \quad (5)$$

$$OCN[RNHCOO\sim OCONHRNHCOOR'OCONH]_nRNHCOO\sim\sim OCONHRNCO$$

The final step may begin to take place while the second is still in process, and may continue slowly for several hours or even days, depending upon the system and the temperature. This final curing step (eq. 6) may be assumed to involve reaction of terminal isocyanate groups with active hydrogen-containing groups in the polymer chain, e.g., urethane groups, to give allophanate branch points:

$$\sim R{-}\underset{H}{N}COO\sim OCO\underset{H}{N}{-}R{-}\underset{H}{N}COO{-}R'{-}OCO\underset{H}{N}{-}R\sim \; + \sim R{-}NCO \rightarrow$$

$$\sim R{-}\underset{H}{N}COO\sim OCO\underset{\underset{\underset{H}{CON}-R\sim}{|}}{N}{-}R{-}\underset{H}{N}COO{-}R{-}OCO\underset{H}{N}{-}R\sim \qquad (6)$$

When the polymer chain also contains urea groups, e.g., from water in the system or from amine chain extenders, the reaction of isocyanate with urea groups will lead to biuret branch points (eq. 7).

$$\sim R{-}NHCONH{-}R\sim + \sim R{-}NCO \rightarrow \sim R{-}\underset{\underset{CONHR\sim}{|}}{N}CONH{-}R\sim \qquad (7)$$

When both urea and urethane groups are present in the polymer chain in nearly equal amounts, most branch points may be expected to be biuret, because of the much faster rate of reaction of urea groups with isocyanate, compared to the urethane-isocyanate reaction. The relative rates of formation and thermal stability of these branch points were reviewed recently (55); see also Chapter IV.

In such systems the extent of cross linking may be controlled by the ratio of isocyanate groups to total active hydrogen groups. The ratio must be greater than 1.0 to provide cross linking. One may also add a trifunctional reactant to provide the desired degree of cross linking.

These reaction sequences apply primarily to uncatalyzed reactions. The choice of catalyst can force certain of these reactions at accelerated rates, and may also introduce other reactions such trimerization and carbodiimide formation (see Chapter V).

Obviously, a great variety of structures in the polymer chain is possible, depending on the nature and molecular weight of the diol and the ratios of reactants. One may consider the urethane elastomers to be block copolymers, where the length and structure of each block may be controlled within broad limits. Thus a typical elastomer may be represented by formula (VIII), in which *E* designates the repeating ester unit, *A* the aromatic portion of the isocyanate, *U* the urethane group, *G* a glycol extender, and *UU* the allophanate branch point. Thus, the polymer contains a moderately flexible, long, linear polyester segment, then a relatively stiff segment composed largely of aromatic and urethane groups. Branching can occur only at these stiff segments

```
~~[EEEEEEEEEEUAUGUAUGUAU]nEE~~
                     U
                     A
                     U
                     G
                     U
                     A
                     U
                     E
                     E
                     ~
```

(VIII)

(if the polyester or polyether was linear). The average length of the stiff aromatic-urethane segment can be controlled, as can the number of branch points. Furthermore, the flexibility of the linear portion may be controlled by the choice of a very flexible polyether or polyesters of moderate to low flexibility. The stiffness of the aromatic-urethane portion may be controlled in part by the choice of isocyanate, e.g., 1,5-naphthalene diisocyanate providing greater rigidity than 2,4-tolylene diisocyanate (or, in an extreme case, than 1,6-hexamethylene diisocyanate). The urethane portion may also serve as a means of control, with greater rigidity being obtained from glycol extenders which contain aromatic nuclei, compared to aliphatic glycols. Even greater rigidity is realized if one uses an aromatic diamine as an extender, giving urea groups in the chain. The amount of cross linking may be controlled by adjusting the ratio of isocyanate groups to the total of all active hydrogen groups in the reactants, or by using tri (or higher) functional chain extenders, such as triols.

In terms of polymer interactions, one may consider that the properties of these elastomers are the result of a combination of segment flexibility, chain entanglement, orientation of segments, hydrogen bonding and other van der Waals forces, the rigidity of aromatic units, and cross linking. The urethane elastomers differ from the more familiar olefin-derived elastomers in that hydrogen bonding and other van der Waals forces play a much more pronounced role in the urethane systems.

This interpretation of the chemistry of elastomer structure is an extension of the early discussions of Bayer and co-workers, the pioneers in the field (8,41). More recently Bayer and Müller (9,42) published discussions of the chemistry of elastomer formation and structure similar to this presentation.

The first work in the elastomer field used polyesters for the flexible portion of the molecule. Later work with polyethers of the 1,4-oxybutylene and 1,2-oxypropylene types extended the range of flexibility and softness, as a result of the more flexible polyether chain.

1. Polyester-Urethane Elastomers

The initial research with polyester urethane elastomers by Bayer and co-workers (8) employed water as a curing agent, rather than the glycol used in the illustration of the urethane elastomer chemistry. With poly(ethylene adipate) and water as the curing agent, the effect of isocyanate structure on elastomer properties is illustrated in Table IV. The polyester molecular weight was 2000; 30% excess diisocyanate was used, based on the polyester. It was concluded from these and other similar data that large, bulky aromatic rings contributed greatly to the strength of the elastomer. The effect of polyester structure on properties of this system, with 1,5-naphthalene diisocyanate, is illustrated by examples in Table V. The weakening effect of the substituent methyl groups, forcing chains apart, is apparent.

TABLE IV[a]
Effect of Isocyanate Structure on Elastomer Properties

Diisocyanate	Tensile strength, p.s.i.	Elongation, %	Tear strength,[b] p.s.i.
Hexamethylene	"Worthless"	—	—
2,4-Tolylene	2850–3550	730	1180
1,5-Naphthalene	4400	765	2370
2,7-Fluorene	6200	660	2020

[a] Taken from refs. 8, 56.
[b] Measured on rings cut from 4 cm. plates, 1 mm. notched, converted to p.s.i., "ring method."

TABLE V[a]
Effect of Polyester Structure on Elastomer Properties

Glycol	Acid	Tensile strength, p.s.i.	Elongation, %	Tear strength,[b] p.s.i.
Ethylene	Succinic	3900	625	1700
Ethylene	Adipic	5000	640	2250
Ethylene	Diglycolic	3800	570	2100
1,2-Propylene	Adipic	3100	780	1300
2,3-Butylene	Adipic	2550	630	1300

[a] Taken from refs. 8, 56.
[b] Ring method, see footnote Table IV.

Poly(ethylene adipate) was chosen to illustrate the relation between polyester molecular weight and properties. In these experiments the naphthalene diisocyanate concentration was changed progressively, so that property changes reflect the influence of changes in molecular weight of the polyester, weight per cent urethane, and aromatic and urea groups (Table VI). These changes in polyester molecular weight

TABLE VI[a]

Effect of Changing Polyester Molecular Weight and Diisocyanate Content

Polyester mol. wt.	Diisocyanate, g./100 g. ester	Tensile strength, p.s.i.	Elongation, %	300% modulus, p.s.i.	Tear strength,[b] p.s.i.	Elasticity, %	Hardness (Shore A)
2290[c]	15.2	5600	680	1330	2700	58	65–71
3500	11.9	4950	560	1860	3560	65	67–73
3100	12.6	4300	610	1580	2450	59	68–73
2440	14.6	5000	645	1600	2650	59	71–76
2080	16.2	5500	635	1850	2650	60	71–76
1385	21.6	5300	645	1560	1780	50	74–77

[a] Taken from refs. 8, 56.
[b] Ring method, see footnote Table IV.
[c] This polyester sample was not purified by fractionation; others were.

and other structural features had only moderate influence on initial properties, but upon storage the elastomers from the higher molecular weight polyesters crystallized slowly. The lowest molecular weight polyester (1385) gave elastomers with the least tendency to crystallize. Because of relatively low tear strength and elasticity with this molecular weight, a weight of approximately 2000 was preferred.

Other experiments in which the polyester molecular weight was varied from 1180 to 4680, using in each case approximately 50% excess naphthalene diisocyanate, showed that modulus and hardness increased somewhat, while tensile, elongation, and tear strength decreased moderately as the molecular weight of the polyester decreased. Relatively little difference was noted in these properties for molecular weights in the range of 2160 to 4680, most of the change occurring between 1180 and 2160. Again crystallization of the elastomer was more extensive at the higher polyester molecular weights.

Based on these studies, a polyester molecular weight of approximately 2000 was chosen as optimum. With poly(ethylene adipate) of this molecular weight, and 16 parts by weight of 1,5-naphthalene diisocyanate per 100 of polyester, the effect of several curing agents is shown in Table VII (41). The use of the thiodiethylene glycol,

TABLE VII[a]
Effect of Curing Agent on Polyester Elastomers

Curing agent	Tensile strength, p.s.i.	Elongation, %	300% modulus, p.s.i.	Tear strength,[b] p.s.i.	Elasticity, %	Hardness (Shore A)
Water[c]	5600	680	1330	2700	58	65–71
1,4-Butanediol	4800	700	1050	2100	59	84
Thiodiethylene glycol	3400	545	480	1750	69	62
o-Dichlorobenzidine	3000	271	1500	2800	53	80

[a] Taken from refs. 41, 56.
[b] Ring method, see footnote Table IV.
[c] Data from ref. 8, included for comparison.

containing the flexible thioether group, resulted in lower modulus, tear strength, and hardness, but greater elasticity. In contrast, the use of the aromatic diamine, introducing additional rigid aromatic rings and the strongly polar urea groups, gave high modulus and tear strength, but reduced elasticity.

A further study of the effect of diamine (41) compared to water (8) as curing agent is shown for several diisocyanates in Table VIII.

These original investigations showed the beneficial effect of strong intermolecular attractions (high modulus and tear strength with diamine curing, leading to urea groups) and considerable rigidity in a portion of the chain (bulky aromatic diisocyanates and aromatic diamine curing agents) favoring high tear strength and modulus. Extending the linear, polyester component of the chain to too great a segment length favored crystallization during storage. The introduction of small substituents on the polyester chain (methyl side groups in the glycols) apparently reduced the effectiveness of intermolecular forces, lowering tensile strength, modulus, and tear strength. Flexible groups such as thioether in the curing agent reduced tensile strength, modulus, tear strength, and hardness.

More recent data reported by Pigott and co-workers (47) confirm the results of Bayer and co-workers and add considerably to an understanding of the elastomers.

In all of these experiments the equivalent ratios were maintained constant (0.1 equivalent of polyester, 0.32 of diisocyanate, and 0.2 of of extender). Using 1,4-butanediol as the chain extender and poly-

TABLE VIII[a]

Comparison of Diamine[b] and Water as Curing Agents

Diisocyanate	Curing agent	Tensile strength, p.s.i.	Elongation, %	300% modulus, p.s.i.	Tear strength,[c] p.s.i.	Elasticity, %	Hardness (Shore A)
2,4-Tolylene	Dianisidine	3900	635	450	2600	37	58
2,4-Tolylene	2,4-TDA	4000	720	500	2050	51	60
2,4-Tolylene	Water	2850–3550	730	—	1180	—	—
Hexamethylene	MDA	3850	680	1150	3000	53	90
Hexamethylene	Dianisidine	3100	650	720	1450	55	77
Hexamethylene	2,4-TDA	3800	710	570	2050	57	69
Hexamethylene	2,4-TDA[d]	1800	707	370	1600	54	70
Hexamethylene	Water[d]	3350	1000	—	825	—	—

[a] Taken from refs. 8, 41, 56.

[b] TDA is tolylenediamine, MDA is 4,4′-diaminodiphenylmethane.

[c] Ring method, see footnote, Table IV.

[d] Prepared with poly(1,2-propylene adipate), others with poly(ethylene adipate), both polyesters of molecular weight 2000.

(ethylene adipate) of molecular weight 2000, the study of diisocyanate structure was repeated. General trends are similar to those observed by Bayer in the water-extended systems (Table IX). It can readily

TABLE IX[a]
Physical Properties of Glycol-Cured Polyester-Urethane Elastomers as Influenced by Diisocyanate

Diiso-cyanate[b]	Tensile strength, p.s.i.	Elongation, %	Elongation Set, %	Modulus, p.s.i. (300% elong.)	Tear strength,[c] lb./in.	Hardness (Shore B)
NDI	4300	500	85	3000	200	80
p-PDI	6400	600	25	2300	300	72
TDI	4600	600	1	350	150	40
MDI	7900	600	10	1600	270	61
DMDI	5300	500	0	600	40	47
DPDI	3500	700	10	300	90	56
TODI	4000	400	10	2300	180	70

[a] Taken from ref. 47.
[b] NDI, 1,5-naphthalene diisocyanate. *p*-PDI, *p*-phenylene diisocyanate. TDI, 2,4-tolylene diisocyanate. MDI, 4,4′-diphenylmethane diisocyanate. DMDI, 3,3′-dimethyl-4,4′-diphenylmethane diisocyanate. DPDI, 4,4′-diphenylisopropylidine diisocyanate. TODI, 3,3′-dimethyl-4,4′-biphenyl diisocyanate.
[c] Split sample, FTMS-601/M4221 method.

be seen that large and rigid aromatic ring structures (NDI, TODI), symmetrical structure (NDI, *P*-PDI, MDI, TODI), and absence of methyl substituents (as present in TDI, DMDI, DPDI) favor high modulus, tear strength, and hardness.

The influence of the diisocyanate on low temperature properties of these urethane elastomers is shown in Figure 3, a plot of Clash-Berg torsional modulus against temperature. This figure indicates that the glass transition temperature was affected only moderately by the structure of the diisocyanate when compared to other changes to be discussed later.

Gross changes in the properties of the urethane elastomers could most readily be introduced by varying the structure of the major component of the polymer; i.e., the polyester. In all cases the elastomers were prepared from diphenylmethane diisocyanate and extended with 1,4-butanediol. Physical properties of the elastomers prepared from these polyesters are listed in Table X.

The following explanations of data in Table X are considered appropriate for polymers containing both ester groups and hydrogen

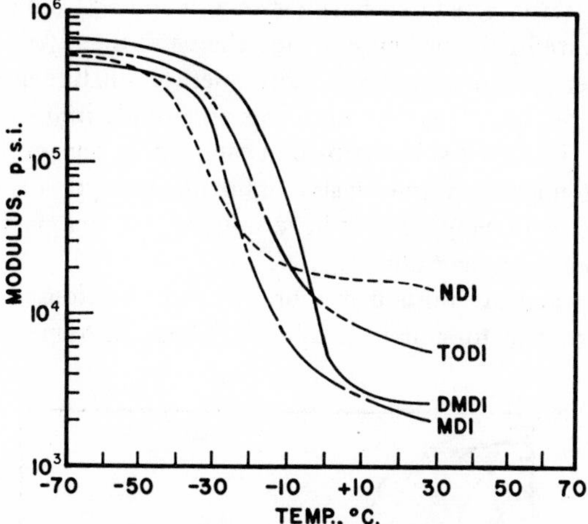

Fig. 3. Effect of diisocyanate on Clash-Berg modulus of polyester-urethane elastomers. System: poly(ethylene adipate), diisocyanate, 1,4-butanediol. NDI, 1,5-naphthalene diisocyanate; TODI, 4,4′-tolidine diisocyanate; DMDI, 3,3′-dimethyl-4,4′-diphenylmethane diisocyanate; MDI, 4,4′-diphenylmethane diisocyanate. (Taken from ref. 47.)

TABLE X[a]

Physical Properties of Cast Urethane Elastomers as Influenced by Polyester Structure

Polyester	Tensile strength, p.s.i.	Elongation %	Elongation Set, %	Modulus, p.s.i. (300% elong.)	Tear strength,[a] lb./in.	Hardness (Shore B)
Ethylene adipate	6900	590	15	1550	240	60
1,4-Butylene adipate	6000	510	15	1900	280	70
1,5-Pentylene adipate	6300	450	10	1800	60	60
1,3-Butylene adipate	3200	520	15	1100	100	58
Ethylene succinate	6800	420	40	3200	200	75
2,3-Butylene succinate	3500	380	105	[c]	520[d]	85
Neopentyl succinate	2600	400	70	2000	230	67

[a] Taken from ref. 47.
[b] Split sample FTMS-601/M4221 method.
[c] Exhibited cold drawing.
[d] Because of cold drawing this result is probably not a true tear value.

donor groups, e.g. urethane, so that the ester groups may participate in hydrogen bonding. Thus, the relations are somewhat different from what would be expected for pure polyesters.

Generally it was noted that tensile strength and 300% modulus were influenced more by the presence of side chains in the glycol component than by ester group separation, with methyl substituents reducing tensile and modulus. Tear strength was apparently influenced by both the presence of methyl side chains and ester group separation, since it decreased significantly in the elastomers made with poly(1,5-pentylene adipate) and with poly(1,3-butylene adipate) as compared to those made from poly(ethylene adipate).

Another practical consequence of this investigation is shown in Figure 4, a plot of torsional modulus for these elastomers as a func-

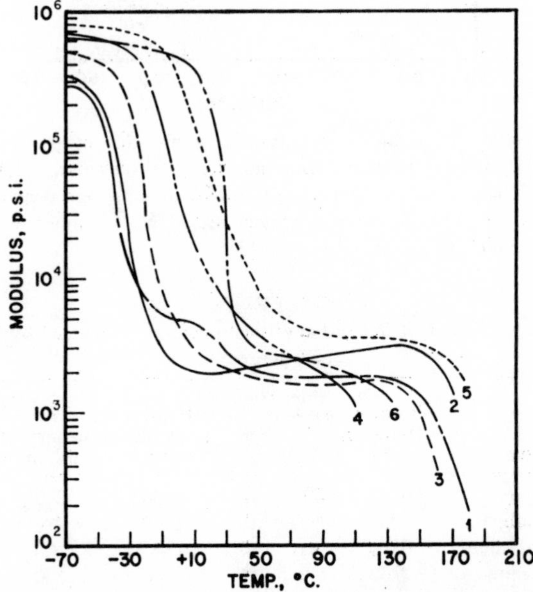

Fig. 4. Effect of polyester on Clash-Berg torsional modulus of polyester urethane elastomers. System: polyester, diphenylmethane diisocyanate, 1,4-butanediol. Polyesters: PBA, poly(1,4-butylene adipate); PPA, poly(1,5-pentylene adipate); PEA, poly(ethylene adipate); PNPS, poly(neopentyl succinate); PBS, poly(2,3-butylene succinate); PES, poly(ethylene succinate). Legend: (1) PBA; (2) PPA; (3) PEA; (4) PNPS; (5) PBS; (6) PES. (Taken from ref. 47.)

tion of temperature. The stiffening at low temperatures varied widely and was apparently dependent on the concentration of ester groups within the polyester. Curves (1) and (2) represent poly(1,4-butylene adipate) and poly(1,5-pentylene adipate) elastomers. These showed a significant decrease in the glass transition temperature compared to the polyethylene adipate elastomer, shown in curve (3). Closer spacing of ester groups as in the polyesters of succinic acid, curves (4), (5), and (6), resulted in the transition occurring at a higher temperature.

Generally, this study of variations in structure of polyesters showed that reducing the ester group concentration improved the low temperature flexibility and reduced the tear strength. An increase in the ester group concentration reduced flexibility at low temperatures, and at room temperature favored higher hardness values, higher modulus, and a marked increase in permanent elongation. These results may be attributed to increased van der Waals attractive forces.

To show the effects of different glycol chain extenders, Table XI lists the physical properties of elastomers from MDI and poly(ethylene adipate), extended with a homologous series of aliphatic glycols and one aromatic glycol. The changes in aliphatic glycol extender showed

TABLE XI[a]

Physical Properties of Cast Urethane Elastomers as Influenced by Glycols

Glycol	Tensile strength, p.s.i.	Elongation %	Elongation Set, %	Modulus p.s.i. (300% elong.)	Tear strength,[b] lb./in.	Hardness (Shore B)
Ethylene glycol	6500	500	20	2000	230	61
1,3-Propanediol	6600	600	15	950	270	61
1,4-Butanediol	7900	600	10	1000	270	61
1,5-Pentanediol	7100	600	10	900	280	62
1,6-Hexanediol	7400	500	5	850	170	60
Xylene-α,α'-diol	6600	500	20	2200	300	73

[a] Taken from ref. 47.

[b] Split sample, FTMS-601/M4221 method.

relatively little effect on properties, except for higher modulus with ethylene glycol. The physical properties of elastomer extended with the aromatic glycol showed higher tear, modulus, and hardness than for specimens extended with aliphatic glycols. These changes may be attributable to the greater rigidity of the aromatic glycol.

The influence of chain extenders was not as pronounced as that of either polyesters or diisocyanates. This was undoubtedly due to the relatively small quantity of extender used in comparison to the other constituents.

To this point, the influence of structural changes within the elastomeric polymer chain had been studied while maintaining essentially constant the type and amount of the primary cross linking present. Studies were also made on the effect of type and amount of chemical cross linking in the polymer. As pointed out previously, normal cross linking in the urethane elastomer of this type is reported to occur by reaction of terminal isocyanate groups with urethane groups to form allophanate linkages (8). Chemical cross linking was also obtained and controlled in another manner in these MDI-poly(ethylene adipate) elastomers: by substitution of a trifunctional hydroxyl compound in place of the normal glycol extender (47). In this case the degree of cross linking was a function of the amount of triol used.

Data for samples prepared by substituting trimethylolpropane for 1,4-butanediol are listed in Table XII in order of increasing average molecular weight per branch point, $\overline{M}_c$, or decreasing degree of cross-linking, calculated from the triol content of the reactants. (These

TABLE XII[a]

Physical Properties of Cast Polyester-Urethane Elastomers as Influenced by Chemical Cross Linking

M_c	Tensile strength,[b] p.s.i.	Elongation[b] %	Elongation[b] Set, %	Modulus, p.s.i. (100% elong.)[b]	Tear,[c] lb./in.	Hardness[d] (Shore B)	Compression,[e] set, %
2100	1800	170	0	570	30	57	1.5
3100	1750	200	0	420	25	53	16
4300	1450	280	0	300	30	49	10
5300	2800	350	0	270	30	46	5
7100	4500	410	0	330	40	51	25
10900	5600	490	5	460	60	55	40
21000	5500	510	10	500	140	56	45
∞	6750	640	15	630	300	61	55

[a] Taken from ref. 47.
[b] Tensile strength, elongation, elongation set, and modulus—ASTM 412.
[c] Tear strength measured with a split sample, FTMS-601/M4221.
[d] Hardness—ASTM 676.
[e] Compression set—ASTM 395, Method B, 70°C., for 22 hrs.

calculated values may be somewhat lower than the true values, but, as will be noted later, certain other systems free from monofunctional impurities have given good agreement between values calculated from the reactants and values calculated from the equilibrium modulus.) Decreasing the M_c values from 21,000 to 5300 resulted in decreased hardness, tensile, elongation, modulus, and tear strength, but increased elasticity and reduced creep as indicated by lower elongation set and compression set.

The relation between tensile modulus, volume swell in dimethylacetamide at 25°C. and calculated M_c values for these elastomers is shown in Figure 5. The volume swell data, a function only of primary

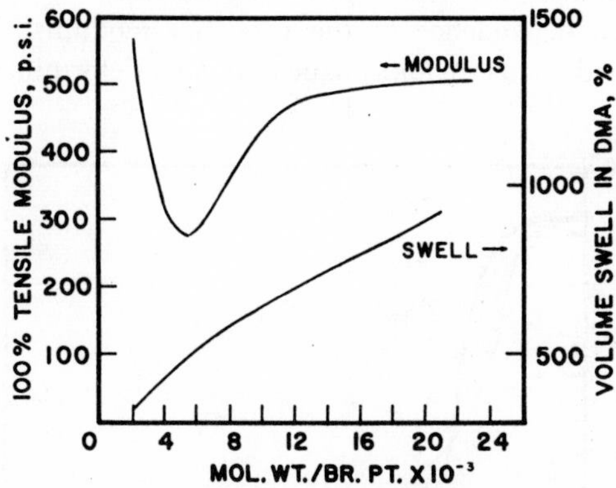

Fig. 5. Effect of M_c on modulus and swelling of a polyester urethane elastomer. System: poly(ethylene adipate), diphenylmethane diisocyanate, 1,4-butanediol, trimethylolpropane. DMA, dimethyl acetamide. (Taken from ref. 47.)

chemical cross links, confirm that progressive changes in cross linking were obtained as anticipated. These observations are contrary to results of similar work with hydrocarbon elastomers (e.g., see reference 32, p. 238), where increased cross linking results in increased modulus. In the case of the polyester-urethane elastomers it appears that increased chemical cross linking actually causes a general weakening of the polymer at room temperature. This is believed due to a reduction in orientation of chains and hence a reduction in probability of obtaining hydrogen bonding and benefit of other intermolecular attractive forces. In other words, with increased chemical cross linking, there is obtained a spatial separation of chains that reduces effective intermolecular attractions. A similar interpretation of this effect of cross linking has also been given by Quant (49). This observation in part confirms the belief that a major portion of the strength of urethane elastomers is due to forces other than primary valence bonding. In fact, Schollenberger and co-workers (59) have described a polyester-urethane elastomer which is reported to be linear, which is soluble in certain solvents, and which has excellent mechanical properties at room temperature. The properties of this elastomer were similarly attributed in large part to the intermolecular forces.

In this series, in the M_c range of 5300 to 2100, the modulus increased with lower M_c values, indicating that the primary cross links eventually became dominant in controlling modulus.

Temperature dependence of the torsional modulus of elastomers cross linked with trimethylolpropane was also determined. Figure 6

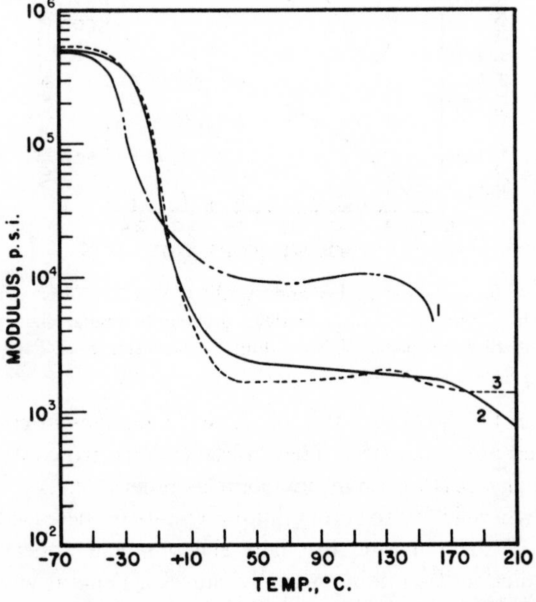

Fig. 6. The Clash-Berg torsional modulus of polyester-urethane elastomers. System: poly(ethylene adipate), diphenylmethane diisocyanate, Multrathane Extender XA, trimethylolpropane (TMP). Legend: (1) 0% TMP in extender; (2) 70% TMP in extender; (3) 100% TMP in extender.

shows the Clash-Berg torsional modulus for a series of Multrathane XA (an aromatic glycol)-trimethylolpropane cured elastomers. The modulus of a specimen containing no cross linking through triol cure (curve 1) was highest at 25°C. but fell off rapidly at 130–150°C. When 70% of the diol extender was replaced with the triol (curve 2), the room temperature modulus was lower but did not exhibit a significant decrease until a temperature of 170 to 190°C. had been reached. Complete substitution of triol for diol resulted in a still further extension of the temperature at which loss of modulus occurred (curve 3). This may be explained by consideration of the fact that hydrogen bonding and van der Waals forces are more readily disrupted by thermal means than is primary valence bonding. Where the hydrogen bonding and van der Waals forces were present in the greatest amount, as for curve 1, a material stronger and harder at room temperature was obtained, although its thermal stability was not as great as was that of the triol cross-linked elastomers. While the foregoing explains to a large extent the reasons for improved thermal stability of the polymers containing more cross linking obtained from the triol, it does not appear to be a complete explanation. It is believed that part of the improvement is due to the greater thermal stability of the urethane linkages (in the triol cross link) compared to that of the allophanate cross link (38,55).

As expected, increases in the degree of cross linking shifted the glass transition region somewhat toward higher temperatures.

A later paper by Pigott *et al.* (48) reported properties of polyester-urethane elastomers prepared similarly from an MDI-poly(ethylene adipate) prepolymer, Multrathane F-66, but with increasing amounts of MDI and 1,4-butanediol as a curing agent. Properties are shown in Table XIII. This series is particularly interesting because the changes in properties resulted from the increased aromatic and urethane contents, other structural features being kept essentially constant. Selected average properties are plotted against the aromatic (C_6H_4) content and urethane (NHCOO) content, calculated from the MDI content of the reactants. For convenience, the curve relating solenoid brittleness to properties was transposed by adding 60°C. to the experimental value, and multiplying by 80. This transposition exaggerates the effect, but permits showing the trend in convenient comparison with the trends in other properties (Fig. 7).

Several of the effects of polyester and diisocyanate structure reported by Pigott and co-workers were confirmed by Smith and Peterson (61). The effect of polyester structure on the elastomer brittle point was investigated in more detail. The most favorable example

TABLE XIII[a]

Relation of MDI-Polyester Elastomer Properties to Aromatic and Urethane Contents of the Polymer

F-66	100	100	100	100	100	100
Butanediol	6.5	9.1	11.7	16	21	26
MDI	—	7.2	14.3	28.7	42.8	57
Properties:						
Hardness, Shore A	80–85	83–85	88–91			
Shore D				50–55	55–60	66–69
Tensile, p.s.i.	6500–8000	6500–7500	6000–7000	5000–6000	4000–4500	3500–4500
Tensile modulus, p.s.i.						
100%	700–900	900–1050	1400–1600	2300–2400	—	—
200%	1000–1250	1450–1600	1900–2100	2750–2950	—	—
300%	1800–2000	2300–2700	2550–2750	3400–3800	—	—
Yield modulus, p.s.i.	—	—	—	—	2800–3100	3500–3800
at elongation, %	—	—	—	—	30–40	30–40
Elongation, %	550–650	500–600	500–600	380–480	250–350	300–350
Elongation set, %	10–20	15–30	40–60	60–80	—	—
Tear strength, lb./in.[b]	200–300	200–350	400–600	600–700	450–600	500–650
Solenoid brittleness, °C.	−50	−40	—	—	−20 to −30	−10 to −20
Compression deflection, p.s.i.						
at 4% deflection		80	310	575	765	1300
at 10% deflection		235	720	1500	1680	3350

[a] Taken from ref. 48.

[b] Split tear, FTMS-601/M4221.

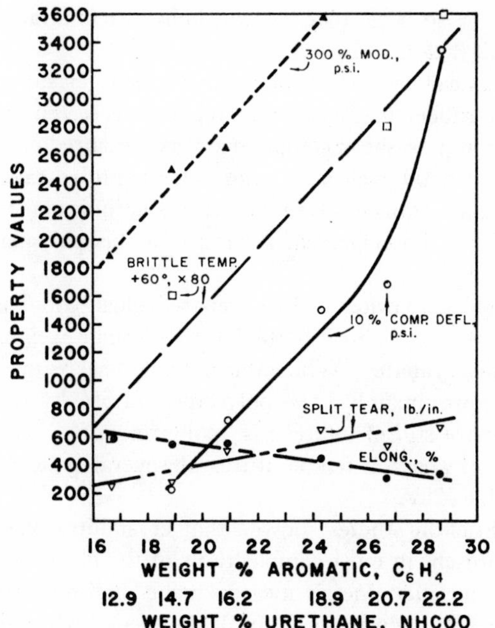

Fig. 7. Relation between properties of certain polyester-urethane elastomers and aromatic plus urethane content. (Data from ref. 48.)

was the elastomer from MDI and the adipate polyester from a 70:30 mixture of 1,5-pentanediol and diethylene glycol, the prepolymer being cured with 1,4-butanediol. The low temperature brittleness (by an unspecified method) was −80°C.

The effect of short branches in polyester-urethane elastomers was studied by Boivin (11), with emphasis being placed on the low temperature flexibility of the polymers. The polyesters were prepared from a series of glycols, $RN[CH_2CH(CH_3)OH]_2$ and cured with TDI. The Gehman freeze point was measured for each elastomer. Although the results were not conclusive, the data indicated that, as R progressed from C_3 to C_6, the freezing temperature was lowered. When R was increased above C_6, the freezing temperature increased. This result is similar to the effect of the size of the short branch in polymeric *n*-alkyl acrylates (50). The C_{3-6} branches may serve to hold chains apart, yet not be so large as to hinder rotation of polymer segments by their own bulk. On the other hand, the branch larger than C_6 may be so large that its own bulk is a hindrance to rotation, with the result that T_g is raised.

The mechanical properties of a polyurethane elastomer, Vulkollan 18/40, in the rubber-to-glass transition zone were reported by Landel (39). The complex shear compliance was measured over a frequency range of 45 to 6000 cycles/sec. and a temperature range of —16 to 39°C. The glass transition temperature was indicated to be approximately —35°C. The chemical structure of this polymer was not revealed in detail.

Iwakura and co-workers (36) prepared block copolymers by joining two polyesters, each of 2000–3000 molecular weight, with hexamethylene diisocyanate. While the polymers were prepared from a mixture of approximately 95% polyester and 5% by weight of diisocyanate, they are still of interest as "polyurethanes." Tensile properties and glass transition temperatures of several typical polymers are shown in Table XIV.

X-ray diffraction studies showed that crystallites of each polyester block were present in most compositions of the block copolymers. In addition, volume dilatometric measurements indicated transition temperatures close to the melting point of the second polyester component of each copolymer.

These copolymers are analogous in some ways to the harder polyester-urethane elastomers, in which the diisocyanate-glycol derived polyurethane block would be analogous to the poly(ethylene terephthalate) block. As in the polyester-urethanes, increasing the percentage of stiff, aromatic-rich block, poly(ethylene terephthalate), raised the tensile modulus, reduced the elongation, and raised the glass transition temperature.

The effect of isocyanate structure on the properties of diamine-cured polyester urethanes was investigated by Blaich and Sampson (10) using methods similar to those of Pigott *et al.* The polyester was poly(ethylene adipate) of molecular weight 2000, and the diisocyanate/polyester molar ratio was 3.0; the prepolymers were cured with 3,3′-dichloro-4,4′-diaminodiphenylmethane. Results are shown in Table XV. Similar to the earlier experiments of Bayer and co-workers (e.g., see Table VII), the diamine-cured elastomers of Table XV had higher modulus, higher tear strength, and frequently higher tensile strength and lower elongation than the corresponding glycol-cured elastomers of Pigott and co-workers (Table IX). In addition, in the

TABLE XIV[a]

Properties of Block Copolymers from Poly(ethylene Terephthalate) (PET) and a Second Polyester

Second polyester	15 mole % PET			35 mole % PET			50 mole % PET		
	Tensile str., p.s.i.	Elong., %	T_g, °C.	Tensile str., p.s.i.	Elong., %	T_g, °C.	Tensile str., p.s.i.	Elong., %	T_g, °C.
Poly(ethylene succinate)	1560	6.7	5			27			35.5
Poly(ethylene adipate)	3400	700	−60	4050	500	−41	5300	100	−20
Poly(diethylene adipate)	1700	200		1900	113		4000	90	
Poly(ethylene azelate)	1650	400	−34	1280	13	−30			− 6
Poly(ethylene sebacate)			−24	2400	27	−15	2850	10	0

[a] Taken from ref. 36.

TABLE XV[a]

Effect of Isocyanate Structure on Properties of Diamine-Cured Polyester-Urethane Elastomers

Isocyanate	Hardness (Shore)	Tensile strength (p.s.i.)	Elongation, %	Modulus, p.s.i.		Split tear,[b] lb./in.	Compression set (B), %
				100%	300%		
2,4-Tolylene diisocyanate	40D	5700	490	1575	3340	270	—
m-Phenylene diisocyanate	85A	6800	500	1000	2960	550	74
p-Phenylene diisocyanate	53D	5960	450	1490	3980	350	—
m-Xylylene diisocyanate	87A	6000	550	1050	2750	170	30
4,4′-Diphenylmethane diisocyanate	42D	6975	430	1910	4490	300	26
3,3′-Dimethyl-4,4′-diphenylmethane diisocyanate	48D	5350	450	2320	4230	685	56
3,3′-Dimethyl-4,4′-biphenyl diisocyanate	53D	6550	450	2580	4745	690	57
3,3′-Dimethoxy-4,4′-biphenyl diisocyanate	45D	7500	510	1425	3400	—	—

[a] Taken from ref. 10. [b] Modified ASTM D571-52T.

amine-cured series the presence of methyl substituents on the isocyanate appeared to have somewhat less effect on properties than in the glycol-cured elastomers (Table IX).

A study of peroxide-cured polyester-urethane elastomers by Gruber and Keplinger (28) showed that increased concentrations of peroxide, which may be assumed to correspond to increases in degree of cross linking, caused a reduction in compression set and heat build-up in the Goodrich flexometer. At the same time the number of flexures before cracking in the DeMattia test was reduced as peroxide was increased. When loaded with 25% carbon black, both modulus and hardness increased with increasing peroxide. Data are not available to show the relation conclusively, but these increases in modulus and hardness may be associated with the presence of the filler, in light of the results of Pigott *et al.* (47) and data from Gruber and Keplinger showing that the modulus of the unloaded stock increased only slightly with cure time.

Gruber and Keplinger concluded from their study that the cross links in a peroxide-cured polyester-urethane elastomer were more stable with regard to creep and compression set at elevated temperatures and flexing than were the cross links in an "isocyanate-cured" elastomer. As noted by their observation that their isocyanate-cured elastomer was soluble in dimethylacetamide at advanced stages of cure, that elastomer almost surely was less cross linked than was the peroxide-cured elastomer. Furthermore, the cross links in their isocyanate-cured elastomer were most probably the relatively weak allophanate or biuret groups.

Tobolsky and co-workers have also studied the stress relaxation of urethane elastomers (19,44). Solvent swelling data were not available to show if the elastomers studied were actually cross linked by primary chemical bonds, and the methods of preparation also did not clarify this point. As noted by Gruber and Keplinger, certain glycol-cured elastomers may be soluble and hence not cross linked but at best only branched (28). Furthermore, if cross links were present they must have been of the relatively weak biuret or allophanate type. Stress relaxation was at the same rate for a polyether sample as for polyester-urethane elastomers, thus indicating that ester groups did not contribute to the rate of stress relaxation.

Thus far in the commercial growth of cast polyester-urethane elastomers the elastomers have probably been linear, branched, or only very slightly cross linked with primary chemical bands which were the relatively weak allophanate or biuret groups. Hydrogen bonding and other intermolecular forces have contributed largely to the strength. The research of Pigott and co-workers has indicated the improvements which may be achieved in compression set and high temperature modulus by cross linking with a triol, giving relatively strong cross links. It remains to be shown if the same cross links will also improve stress relaxation and flex fatigue.

2. *Polyether-Urethane Elastomers*

There has been extensive industrial research directed toward the production of urethane elastomers from polyethers of several structures. Elastomers from poly(1,4-oxybutylene) glycols have been prepared with many properties equal to those obtained from the polyester-urethanes. Elastomers having a wide variety of properties have also been prepared from the poly(1,2-oxypropylene) glycols.

Data are available for a series of polyether-urethane elastomers based on a prepolymer which may be assumed to have been obtained from two moles of 2,4-tolylene diisocyanate and poly(1,4-oxybutylene) glycol of 1600 to 1700 molecular weight (2,3,49).

The effect of changes in weight per cross link, calculated from the formulations given by Quant (49), are shown in Table XVI for a glycol-triol cured elastomer. The prepolymer was assumed to have a molecular weight of 2000 and the poly(oxypropylene) triol, "11-80," was assumed to have a molecular weight of 700.

TABLE XVI[a]

Effect of Changes in M_c for Glycol-Triol Cure of Poly(oxy-1,4-butylene) Glycol-Diisocyanate Prepolymer (1.00 equivalent of prepolymer)

Curing agents, equiv.	M_c	Tensile strength, p.s.i.	Elongation, %	100% Modulus,[b] p.s.i.	Hardness (Shore A)	Graves tear, lb./in
Hexanetriol, 1.0	2090	475	235	250	55	45
11-80, 1.0	3700	555	380	170	43	40
11-80, 0.6, plus pentanediol, 0.4	5800	1340	645	105	38	85
11-80, 0.6, plus P-425,[c] 0.4	6150	945	625	80	37	65

[a] Taken from refs. 49, 56. [b] Secant modulus, ASTM D638-52T. [c] Poly(oxypropylene glycol), mole weight 425.

In this series the modulus and hardness increased; the elongation and tear strength decreased as values of M_c decreased. This effect on modulus and hardness is opposite to that obtained with the polyester elastomers, indicating that the glycol-triol cured polyether elastomers do not benefit from the same degree of intermolecular forces as evidenced in the polyester series. The polyether-derived elastomers are more like the hydrocarbon elastomers in this respect. Such a relationship was to be anticipated from the very flexible character of the polyether chain segment.

The poly(oxy-1,4-butylene) glycol prepolymers, when cured with aromatic diamines (2,3), give relationships very similar to those obtained in the polyester systems. With the increased aromatic structure and greatly increased hydrogen bonding from the urea groups thus obtained, these polyether-urea-urethanes derive a large part of their strength from intermolecular forces, similar to the polyester-urethane elastomers.

The qualitative effect of changing the degree of cross linking is shown in Table XVII, in which the diamine curing agent, methylenebis(*o*-chloroaniline) (MOCA), was varied from 50 to 100% of that equivalent to the NCO of the prepolymer (2).

TABLE XVII[a]

Effect of Changes in Cross Linking on Poly(1,4-oxybutylene) Glycol, Amine-Cured Elastomers

MOCA, p.h.r.	6	9	11	13
NCO/NH_2 ratio	2.0	1.4	1.2	1.0
Tensile strength, p.s.i.	3500	4000	5000	4200
Elongation, %	350	350	440	480
Modulus, 100%, p.s.i.	800	1000	1000	1000
Hardness, Shore A	86	89	90	88
Compression set, 22 hr., 70°C., %	20	20	26	37
Split tear, ASTM D-470, lb./in.	22	35	50	75
Graves tear, lb./in.	450	490	500	490

[a] Taken from ref. 2.

At high NCO/NH_2 ratios one may assume that the excess NCO was consumed in the formation of biuret branch points. Thus increases in cross linking (increases in NCO/NH_2 ratio) resulted in reduced modulus, elongation, compression set, and tear strength (by the split tear method), as in the polyester elastomers. These data also illustrate the great differences in tear strengths obtained by different methods. Other data by Athey (3) showed that similar increases in cross linking resulted in lower hardness and compression set.

Sampson and Blaich (53) evaluated several aromatic diamines as curing agent for the TDI-poly(1,4-oxybutylene) glycol prepolymer having 4.0–4.3% NCO content. Each amine was used in a concentration equivalent to 87% of an NCO content of 4.0%. Data are shown in Table XVIII. When an amine with a functionality of 3.6 was used for curing, the final elastomer was low in tensile, elongation, and tear strength, apparently because of too much cross linking.

TABLE XVIII[a]
Properties of Diamine-Cured TDI-Poly(1,4-oxybutylene) Glycol Elastomers

Diamine	Hardness (Shore A)	Tensile strength, p.s.i.			Elongation, %	Graves tear, lb./in.
		Ultimate	100% modulus	300% modulus		
4,4′-Diaminodiphenylmethane	86	4420	1150	2050	520	535
3,3′-Dichloro-4,4′-diaminodiphenylmethane	91	5000	925	2100	450	475
Benzidine	86	4340	1190	2330	470	565
3,3′-Dimethylbenzidine	95	7000	1845	3130	550	675
3,3′-Dimethoxybenzidine	93	2470	745	1100	550	415
3,3′-Dichlorobenzidine	94	5450	1700	4070	390	625
p-Phenylenediamine	91	2320	1560	2320	300	645

[a] Taken from ref. 53.

It is apparent from these data that the *ortho* methyl and chlorine groups in these amine curing agents did not cause a reduction of properties as *ortho* methyl groups on the isocyanate did in the glycol-cured polyester-urethanes (Table IX). This result is similar to the experience with the diamine-cured polyester-urethanes (Table XV). The elastomers of Table XV and XVIII have in common the diamine cure, leading to urea groups in the polymer. In contrast the glycol-cured urethanes have essentially no urea groups. The data suggest that an *ortho* substituent on the aromatic ring adjacent to a urea group is less effective in reducing intermolecular forces than is an *ortho* substituent on an aromatic ring adjacent to the nitrogen in a urethane group.

The effect of cross link structure on the properties of similar polyether-urethane elastomers was investigated by Cluff and Gladding (16). The linear polyurethane used in this study had the structure IX

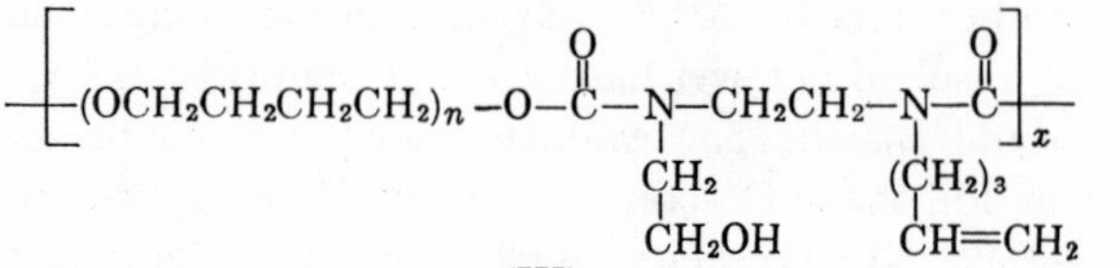

$$\left[(OCH_2CH_2CH_2CH_2)_n-O-\overset{O}{\overset{\|}{C}}-\underset{\underset{\underset{CH_2OH}{|}}{\underset{CH_2}{|}}}{N}-CH_2CH_2-\underset{\underset{\underset{CH=CH_2}{|}}{\underset{(CH_2)_3}{|}}}{N}-\overset{O}{\overset{\|}{C}} \right]_x$$

(IX)

and was synthesized by reacting the bischloroformate of poly(1,4-oxybutylene) glycol with *N*-(2-hydroxyethyl)-*N′*-pentenylethylenediamine in chloroform solution, using aqueous sodium carbonate as the acid acceptor. This polymer contained two types of cross-linking sites: pendant hydroxyl groups, suitable for curing with diisocyanates, and pendant vinyl groups for vulcanization with sulfur. The cross-linked elastomers were produced from the same linear polymer, thus keeping molecular weight, molecular weight distribution, interchain forces, and curing site distribution essentially constant. The average spacing of the cure sites along the chain was approximately 1200 molecular weight units. The molecular weight of the polymer as determined by light scattering was 195,000, and was 54,000 as measured by osmotic pressure.

Three curing agents were used for cross linking:

(*a*) 3,3′-Dimethoxy-4,4′-biphenyl diisocyanate.

(*b*) Isocyanate-terminated prepolymer of approximately 5000 molecular weight obtained by reacting four moles of poly(1,4-oxybutylene) glycol of approximately 1000 molecular weight and 5 moles of the above diisocyanate.

(*c*) A sulfur-accelerator system consisting of:

	Parts per hundred parts of elastomer
Sulfur	1.0
Mercaptobenzthiazole disulfide	4.0
Mercaptobenzthiazole	2.0
Mercaptobenzthiazole·$ZnCl_2$	0.7
Cadmium stearate	1.0

The vulcanizates were cured at 150°C. for two hours.

The cross link densities were determined by swelling elastomer samples in toluene and measuring the moduli either in extension or in compression. The cross link densities were computed from equation (8), in which ν_e/V are the moles of effective network chains per milli-

$$\nu_e/V = FV_r^{1/3}/[ART(\alpha - \alpha^{-2})] \qquad (8)$$

liter of polymer, F is the force in grams required to obtain an extension ratio of α, V_r is the volume fraction of the elastomer in the swollen sample, A is the cross sectional area of the unswollen sample, R is the gas content, and T is the absolute temperature. This equation has been shown to be valid for systems in which V_r is less than 0.25 (26,27).

Concentration of effective network chains, a measure of cross link density, was employed as a parameter to correlate physical properties and cross link structure. Modulus, hardness, and resilience (25 and 150°C.) of the cured polyether-urethane elastomer were found to be independent of both the chemical nature and the chain length of the curing agent. These conclusions were drawn from the results shown in Figure 8. However, compression set data (22 hr. at 70°C. and

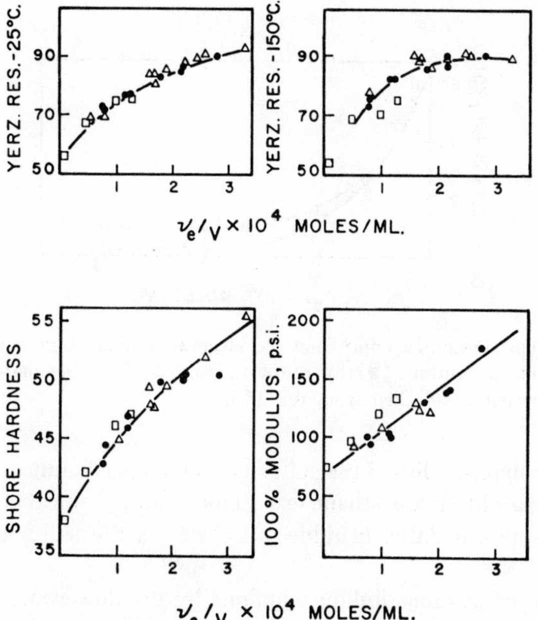

Fig. 8. Dependence of resilience, modulus, and hardness on network chain concentration: (△) vulcanization by sulfur, (●) by diisocyanate, (□) by isocyanate-terminated polyether urethane. (Taken from ref. 16.)

70 hr. at 100°C.) distinguished between the isocyanate and sulfur cure, with the sulfur cures exhibiting consistently higher set values at equiva-

lent cross link densities. This relationship is shown in Figure 9. The dfference in compression set can at least be partly explained by the

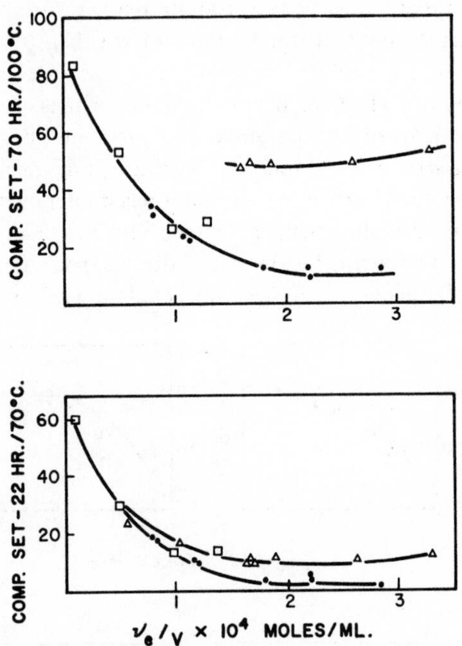

Fig. 9. Dependence of compression set on network chain concentration: (△) vulcanization by sulfur, (●) by diisocyanate, (□) by isocyanate-terminated polyether urethane. (Taken from ref. 16.)

poorer thermal stability of the sulfur cross link, predominantly disulfide type, compared to the urethane cross link. Both physical and chemical evidence supported the disulfide structure for the sulfur-cured cross link.

The degree of cross linking obtained by the diisocyanate cure was found to be essentially theoretical. Thus the degree of cross linking calculated from the quantity of isocyanate used was the same as that calculated from the above equation relating the effective network chains per unit volume to the swelling by a solvent..

Additional experiments by Cluff, Gladding, and Rogan (18) provide further information on the effect of branched chain structure and cross linking on the properties of the polyether-urethane elastomers. A polymer of the following structure was used in these studies:

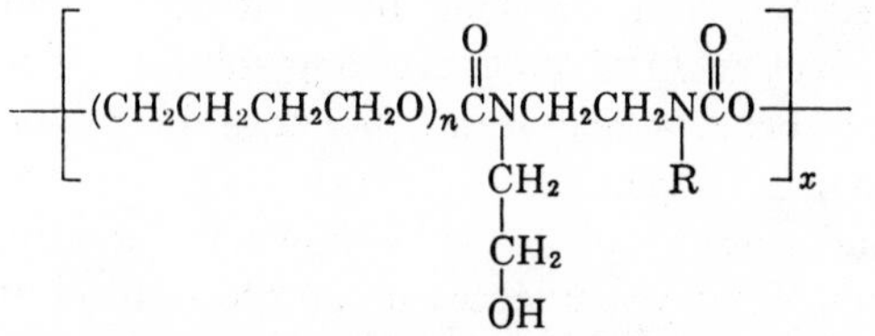

$$\left[-(CH_2CH_2CH_2CH_2O)_n\overset{\overset{O}{\|}}{C}\underset{\underset{\underset{OH}{|}}{\underset{CH_2}{|}}}{\underset{CH_2}{\underset{|}{N}}}CH_2CH_2\underset{\underset{R}{|}}{N}\overset{\overset{O}{\|}}{C}O- \right]_x$$

(I) R = H
(II) R = $(CH_2)_3CH{=}CH_2$

The technique of preparing this polymer was similar to that used previously by Cluff and Gladding (16).

Short chain branches were introduced by reaction of the pendant hydroxyl group with monoisocyanates of several structures. As the concentration of these short urethane branches was increased the ease of crystallization of the polymer was reduced. At a phenylurethane branch point concentration of 8.6×10^{-4} per gram, no crystallization could be induced at 0°, whereas only 0.7 hour was required for 50% of the ultimate crystallization to occur in the unsubstituted polymer.

Other more polar branches were introduced, as shown in Table XIX. In these experiments the monoisocyanate used was equivalent to 90% of the hydroxyl groups. Table XIX shows the effect of the polar

TABLE XIX[a]
Effect of Branch Structure on Polymer Properties

Structure of branch	Plasticity		Recovery		Intrinsic viscosity at 30°C.	
	30°C.	80°C.	30°C.	80°C.	THF/DMF	Benzene
$-CH_2CH_2-OH$ (Control)	90	48	6	0	1.24	1.08
$-CH_2CH_2O\overset{O}{\overset{\|}{C}}NHC_{10}H_7$	108	53	6	1	1.14	1.17
$-CH_2CH_2O\overset{O}{\overset{\|}{C}}NHC_7H_6NH\overset{O}{\overset{\|}{C}}OCH_3$	158	69	38	1	1.15	0.90
$-CH_2CH_2O\overset{O}{\overset{\|}{C}}NHC_7H_6NH\overset{O}{\overset{\|}{C}}NHC_7H_7$	196	91	59	6	1.29	0.60

[a] Taken from ref. 18.

branch on Williams plasticity at 30 and 80°C. and on the Williams recovery, as well as intrinsic viscosity in a good solvent (86.2% by weight tetrahydrofuran (THF), 13.8% dimethylformamide (DMF)) and in a poor solvent (benzene). The results suggest that the more polar side groups introduced interchain forces which increased the bulk viscosity and persisted for relatively long times at 30°C., but which had relatively little effect at 80°C. or in a strong solvent. The effect on intrinsic viscosity in benzene may be attributed to the coiling of the polar molecules in the poor solvent.

These short urethane and urea branches were shown to have no significant effect on modulus, Yerzley resilience, or compression set at 70°C.

A somewhat different type of polyether-urethane was also prepared for use in the further study of the effect of cross linking on properties. This polymer was prepared by the condensation of poly(1,4-oxybutylene) glycol of about 1000 molecular weight, trimethylolpropane, and 2,4-hexadiene-1-ol with 2,4-TDI. This provided a branched polymer terminating in a 1,3-diene structure. Curing was effected using a Diels-Alder reaction with a bisdieneophile, *m*-phenylenebismaleimide. It was found that curing such a branched polymer with 50–100% of the theoretical dienophile increased the modulus and Yerzley resilience and decreased the compression set as the curing agent concentration approached theoretical. This was interpreted to mean that elimination of long branches or free ends resulted in improving those properties. Since the increase in degree of cross linking achieved would also have given the same effect on the physical properties, the influence of the free ends does not appear to have been clearly established from these experiments. Other results did indicate, however, that the resilience of the polymer was reduced as the long chain branches were increased.

In a series of similar polymers having varying amounts of trimethylolpropane, complete cure of end groups was attempted; long chain branches were therefore kept to a minimum. The modulus and compression sets of these polymers were measured, as indicated in Figure 10.

During the course of their study of urethane elastomers, Cluff and co-workers (17) developed a rapid method for determining the degree of cross linking in elastomers. Previous physical methods for measuring the degree of cross linking involve determination of either equilibrium volume swell or equilibrium moduli (25,26). Equilibrium moduli are often determined in extension of solvent-swollen specimens. Instead of the measurement of equilibrium moduli in extension, which is more time consuming and more complicated, Cluff and co-

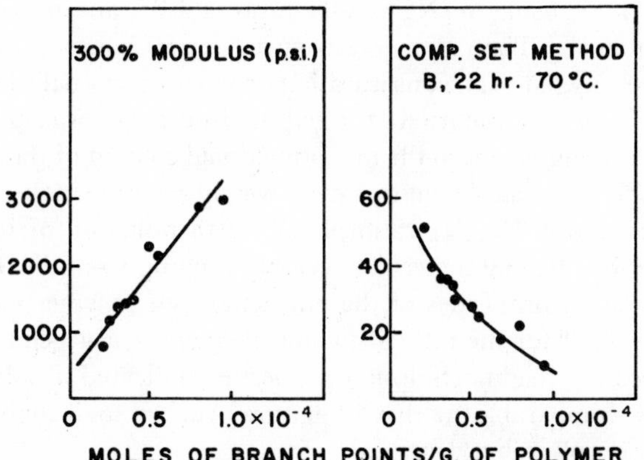

Fig. 10. Dependence of modulus and compression set in polyether-urethane elastomers on branch point concentration. (Taken from ref. 18.)

workers measured equilibrium compression at very small deformation on swollen samples of polyurethane elastomers. The measurements gave data suitable for the calculation of ν_e/V. The values of ν_e/V obtained from both compression and extension methods agreed within 1–3%. They were also in reasonable agreement with theoretical values for the elastomers studied, calculated from the amount of sulfur used in the vulcanization, the number-average molecular weight (about 100,000), and the assumption that cross links were of the disulfide type.

Poly(oxypropylene) glycols also have been used to prepare elastomers, often with a relatively low level of properties but with good elongation and good low temperature flexibility. Early research by Heiss and co-workers (30) in 1954 indicated the usefulness of these polyether glycols, and the screening of a wide variety of polyethers by Dickinson (24) in 1957 showed that a polyether molecular weight of 2000, with its associated lower percentages of aromatic and urethane groups in the elastomer, gave better low temperature flexibility than did a molecular weight of 1000. Poly(oxyethylene) glycols gave similar results, whereas the poly(1,4-oxybutylene) glycol elastomers gave the lowest approximate glass transition temperature of the types studied.

The dilute solution properties of a linear polyether-urethane were reported by Moacanin (40). This polymer was prepared by the bulk polymerization of poly(oxypropylene) glycol of molecular weight 2000 with 2,4-TDI, using an NCO/OH ratio of 1.05, and ferric acetylacetonate catalyst. The polymer was cured for 50 hours at 60°C. in the absence of oxygen. The unsaturation or monofunctional content of the polyether was not reported; the excess isocyanate was probably approximately equivalent to the monofunctional content of the polyether.

This polymer was shown to have a weight-average molecular weight of 36,500, and a M_w/M_n ratio of 1.7. Fractionation of the polymer gave fractions having molecular weights ranging from 8300 to 67,000. Dilute solution properties of the unfractionated polymer gave a value of 0.57×10^{-16} for the ratio of the mean-square end-to-end distance to the molecular weight. Solution properties indicated a polymer chain flexibility comparable to that of natural rubber and slightly greater than that of polyisobutylene.

A careful study of elastomers from poly(oxypropylene) glycol of 1790 molecular weight was reported by Smith and Magnusson (62). Dipropylene glycol or trimethylolpropane was added as necessary to control the concentration of urethane and aromatic groups and weight per cross link; 2,4-tolylene diisocyanate or hexamethylene diisocyanate was used.

Properties of the tolylene diisocyanate (TDI) elastomers are shown in Table XX, and those of the hexamethylene diisocyanate (HDI) elastomers are shown in Table XXI. (For consistency with other data

TABLE XX[a]
Properties of TDI-Poly(oxypropylene) Glycol Elastomers

M_c	Urethane wt., %	Aromatic wt. %	Tensile strength, p.s.i.	Elongation, %	T_g, °C.	Solvent[b] swell, vol. %
8500	8.4	5.8	110	190	−51	524
8500	9.3	6.5	110	180	−48	492
8500	10.9	7.6	140	220	−43	450
8500	13.6	9.5	250	340	−34	368
8500	17.0	11.9	2000	720	−24	300
2500	13.6	9.5	280	110	−34	216
4500	13.6	9.5	250	200	−34	275
6500	13.6	9.5	350	350	−34	322
8500	13.6	9.5	230	330	−34	368
10,500	13.6	9.5	350	520	−34	421
12,500	13.6	9.5	320	—	−34	419
20,000	13.6	9.5	320	710	−34	629

[a] Taken from ref. 62.
[b] Benzene.

TABLE XXI[a]
Properties of HDI-Poly(oxypropylene) Glycol Elastomers

M_c	Urethane wt., %	Tensile strength, p.s.i.	Elongation, %	T_g, °C.	Solvent[b] swell, vol. %
8500	8.4	80	150	−65	619
8500	10.9	120	150	−62	452
8500	13.6	135	160	−59	384
8500	17.0	225	280	−55	315
2500	13.6	200	110	−59	294
4500	13.6	220	190	−59	342
8500	13.6	130	160	−59	384
12,500	13.6	160	310	−59	467

[a] Taken from ref. 62.
[b] Benzene.

in this chapter the weights per branch point have been calculated, which are 50% greater than the average weight between branch points reported by Smith and Magnusson. Properties have been derived from the original curves as necessary to give approximate room temperature values.) A plot of the values of T_g against the urethane content (U) expressed as moles of urethane per 1000 grams of polymer is shown in Figure 11 for both the TDI and the HDI elastomers.

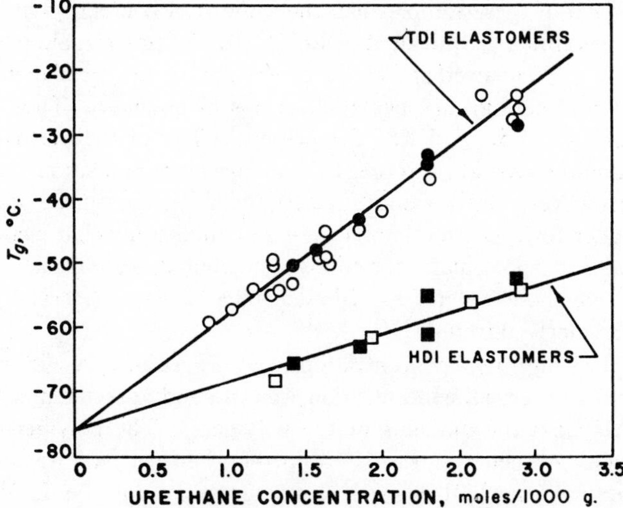

Fig. 11. Glass transition temperature of T_g of polyether-urethane elastomers plotted against the concentration of urethane groups. (Taken from ref. 62.)

These results showed several structure-property relationships. With both the HDI and the TDI elastomers at constant M_c values an increase in urethane content resulted in an increase in tensile strength, modulus, and the glass transition temperature (T_g), and a reduction in swelling by a solvent, benzene. Again, in both series, an increase in weight per branch point at constant urethane content resulted in increased elongation and solvent swelling, and in reduced modulus. In contrast to numerous other observations, changes in M_c had no effect on the glass transition temperature within the limits of the experimental error in measuring T_g. No explanation for this unexpected observation is apparent.

Comparison of the TDI and HDI elastomers at equal urethane contents and M_c values showed that the introduction of aromatic groups resulted in greater tensile strength and elongation, higher T_g values, and slightly less swelling by a solvent, all measured at room temperature.

The effects of the urethane group and aromatic group concentrations on properties was due in part to their influence on the glass transition temperature. For example, a plot of the log of the tensile strength against temperature expressed as $(T - T_g)$, in which T is the test temperature, is shown in Figure 12 for a series of TDI-based elastomers. All of these samples had the same triol content, giving a degree of cross linking equivalent to 1.87×10^{-4} effective chain per milliliter (ν_e/V). The urethane group concentration (U) is shown as the moles of urethane groups per 1000 grams of polymer. Thus, for U values of 1.42, 1.57, and 1.85 the primary effect of the urethane and corresponding aromatic groups was on the glass transition temperature. However, for U values of 2.30 and 2.89, the tensile strengths were higher for given levels of $(T - T_g)$, indicating that chain stiffness and intermolecular attractions contributed significantly to the strength of these polymers. Similar effects were observed in the elastomers derived from HDI.

Except at high triol concentrations, the degree of cross linking calculated from the triol concentration was in good agreement with that calculated from the modulus of the polymers. The polymer-solvent interaction parameter χ_1, was determined for benzene, and was found to be larger for the TDI-derived elastomers than for the HDI-based elastomers, 0.45 and 0.41, respectively at U of 2.30. Values were higher at higher urethane concentrations.

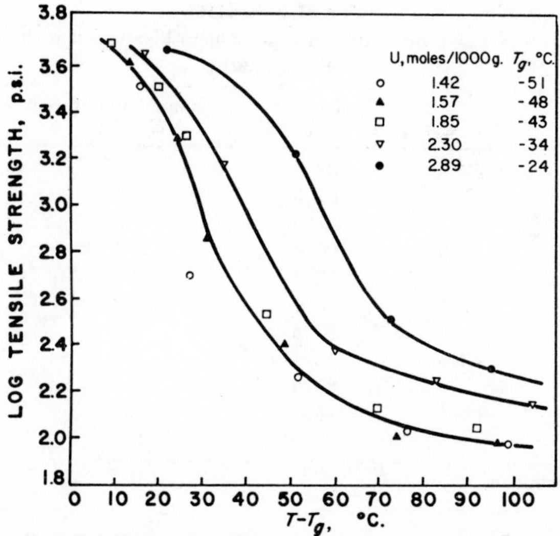

Fig. 12. Temperature dependence of tensile strength of a series of TDI elastomers having $\nu_e/V = 1.87 \times 10^{-4}$/ml. and different concentrations of urethane groups. (Taken from ref. 62.)

In a continuation of this study, Smith and Magnusson (63) showed that intermolecular forces in a series of plasticized polyether-urethane elastomers affected the modulus only as they affected T_g. The elastomers were prepared from poly(oxypropylene) glycol of molecular weight 2000, dipropylene glycol, trimethylolpropane, and 2,4-TDI. The concentrations of reactants were selected to give 1.42 moles of urethane groups per 1000 grams of polymer and 1.87×10^{-4} effective chains per milliliter calculated from the triol content. The plasticizer, isodecyl pelargonate, was used at 0, 5, 10, 15, and 20% concentration. Table XXII shows the glass transition temperature, Young's modulus (E) at several test temperatures expressed as degrees of temperature above the glass transition temperature ($T - T_g$), and the reduced modulus, $(298/T)E$, for these elastomers. The reduction in T_g as the plasticizer concentration was increased was assumed to be the result of separating chains, decreasing their interactions and increasing their mobility. As shown in Figure 13 and 14, the plots of the tensile strength and elongation vs. ($T - T_g$) were independent of plasticizer concentration, hence of intermolecular forces.

A series of elastomers was prepared similarly, having the same

TABLE XXII[a]
Properties of Polyether-Urethane Elastomers Plasticized with Isodecyl Pelargonate

IDP, wt. %	T_g, °C.	Test temp., $T - T_g$, °C.	Young's modulus E, p.s.i.	$(298/T)E$
0	−52.5	123.5	192	166
		101.5	186	172
		77.5	180	180
5	−57.5	106.4	172	159
		82.5	160	160
10	−61.5	110.4	163	151
		86.5	163	163
15	−63.5	112.4	150	139
		88.5	148	148
20	−66.5	115.4	150	139
		91.5	148	148

[a] Taken from ref. 63.

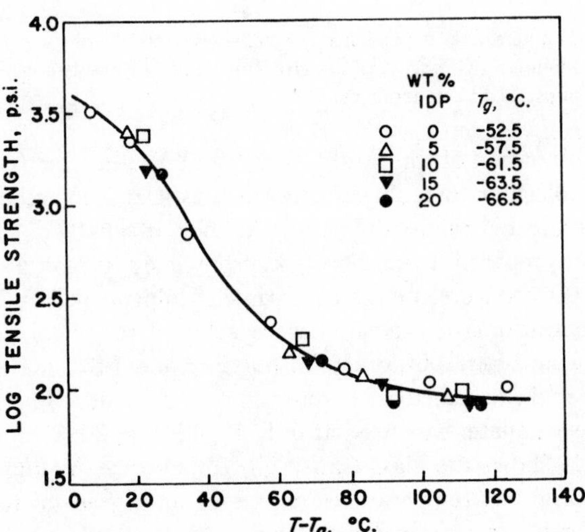

Fig. 13. Relation between tensile strength and $T—T_g$ for isodecyl pelargonate (IDP) plasticized polyether-urethane elastomers. (Taken from ref. 63.)

urethane content and degree of cross linking, but using hexamethylene diisocyanate (HDI), *m*-phenylene diisocyanate (PDI), or 1,5-naphthalene diisocyanate (NDI) to compare with the 2,4-TDI. The T_g values for these elastomers were —67.5, —50.5, —17, and —52.5°,

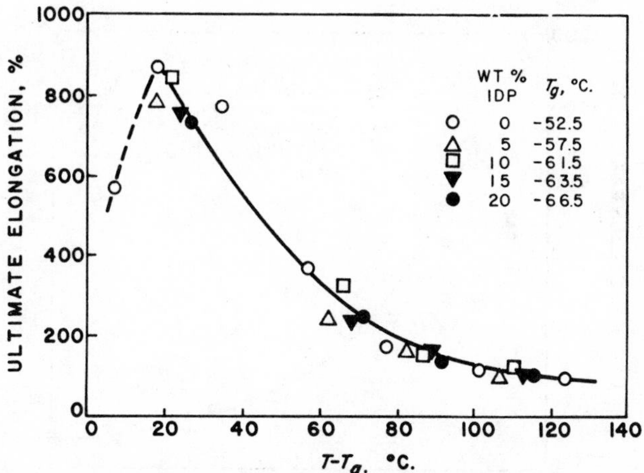

Fig. 14. Relation between elongation and $T - T_g$ for isodecyl pelargonate plasticized polyether elastomers. (Taken from ref. 63.)

respectively. Plots of tensile and elongation vs. $(T - T_g)$ are shown in Figures 15 and 16. With the possible exception of the NDI elastomers the ultimate properties were essentially the same at any given value of $(T - T_g)$.

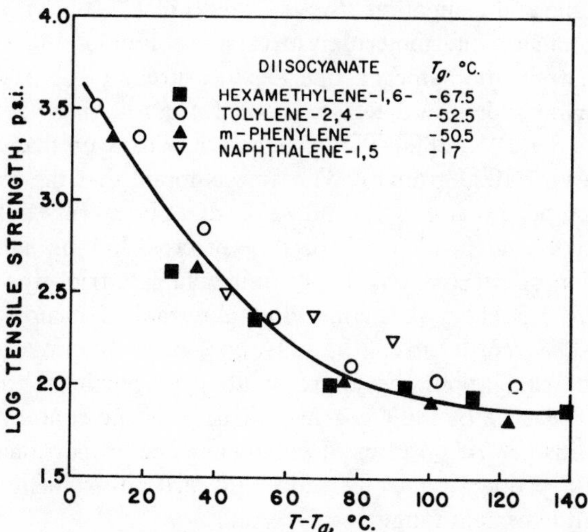

Fig. 15. Tensile strength plotted against $T - T_g$ for polyether-urethane elastomers prepared with different isocyanates. (Taken from ref. 63.)

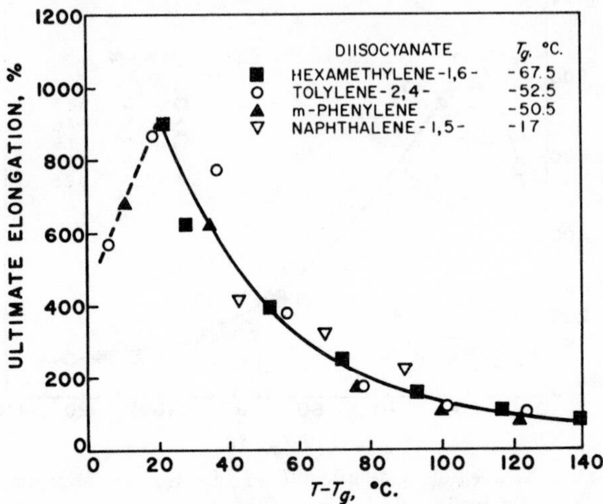

Fig. 16. Elongation plotted against $T—T_g$ for polyether-urethane elastomers prepared with different isocyanates. (Taken from ref. 63.)

Thus, a range of polyether-urethane elastomers with a fairly low urethane and aromatic content, some with plasticizers, had the same ultimate tensile and elongation at given values of $(T - T_g)$. In these specific elastomers intermolecular attractions did not make a large contribution to the mechanical properties measured.

Several trifunctional and tetrafunctional cross-linking agents were evaluated in the PPG-2000-TDI elastomers with a urethane content of 15.7 moles for 1000 grams (63). It was found that the tensile and elongation properties at 4.5, 25, and 71°C. at a given cross link density were essentially independent of the type of cross-linking agent. (In the calculation of effective chains per unit volume a triol was assumed to contribute 1.5 effective chains, and a tetraol, 2 chains per unit volume.) The tensile strength was approximately proportional to $\nu_e^{1/2}$, and the elongation was approximately proportional to $1/\nu_e$, in which ν_e, a measure of the cross link density, is the concentration of effective chains per 1000 grams of polymer. The proportionality constants were dependent on temperature and also on urethane and aromatic content in certain ranges.

The reduced modulus of the PPG-2000 elastomers was usually somewhat less than that calculated from the triol content of the system

(63). Young's modulus should be related to the cross link density by the equation:

$$E = 3(\nu_e/V)RT$$

in which R is the gas constant and T is the temperature. The value (ν_e/V) was calculated from the triol content by the equation:

$$\nu_e/V = 3/2 \text{ (moles triol/ml. elastomer)}$$

Elastomers having a calculated value of (ν_e/V) of 1.87×10^{-4} chain per milliliter had experimental modulus values of 130–174 p.s.i., compared to calculated values of about 200 p.s.i. This deviation apparently was due to the monofunctional content of the polyethers, which had an unsaturation of 3.2×10^{-5} mole per gram, corresponding to about 6 mole per cent monofunctional. When specially purified PPG-2000 having no monofunctional content was used the value of (ν_e/V) calculated from the triol content was essentially the same as that obtained from the modulus data.

To compare with the polyether-based elastomers, a series of elastomers was prepared from polyesters, 2,4-TDI, triethylene glycol, and trimethylolpropane (63). The polyesters were: (*1*) a "50:50 polyester," obtained from the copolymerization of a 50:50 molar mixture of ε-caprolactone and methyl ε-caprolactone using ethylene glycol as initiator, average molecular weight 2150; and (*2*) an "80:20 polyester" prepared similarly from an 80:20 molar ratio of ε-caprolactone and methyl ε-caprolactone, molecular weight 2260. The urethane and aromatic contents of the elastomers were varied, but the triol content was constant, corresponding to 1.87×10^{-4} chain per milliliter.

The elastomers from the 50:50 polyester, and having urethane contents of 1.28, 1.85, and 2.30 moles per 1000 grams, had T_g values of −50.5, −43.5, and −40°C. Thus, T_g increased linearly with urethane content, as in the polyether series. Reduced modulus values were 265–347 p.s.i., increasing with increasing urethane (and aromatic) content. The modulus calculated from the triol content was 200 p.s.i. This difference suggests that the modulus in the polyester-based elastomers was influenced greatly by intermolecular forces, in addition to the primary cross links. It will be recalled that the modulus of the ether-based elastomers was equal to or less than the value calculated from the triol content, suggesting that the modulus of the ether-based elastomers was influenced almost completely by the primary cross links, not by the intermolecular forces.

A comparison of the tensile and elongation properties of elastomers from the 80:20 polyester, the 50:50 polyester, the PPG-2000, all at 1.42 moles of urethane per 1000 grams and 1.87×10^{-4} chain per milliliter, and SBR rubber (about 1.2×10^{-4} chain per milliliter) is shown in Figures 17 and 18 (63). It may be seen from these figures

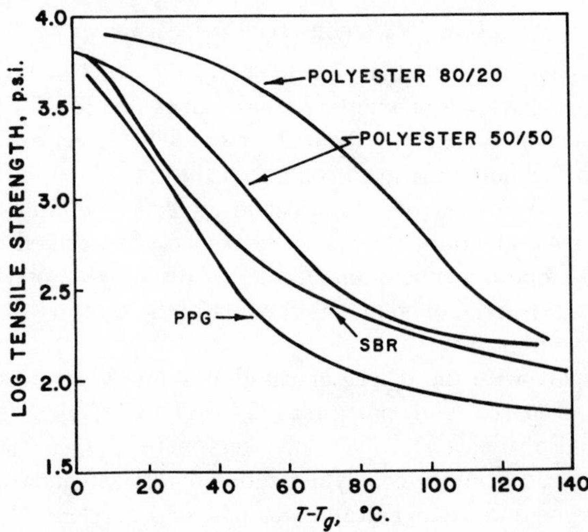

Fig. 17. Comparison of tensile strengths of three types of polyurethane elastomers and an SBR rubber. (Taken from ref. 63.)

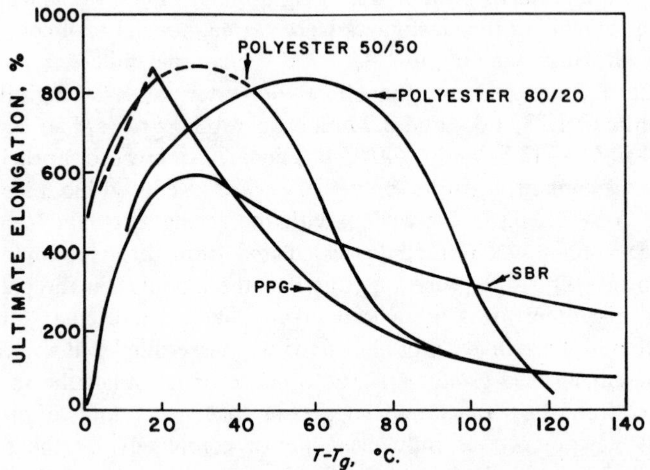

Fig. 18. Comparison of ultimate elongations of three types of urethane elastomers and SBR rubber. (Taken from ref. 63.)

that the tensile and elongation properties of a urethane polymer at any given temperature interval above its T_g depend to a large extent on the chemical structure of the polymer chain.

Polymer-solvent interactions have also been studied by Conway (20,21), using poly(oxypropylene) glycol-triol elastomers cured with 2,4-TDI. The average chain weight between cross linking sites was 10–30% greater when obtained from solvent swelling data than when calculated from the triol content. This difference could be due, at least in part, to the monofunctional content of the polyethers.

Poly(oxypropylene) glycol-2,4-TDI elastomers containing urea groups have also been prepared. Axelrood and Frisch (4) prepared prepolymers from 2,4-TDI and varying molecular weight polyether glycols, each at NCO/OH of 2:1, and cured them with MOCA. The prepolymer/MOCA ratio was calculated to give one biuret branch point for every 6850 molecular weight units. Typical properties are shown in Table XXIII.

TABLE XXIII[a]
Properties of Elastomers Prepared from Poly(oxypropylene) Glycols, 2,4-TDI, and MOCA
(NCO/OH = 2:1 in prepolymer)

PPG mole wt.	1000	1250	1500	2000
Properties:				
Tensile strength, p.s.i.	5050	4500	3500	1200
Elongation, %	—	860	—	—
Modulus, p.s.i., at 300%	2100	1000	600	400
Tear strength, Graves, lb./in.	310	240	225	125
Hardness, Shore A	88	77	67	60
Abrasion, Taber, mg. loss/1000 cycles	85	60	25	8
Brittle pt., Tinius Olsen, °C.	−40	−50	−55	−56
Rebound resilience, Bashore, %	24	20	22	38

[a] Taken from ref. 4.

The weight per cent of urea (NHCONH), urethane (NHCOO), and aromatic (C_6H_3) have been calculated and are plotted against properties in Figure 19. Although the calculated weight per cent urethane averaged 0.1% higher than the urea, the two are shown as being the same in this figure. In order to indicate trends conveniently, the hardness values were multiplied by 30, and the brittle point was converted by adding 60°C., then multiplying by 200.

Similar results were obtained using a "one-shot" method in which

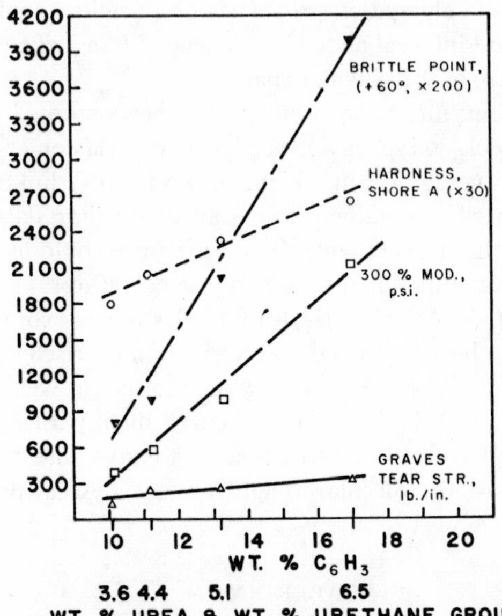

Fig. 19. Effect of polymer composition on properties of poly (oxypropylene) glycol-TDI-MOCA elastomers. (Data from ref. 4.)

the TDI, glycol, and MOCA were mixed simultaneously (5). With the same starting materials the one-shot method gave somewhat lower tensile strength than the prepolymer method, but higher tear strength and modulus, better resilience, and compression set.

Similar to the series in which the polyether molecular weight was varied, another series of elastomers was made in which the polyether was kept constant but the TDI and MOCA contents increased progressively. Again, as the aromatic and urea content of the polymer increased, the same trends were noted: hardness, modulus, and tear strength increased. The substitution of 3,3′-dichlorobenzidine for MOCA increased the modulus and the tear strength somewhat (5).

A series of polyurea-urethanes was prepared from tolylene diisocyanate and poly(oxyethylene)glycols by Heiss and others (30). These polymers were linear, with the recurring unit X. By varying

$$\left[-HN-C_6H_3(CH_3)-NHCOO-(CH_2CH_2O)_n-CONH-C_6H_3(CH_3)-NHCO- \right]_n$$

(X)

the molecular weight of the polyether glycol a range of properties was obtained, as illustrated in Table XXIV, where the number following "PEG" (polyethylene glycol) refers to the molecular weight.

TABLE XXIV[a]
Tolylene Diisocyanate-Polyurea-Urethane Film Properties

Property	Polyol used		
	PEG-200	PEG-400	PEG-1000
Urethane, %	21.4	15.6	8.8
Urea, %	10.5	7.7	4.3
Aromatic, C_6H_3, %	27.2	19.9	11.1
M.p., °C.	250	230	210
Yield pt., p.s.i.	3600	1600	0
Ultimate tensile, p.s.i.	3600	3000	300
Ultimate elongation, %	0	400	1000

[a] Taken from ref. 30.

As the glycol molecular weight was increased the weight percentages of urethane, urea, and aromatic groups were reduced, with a trend toward greater elasticity, lower tensile strength and melting point, and greater elongation.

The properties of a wide variety of low durometer cast urethane elastomers have also been reported by Heiss (29), with attention being given to the aromatic, urea, and urethane contents of the polymers. Similar to the results of Smith and Magnusson (63), Heiss found that the type of cross linking (from triisocyanate, triol, or excess isocyanate) had little effect on room temperature properties. On the other hand, polymer "melting points" were higher when the cross links were from triol or triisocyanate than when they were derived from excess isocyanate. This is to be expected since the excess isocyanate may be assumed to have given the thermally unstable allophanate or biuret cross links.

Precise comparisons cannot at this time be made which show structure-property relations as the major component of the elastomer is changed from polyester to polyether to other materials such as castor oil. However, an interesting indication is given in Table XXV, where properties of outstanding published formulations are summarized. It is apparent that excellent properties have been obtained from polyester-diisocyanate-glycol and polyether-diisocyanate-diamine combinations. Thus when the polyester is replaced by a more flexible component, e.g., polyether, best properties are obtained when an aromatic diamine curing agent is substituted for the glycol curing agent. Thus far elastomers of outstanding mechanical properties (except low temperature flexibility) have not been obtained from polyether-diisocyanate-glycol combinations or from castor oil-containing combinations. Similar comparisons were recently published by Müller (42).

TABLE XXV[a]
Summary of Elastomer Systems and Properties

Prepolymer	Curing agent	Tensile strength, p.s.i.	Elongation, %	300% modulus, p.s.i.	Hardness (Shore A)	Ref.
Polyester-MDI	Glycol	7900	600	1600	81	47
Polyester-TDI	Glycol	4600	600	350	60	47
Poly(1,4-	Diamine	6000	460	—	80	13
oxybutylene)-	Glycol	1340	645	—	38	3
glycol-TDI	Castor oil	800	400	—	43	13
Poly(oxypropylene)	Glycol	2000	720	—	—	62
glycol-TDI	Diamine	4500	860	1000	77	4
Castor oil-TDI	Ester	875	400	—	41	45
	Ester	2750	175	—	93	45

[a] Taken from ref. 56.

V. Urethane Foams

Like the urethane elastomers, urethane foams are normally prepared from diisocyanates and hydroxyl-terminated resins such as polyethers and polyesters. Linear or only slightly branched resins are used to provide flexible foams, whereas more highly branched resins produce rigid foams. Foaming is usually accomplished by including water in the system, the reaction between isocyanate and water providing carbon dioxide for foaming. More recent work, especially with rigid foams, has utilized a low boiling liquid such as trichlorofluoromethane as a blowing agent. Appropriate catalysts and stabilizers are used to provide adequate control of the foam formation and cure. The chemistry of foam formation, discussed in detail in Chapter V, is illustrated with a difunctional resin; the reactions would be similar with branched resins, but leading to more cross-linked polymers.

While much foam production is carried out by suitably mixing all ingredients simultaneously (the "one-shot process"), the reactions involved may be more readily illustrated if they are considered in steps (the "prepolymer process"). The first reaction is that between excess diisocyanate and the hydroxyl-containing resins:

$$4R(NCO)_2 + HO{\sim\sim}OH \rightarrow$$
$$OCN—R—NHCOO{\sim\sim}OCONH—R—NCO + 2R(NCO)_2 \quad (9a)$$

This isocyanate-terminated prepolymer and excess diisocyanate are then foamed by reaction with water:

$$\xrightarrow{H_2O} {\sim\sim}OCONHR—NHCONH—RNHCONHR—NHCONHR{\sim\sim} + CO_2 \quad (9b)$$

Thus the polymer contains the resin chain (e.g., polyester or polyether), urethane groups, aromatic rings, and many urea groups. At least trace amounts of free $—NH_2$ end groups are present, and with the "one-shot" method traces of free —OH end groups may also be present.

The balance of reactants may affect the polymer structure and the properties of the foam. For example, the density is usually controlled by regulating the water content: low density foams require more water than higher density foams. The isocyanate content is increased proportionately, so that low density foams contain a higher percentage of aromatic rings and urea groups than do higher density foams. For flexible foams at approximately 2.0 lb./cu. ft. density, about 25% of the isocyanate groups combine with hydroxyl groups of the resin, whereas about 75% react with water.

The balance between isocyanate content and other reactive ingredients is sometimes adjusted to help broaden the range of properties obtained. When less than the stoichiometric requirement of isocyanate is used the foam polymer will have an increased number of free ends terminating in $—NH_2$ or —OH groups or both; with branched resins not all of the branch points in the resin will be built into cross links in the final polymer. When more than the stoichiometric requirement of isocyanate is used the excess isocyanate groups may react with urea groups or urethane groups to provide biuret and allophanate branch points, respectively. In the presence of certain catalysts the formation of isocyanate trimer branch points is also possible. These branching reactions, which are reviewed in Chapter III, are illustrated by equations (10) to (12). Of the first two, biuret formation is more likely in water-blown foams because of the greater number of urea groups, compared to urethane groups, and because of the much faster rate of reaction of isocyanate with urea groups than with urethane. The formation of the biuret and allophanate is reversed

$$\underset{\text{(urea)}}{\sim\text{NHCONH}\sim} + \sim\text{NCO} \rightarrow \sim\underset{\substack{|\\ \text{CONH}\sim}}{\text{N}}\text{CONH}\sim \quad \text{(biuret)} \tag{10}$$

$$\underset{\text{(urethane)}}{\sim\text{NHCOO}\sim} + \sim\text{NCO} \rightarrow \sim\underset{\substack{|\\ \text{CONH}\sim}}{\text{N}}\text{COO}\sim \quad \text{(allophanate)} \tag{11}$$

$$3\sim\text{NCO} \rightarrow \begin{array}{ccc} & \text{CO} & \\ \sim\text{N} & & \text{N}\sim \\ | & & | \\ \text{OC} & & \text{CO} \\ & \text{N} & \\ & \wr & \end{array} \quad \text{(trimer)} \tag{12}$$

at temperatures in the range of 120 to 150°C., thus making these branch points temperature sensitive. In contrast, the trimer ring is quite stable at elevated temperatures.

The influence of these structural features on urethane foams is illustrated by the following discussions of specific foam systems.

1. Polyether-Urethane Foams

Preliminary studies of relations between molecular structure and mechanical properties in foams have been reported in two papers by Bolin and co-workers (12) and by Sandridge and co-workers (54). Foams prepared from poly(oxypropylene) glycols and triols with tolylene diisocyanate (80:20 isomer ratio) by the prepolymer technique and foamed with water have the properties summarized in Table XXVI. The silicone oil used in foaming was of the poly(dimethylsiloxane) type. The calculated weight per branch point was based on the functionality and molecular weights of components used to make the foams (12).

Similar trends were reported for a series prepared with polyether tetrols plus glycols (12).

Clash-Berg torsional stiffness curves are shown in Figure 20 for foams prepared from the polyether triols. The results show the combined effects of reducing the degree of cross linking, aromatic content, and urethane content as noted in Table XXVI, with steady progression toward better low temperature flexibility. In an effort to isolate these variables more, Table XXVII shows a comparison of two foams at about 3375–3385 M_c values, but varying aromatic and urethane contents. With the higher aromatic and urethane contents the modulus

TABLE XXVI[a]

Relationship between Structure and Physical Properties for Polyether-Urethane Foams

Polyether	Triol	Triol	Triol	Triol	Triol	Triol	Triol and glycol	Triol and glycol
Wt./branch pt.	1650	2175	3375	3900	5175	6525[b]	10225	15185
Aromatic, %	16.2	14.9	12.6	11.2	11.0	11.0	14.6	12.3
Urethane, %	10.5	8.3	5.3	4.5	3.4	2.7	7.9	6.0
Urea, %	7.9	7.6	6.6	6.6	6.7	6.6	6.6	7.0
Density, lb./cu. ft.	2.4	2.2	2.5	2.5	2.8	2.4	2.2	2.2
Tensile strength, p.s.i.	30.0	21.0	18.0	20.0	22.0	15.0	24	21
Tensile mod., 100% elong., p.s.i.	—	16	12	10	7	6	—	—
Elongation, %	100	130	155	200	295	340	270	375
Compression strength, p.s.i.								
25%	1.9	0.9	0.5	0.5	0.5	0.3	0.5	0.4
25%R[b]	0.7	0.6	0.5	0.4	0.4	0.3	—	—
50%	2.8	1.3	0.7	0.7	0.7	0.4	0.7	0.4
75%	8.3	4.3	2.1	1.9	1.6	0.9	1.7	1.0
Compression set, 22 hr., 50% deflection, 70°C., %	7.0	3	4	3.0	—	14	3	6
Rebound elasticity, %	16	15	44	49	42	—	25	—
Yerzley resilience, % (at 30% deflection)	N.A.[d]	N.A.[d]	47	63	50	—	21	—
Point load indent, sec.[e]	7100	130	1	1.0	1	—	—	—
Swell index, vol. % (in dimethylacetamide)	145	170	237	240	350	—	390	—

[a] Taken from ref. 12.
[b] Prepolymer prepared under different conditions.
[c] Measured after 1 min. rest.
[d] Not applicable.
[e] Time required to recover from 90% indentation by a 1.13 in. diameter rod, held in indent for 5 min.

TABLE XXVII[a]

Effect of Structural Factors and Branching on Torsional Stiffness (Clash-Berg)

Wt./branch pt.	3375	3385	10,225
Aromatic (C_6H_3), %	12.6	14.7	14.6
Urethane (—NHCOO—), %	5.3	8.1	7.9
Temp., °C. at modulus 50 p.s.i.	−37	−10	−35
Temp., °C. at modulus 100 p.s.i.	−40	−30	−45

[a] Taken from ref. 12.

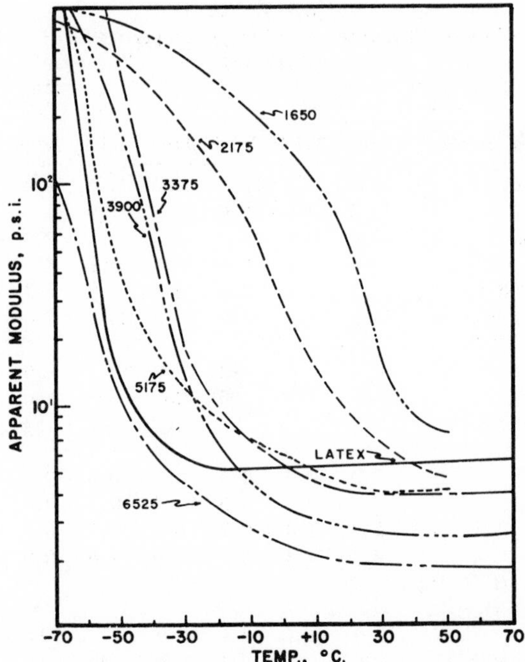

Fig. 20. Effect of calculated M_c values (as shown) and concurrent structural changes (see Table XXVI) on Clash-Berg torsional modulus of polyether-urethane foams. (Taken from ref. 12.)

increased sharply at higher temperatures. Similarly, two foams with approximately equal aromatic and urethane contents were compared. Of these, the one with a higher M_c value retained its flexibility to lower temperatures.

A series of one-shot foams was prepared from a poly(oxypropylene) triol and tetrol with tolylene diisocyanates and water, using a poly-oxyalkylene-polysiloxane copolymer as a foam stabilizer (54). A combination of these data with those of Bolin *et al.* (12) in Figure 21 shows the relations between M_c (and, related to it, the urethane content and aromatic content), tensile modulus, and elongation and volume swell in dimethylacetamide.

A plot of the reciprocal of the compression-deflection values at 25% deflection vs. M_c is shown in Figure 22 for 2.2–2.5 lb./cu. ft. density. The deviation from a linear relation is probably the result of variations

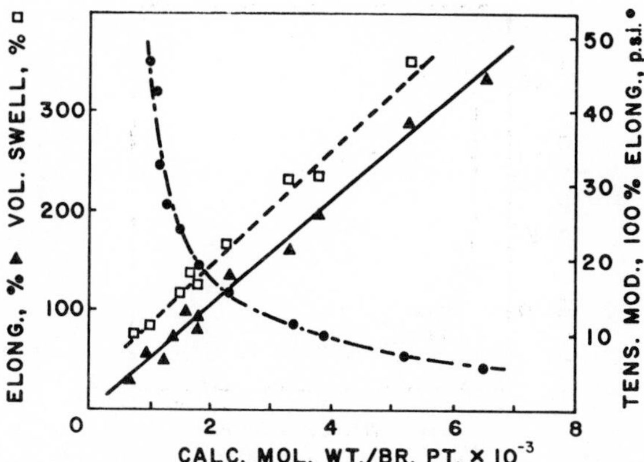

Fig. 21. Relation between calculated M_c and properties of polyether foams. (Taken from ref. 56; data from ref. 12, 54.)

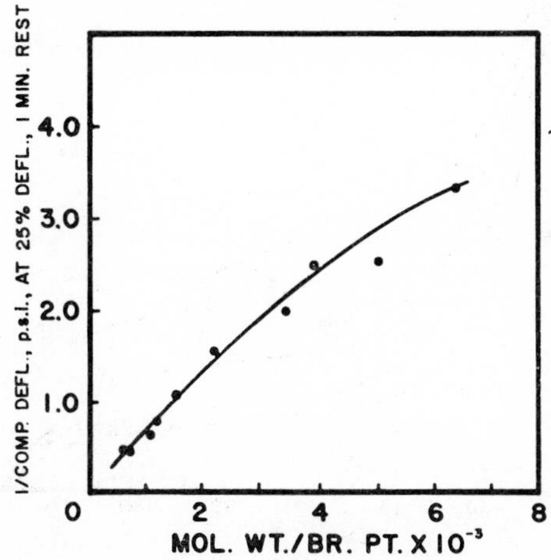

Fig. 22. Reciprocal of compression deflection related to calculated M_c for polyether foam. (Taken from ref. 56; data from ref. 12, 54.)

in the aromatic and urethane contents of the foams. Similar relations were obtained at higher densities, with the higher density foams having greater compression strength.

Figure 23 shows the relation between compression set (70°C.) and M_c values. This relation can be more readily understood if one refers to Figure 24, which shows the Clash-Berg curves for a series of foams

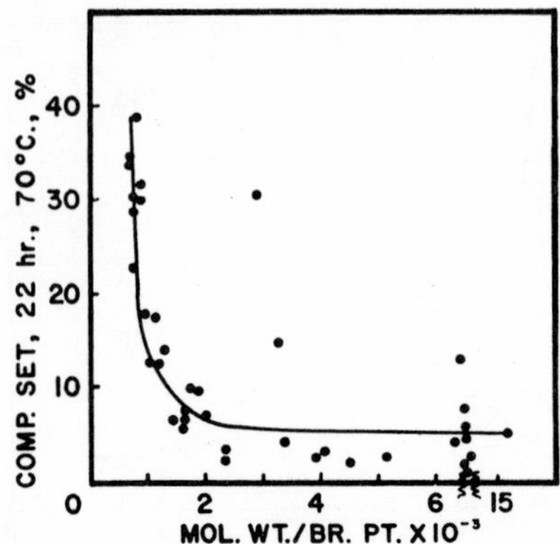

Fig. 23. Compression set related to calculated M_c for polyether foams. (Taken from ref. 54, 56.)

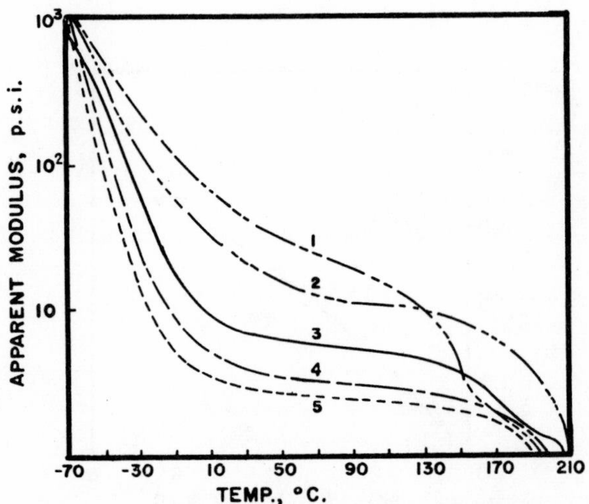

Fig. 24. Clash-Berg torsional modulus, polyether foams:

Curve	Index	M_c	Density, lb./cu. ft.	Compression set, %
1	120	680	3.5	34
2	100	1100	2.7	12
3	120	1350	2.6	6.5
4	100	1600	2.8	5.5
5	90	2000	2.7	7.5

(Taken from ref. 54.)

at 680–2000 M_c values. In the compression set test foam samples are compressed to half their thickness for 22 hours at a temperature of 70°C. and permitted to recover for 30 minutes at room temperature; then the sample thicknesses are measured. If the samples having poor set were given longer recovery periods, the sets continued to improve with a recovery rate dependent upon the M_c value for the foam. In a like manner, all foams showed good set values (ca. 5%) if allowed to recover in the 70°C. oven for 30 minutes. Inspection of Figure 24 reveals a possible explanation. Foams with higher M_c values have a relatively flat modulus curve in the 25–70°C. range encompassed by the set test. Low M_c foams have a greater slope in this region, indicating a more temperature sensitive condition.

It is believed that slow recovery in the standard compression set test, hence high set values, resulted from compression of the foam while in the elastic state (70°C.), followed by recovery in a state approaching the glassy state (25°C.). Thus compression sets measured by the standard method have generally been poor when the M_c value of the foam is less than approximately 1200.

The apparent influence of the temperature sensitive biuret and possibly allophanate cross links in foams was demonstrated by Sandridge *et al.* (54). Foams were prepared using 90, 100, and 120% (90, 100, 120 "index") of the theoretical isocyanate requirement at calculated M_c values in the range of 600 to 1730. The foams prepared at 120 index were attacked by aniline at 140°C. (eqs. 13, 14) very much faster than were foams prepared at 90–100 index. This hot aniline degradation may be used as a quantitative test for biuret plus allophanate in urethane polymers (1). Data are shown in Table XXVIII.

$$\sim\!\!\mathrm{N}(\mathrm{CONH}\!\sim)\!-\!\overset{\mathrm{O}}{\overset{\|}{\mathrm{C}}}\!-\!\mathrm{NH}\!\sim + \mathrm{ArNH_2} \xrightarrow[140^\circ\mathrm{C.}]{\text{fast}} \sim\!\!\mathrm{NH}\!-\!\overset{\mathrm{O}}{\overset{\|}{\mathrm{C}}}\!-\!\mathrm{NH}\!\sim + \mathrm{ArNHCONH}\!\sim \qquad (13)$$

$$\sim\!\!\mathrm{N}(\mathrm{CONH}\!\sim)\!-\!\overset{\mathrm{O}}{\overset{\|}{\mathrm{C}}}\mathrm{O}\!\sim + \mathrm{ArNH_2} \xrightarrow[140^\circ\mathrm{C.}]{\text{fast}} \sim\!\!\mathrm{NH}\overset{\mathrm{O}}{\overset{\|}{\mathrm{C}}}\mathrm{O}\!\sim + \mathrm{ArNHCONH}\!\sim \qquad (14)$$

The swelling in dimethylacetamide (DMA) at 25°C. increased much more after aniline treatment of the 120 index foam than for the 90 and 100 index foams, showing rupture of cross links in the 120 index foam by the aniline.

TABLE XXVIII[a]

Degradation of Polyether Foams in Aniline, Related to Isocyanate Index

Isocyanate index	Calcd., M_c	Foam sample length, cm. Original Dry	Original In DMA	In DMA, after aniline treatment	Time in aniline at 140°C., min.
90	1730	10.0	13.9	14.1	2
100	1100	10.0	13.5	13.7	2
120	660	10.0	12.8	14.3	2
90	1730	10.0	13.9	14.4	5
100	1100	10.0	13.4	14.4	5
120	660	10.0	12.6	16.5	5

[a] Taken from ref. 54.

Closely related to these results were the Clash-Berg torsional modulus curves of the same foams (Fig. 24). Those foams prepared at 90 and 100 index, having at most few biuret and/or allophanate cross links, showed relatively flat modulus curves to approximately 160–170°C. In contrast, 120 index foams showed breaks in the modulus curves with sharp loss of modulus beginning at approximately 110–130°C. This loss of modulus in the 120 index foams may be assumed to be due to rupture of the biuret and/or allophanate cross links at 110–130°C. This temperature range is in agreement with the data of Kogon, who showed that allophanates are in equilibrium with urethanes and isocyanate, with dissociation of the allophanate being measurable at temperatures as low as 106°C. (38).

In addition, the 120 index foams were more readily attacked by steam than were the 90 and 100 index foams, as shown by increases in solvent swelling after hydrolysis (Table XXIX). Again, it may be assumed that the biuret and/or allophanate groups were attacked most readily by the water.

TABLE XXIX[a]

Volume Swell of Polyether Foams in Acetone, Related to Hydrolysis Aging of the Foam

	Isocyanate index 90	100	120
Calcd. M_c	1630	1070	690
Vol. swell, original, %	116	90	83
Vol. swell after 5 hr. steam autoclave, 120°C., %	140	132	155
Net change, %	24	42	72

[a] Taken from ref. 54.

Data on foams prepared from poly(oxypropylene) triols of a similar molecular weight range were also given by Seizinger and co-workers (60). These results support those reported by Bolin *et al.* (12) and by Sandridge *et al.* (54).

2. Polyester Foams

Table XXX shows the properties of various adipic acid polyester foams and their relationship to their molecular structure, as reported by Bolin *et al.* (12). Two of the rigid foam samples were prepared from polyesters containing adipic acid and also a small amount of phthalic anhydride. In the calculation of the aromatic content of such foam samples, the phthalic anhydride is included.

The trends established in Table XXX are in general agreement with those obtained for the polyester series. At similar weights per branch points, the polyether samples were firmer than those obtained from polyethers. Figure 25 shows the low temperature flexibility of a flexible and a semirigid sample, with the former being considerably stiffer at a given temperature than a more cross-linked polyether sample (Fig. 20). A greater degree of intermolecular forces due to the presence of the ester linkages in polyester foams and greater flexibility in the polyether chain are considered to be the principal reasons for the greater compressive strengths and greater apparent moduli of the polyester foams at certain temperatures.

VI. Urethane Coatings

The cure ot urethane coatings in practical application usually involves the reaction of some percentage of the isocyanate with atmospheric moisture. The extent of this reaction has not been adequately established in any report of coatings experiments, with the result that structure-property relations have not been as well established for coatings as for elastomers and foams. Nevertheless, some generalities appear to be valid. Pflueger (46) reported data showing that elongation was reduced while hardness and chemical resistance were increased as the cross linking was increased in a series of polyester-urethane coatings. Hudson and co-workers (35) presented similar data on polyester coatings.

Remington and Athey showed that in coatings based on tolylene diisocyanate and polyethers the elongation increased and hardness decreased as the calculated weight per branch point increased (52).

TABLE XXX[a]

Relationship between Structure and Physical Properties of Polyester-Urethane Foams

Wt./cross link	410	538	755[b]	1370	2170	2460	4220	4760	6700	15,200
Aromatic, %	21.8	22.7	16.6	15.9	15.3	14.7	14.2	13.8	13.9	12.6
Urethane, %	16.6	17.3	7.7	7.9	6.8	5.8	4.7	4.5	4.2	3.7
Urea, %	5.2	5.0	4.8	6.8	7.0	7.1	7.2	7.1	7.3	7.1
Density, lb./cu. ft.	2	2	2.8	2	2.1	2	2	2	2	2
Tensile strength, p.s.i.	55	55	35	27	27.9	26	29	20	33	25
Elongation, %	10	10	60	160	145	270	300	200	380	350
Compression strength at yield (10%), p.s.i.	20	20	8.7	—	—	—	—	0.7	—	0.6
Compression set, %, 22 hr., 50% deflection, 70°C.	—	—	47	26	—	18	9	5	14	5

[a] Taken from ref. 12.

[b] Contains 4.0 p.b.w. plasticizer. Calculations based on actual foam components other than plasticizer.

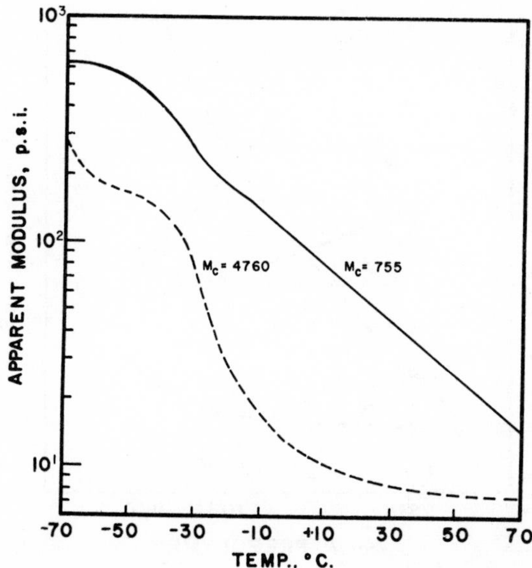

Fig. 25. Effect of M_c on Clash-Berg torsional stiffness of polyester urethane foam. (Taken from ref. 12.)

A series of prepolymers from TDI and polyethers was evaluated as coatings by Damusis, McClellan, and Frisch (23). The prepolymers were prepared from a 400 molecular weight poly(oxypropylene) triol, the triol plus dipropylene glycol, and the triol plus a poly(oxypropylene) glycol of molecular weight 400, all at NCO/OH of 2.0. These prepolymers were applied from solution and were permitted to cure by reaction with atmospheric moisture. The properties of the resulting coatings, related to the average molecular weight per branch point in the prepolymer, are shown in Figure 26. Reducing the degree of cross linking increased the impact resistance and the abrasion resistance, while reducing the solvent resistance and the hardness. Similar trends were shown for several other combinations of polyether triols, tetraols, and glycols.

In studying coatings from caster oil and castor oil derivatives cured with TDI, Bailey and co-workers (6) found that the abrasion resistance increased almost linearly with the "energy of rupture" of the film. The energy of rupture was considered as proportional to the area under the tensile stress-strain curve characteristic of the polymer

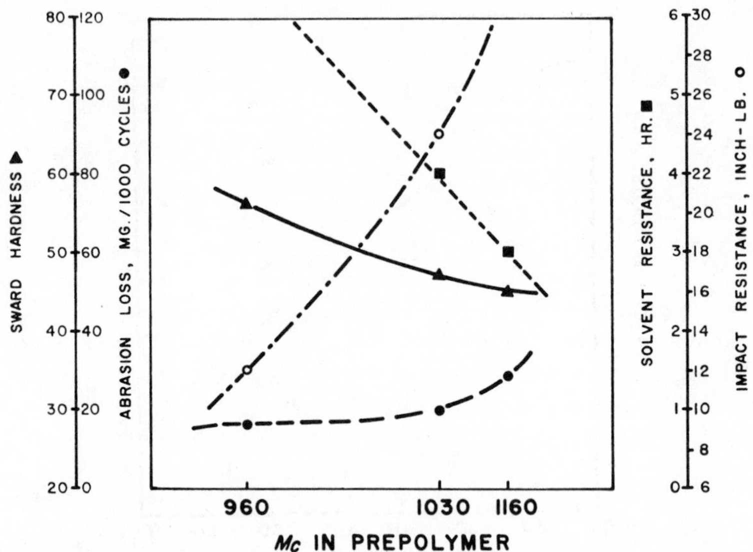

Fig. 26. Mole weight per branch point in prepolymer related to properties of moisture-cured polyether-urethane coatings. (Taken from ref. 23.)

film. The energy of rupture increased as the TDI content of the system increased, and decreased as the degree of cross linking increased. Chemical resistance was improved, however, as the system was cross linked beyond the point of maximum energy of rupture.

VII. Other Urethane Polymer Applications

The generalities which have been established in the elastomer, foam, and coatings fields may be expected to serve as useful guides in other areas of application. Thus caulks and sealants may be treated as elastomers that have been modified by fillers and plasticizers. Adhesives are analogous to the elastomers and coatings insofar as the properties of the adhesive layer itself are concerned. The complication of bonding to the substrate adds a special challenge to the study of adhesives. Potting and encapsulating compounds are usually elastomeric in nature, and will show the structure-property relations typical of the elastomers. As a guide to these and other applications the apparent structure-property relations are summarized in a later section of this chapter.

VIII. Flow, Creep, and Stress Relaxation in Urethane Polymers

Flow, creep and stress relaxation are important characteristics of many or most polymers, especially since they affect the permanence of the polymers' properties during use. The term "flow" is used here to indicate a permanent, nonrecoverable change in the geometric relationship of polymer molecules as a result of stress, wherein the change is the result of permanent slippage or flow of one or more molecules or segments past other molecules or segments. Permanent changes in shape and also permanent loss of mechanical properties are frequent manifestations of flow. "Creep" is considered to be the reversible change in shape with time of a sample under a sustained load. A familiar example is the gradual elongation of a rubber sample which is supporting a constant weight. "Stress relaxation" is considered to be the reduction with time of the load required to give a sample a specified deformation.

Flow in polymers is generally associated with the presence of linear or branched, especially linear, molecules in the polymer. Cross linked polymers (i.e., the gel component of polymers) are not considered to exhibit flow (i.e., permanent deformation) as long as the network structure remains intact. A cross-linked polymer could be deformed and the deformation "frozen in," e.g., by sufficient cooling, but the deformation would not be truly permanent. With sufficient time or heat this polymer should regain its original shape. It is possible, of course, that a cross-linked polymer could undergo degradation, e.g., by hydrolysis, oxidation, or pyrolysis, to give linear and branched fragments which could then exhibit flow behavior.

Creep of cross-linked polymers may occur, as in the compression set test, because the polymer is deformed for a long time and/or at an elevated temperature so that a deformation is established which recovers only slowly when the sample is permitted to relax at room temperature. The rate of recovery will be influenced by the balance of driving forces and restraining forces. The principal driving force is the tendency of the deformed network structure to regain its original shape, a direct function largely of the degree of cross linking. The restraining forces include the internal viscosity of the system, which may be very high near or below the glass transition temperature, the stiffness of chain segments, intermolecular forces, and crystallization established in the deformed state and which must be broken. If any primary chemical cross links were established in the deformed state these would also provide restraining forces. Chain entanglements formed in equilibrium with the deformed state would act like temporary cross links, being restraining forces for a time.

Stress relaxation of polymers may result from the flow of sol portions of the polymers, and by the rupture of cross links with subsequent flow. In many cases new cross links may be formed in equilibrium with the deformed state. Thus, the polymer aggregate strives to reach a configuration which is in equilibrium with the deformed state. Under sufficiently high constant load and with stress relaxation, this deformed state is constantly changing so the test sample will eventually break. Under lighter loads stress relaxation may reach a limiting value, that value being defined by the extent of cross linking and the stability of the cross links and segments between cross links.

Special features of the urethanes which influence creep and stress relaxation are discussed below. Since flow results from the presence of sol in the polymer, no special discussion of flow is required. The sol fraction may be controlled by the proper choice of polyfunctional reactants, elimination of monofunctional reactants, and choice of cure conditions.

1. Factors Related to Primary Chemical Bonds

A consideration of the structure of urethanes reveals several groups which could break and perhaps re-form as a result of stress. These include biuret, allophanate, urethane, and urea groups. Breaking and re-forming these groups might require activation energies in the range of 20–50 kcal./mole. The breaking and re-forming of a primary bond (allophanate) is illustrated in eq. 15. Several related studies give good evidence as to which groups may be most susceptible to breaking and re-forming, and therefore be the worst with respect to stress relaxation. Tobolsky and co-workers have studied the stress relaxation of a variety of elastomers, including urethanes (19,44). Polyether- and polyester-urethanes gave the same results, and, since the ether link is unlikely to break under the conditions used, one may assume the ester link does not contribute to stress relaxation or creep.

While those experiments eliminate the ester groups, other rate studies point toward allophanate and biruet groups as being groups which are easily broken at elevated temperatures. Thus, Kogon (38) showed that an equilibrium exists between urethane and allophanate

```
      O                    O
      ‖                    ‖
  ~NCO~~~~~~~~~~~~~~~~~OCN~~
   |                     |
   H                    CNH~~
                         ‖
                         O                  (15)
              ↓
      O                    O
      ‖                    ‖
  ~NCO———————————————————OCN~~
   |                        |
  CNH~~                     H
   ‖
   O
```

(eq. 16), with considerable dissociation at 106°C. and above. He also demonstrated the similar dissociation of biurets, with rates being appreciable at 120°C. and above (37).

$$\mathrm{R'NH\underset{\underset{O}{\|}}{C}-\underset{\underset{R}{|}}{N}COOR \rightleftharpoons R'NCO + RNHCOOR} \qquad (16)$$

Reilly and Orchin (51) showed that biurets react much more readily with amines than do ureas at 150°C. (eqs. 17,18).

$$\mathrm{R'NH\underset{\underset{O}{\|}}{C}-\underset{\underset{R}{|}}{N}CONHR + Bu_2NH \xrightarrow{fast} R'NH\underset{\underset{O}{\|}}{C}NBu_2 + RNHCONHR} \qquad (17)$$

$$\mathrm{RNHCONHR + Bu_2NH \xrightarrow{slow} Bu_2NCONHR + RNH_2} \qquad (18)$$

These results show the relative instability of allophanate and biuret groups, and hence their undesirability. The urea and urethane groups are also known to dissociate, though less readily, at elevated temperatures (55). Research showing which are the most stable urea and urethane structures should improve the creep and stress relaxation of polyurethanes.

2. *Factors Related to Secondary Bonds*

In addition to the breaking of primary chemical bonds, it is highly probable that the breaking of "secondary bonds," hydrogen bonds and other van der Waals attractive forces, plays a significant role in creep and stress relaxation in urethane polymers (57). All urethane polymers contain a large percentage of groups that can participate in such attractions, and a considerable part of the tensile and compressive strength of these polymers may be assumed to be the result of such intermolecular attractions. Fürthermore, these forces are disrupted relatively easily, so that it is not surprising that an apparent softening of urethane foam occurs on flexing, and recovery of essentially the original strength occurs after an adequate rest period (58). A similar softening of diamine-cured polyether-urethane elastomers on repeated elongation was reported by Trick (65). In the initial state the polymer may be assumed to derive its strength from a combination

$$\begin{array}{c} \sim\mathrm{N(H)\!-\!C(\!=\!O)}\sim \\ \vdots \\ \sim\mathrm{C(\!=\!O)\!-\!N(H)}\sim \end{array} \rightleftharpoons \begin{array}{c} \sim\mathrm{N(H)\!-\!C(\!=\!O)}\sim \\ \\ \sim\mathrm{C(\!=\!O)\!-\!N(H)}\sim \end{array} \qquad (19)$$

of primary chemical bonds and secondary bonds. Vigorous flexing, elongation, or other working disrupts the secondary bonds but does not affect the primary bonds (eq. 19). Consequently after extensive flexing the polymer is softer, having only the strength derived from the primary bonds. With time the secondary bonds re-form, thus restoring the polymer to its original strength, that derived from primary plus secondary bonds.

This softening or weakening of urethanes is similar to the "Mullins effect," the softening of filler-reinforced rubber on repeated extension. Mullins and Tobin (43) assumed the apparent modulus was equal to the sum of the modulus due to the primary cross links plus the modulus due to the secondary forces binding the polymer to the filler. This fraction of the apparent modulus due to the secondary bonds was considered to be disrupted by pre-stressing. The softening of filler-reinforced elastomers has also been discussed by Houwink (34).

The urethanes may be considered to be similar, except that they are "self-reinforced," providing (to varying degrees) their own secondary bonding, as well as primary cross linking.

The breaking and re-forming of secondary bonds could also be expected to contribute to compression set and other manifestations of creep and to stress relaxation. Thus when foam or elastomer is compressed some secondary bonds, initially in equilibrium with the original state, may break and re-form in equilibrium with the compressed state (eq. 20). The rate of such changes could be significant

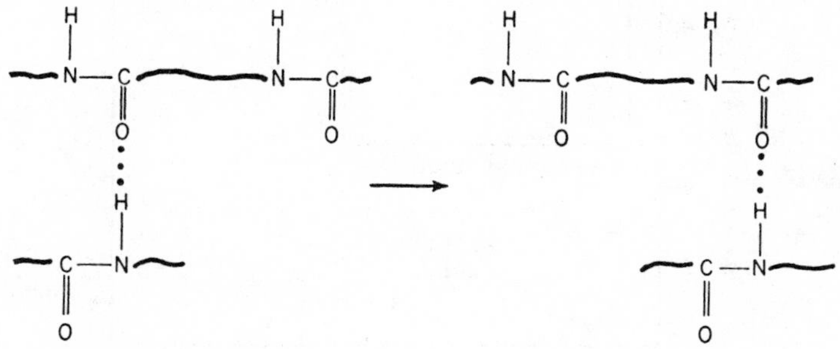

(20)

(in original state) (in compressed state)

at 70°C., the usual temperature of the compression portion of the test. When the sample is removed from the test plates and permitted to recover (at room temperature) those secondary bonds in equilibrium with the compressed state would serve as a temporary restraining force, tending to keep the sample compressed.

3. *Compression Set*

The "compression set" of a solid polymer or foam is usually measured by compressing the sample a desired percentage of its original height (constant deflection method) or compressing it under a desired load (constant load method), storing the compressed sample for a standard time at a standard temperature (e.g., 22 hr. at 70°C.), then at 25°C. removing the load or source of compression, and letting the sample "recover" for 30 minutes at 25°C. The height is then measured. The per cent set may be expressed as the loss in height (original minus final) divided by the original height, multiplied by 100. The set test is usually run at an elevated temperature to give an accelerated test. Although the correlation between such a test and actual service life is not really known, it may be assumed that a cushion in use, for example, may retain its original height better if its "compression set" is low rather than high, other characteristics being equal.

The performance of a typical foam sample in the compression set test, where the deflection is constant at 50%, is illustrated in Figure 27. In this hypothetical sample the recovery is rapid during the

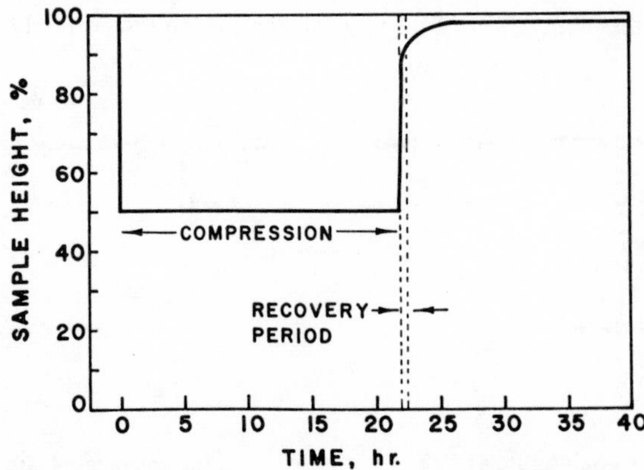

Fig. 27. Typical compression set behavior of flexible urethane foam.

standard 30 minute recovery period, so that the compression set is calculated as being about 8%. If the sample is observed for a longer period of time it will be found that it slowly recovers to within about 1% of the original height. An analysis of this behavior may be made, with consideration of both rate of recovery and extent of recovery, as follows.

The rate of the sample recovery will be controlled by the balance of driving force and restraining forces, as noted previously. The driving force is the tendency of the network structure to regain its original shape. This driving force will depend on the forces anchoring polymer segments in original positions. Such "anchors" may be primary chemical cross links, crystallites (unlikely in foam), hydrogen bonds, and chain entanglements. All of these may be disrupted at sufficiently high temperatures and long times, but the primary chemical cross links are the most stable; hence the driving force is dependent primarily on the degree of cross linking.

The restraining forces are a combination of internal viscosity and any "anchors" formed in equilibrium with the compressed state, primary chemical bonds, hydrogen bonds, other van der Waals forces, crystallites (not likely in foams), and chain entanglements.

The internal viscosity may be reduced by increasing the temperature interval above the glass transition temperature of the polymer $(T-T_g)$. This may be accomplished by using a higher temperature for the recovery period, by reducing T_g of the polymer, e.g., by adding a suitable plasticizer or changing the polymer structure as summarized in Section IX.

The formation of primary chemical bonds during the compression period, i.e., in equilibrium with the compressed state, should be minimized in completely cured foam (i.e., no remaining isocyanate groups) by having as low a concentration as possible of biuret and allophanate groups, as few as possible amine end groups, and a relatively low test temperature. Some catalysts could also be influential.

The formation of hydrogen bonds and other van der Waals forces, and crystallization in the compressed state, will be a function of the sites available for such bonding and the fit of the polymer segment. One can usually change these only by changing the polymer ingredients or by adding a suitable plasticizer.

The formation of new chain entanglements during compression will probably depend on internal viscosity and the concentration of sol fraction and long free ends.

The magnitude of the restraining forces will usually increase with an increase in the time, the temperature, and the extent of the compression. In the case of compression sets run at 90% deflection, one also introduces the possibility of mechanically breaking some cell walls and ribs, and of introducing a surface effect, where surface tackiness could also provide a restraining force.

The degree of recovery of the foam may be assumed to be influenced primarily by the balance between the driving (recovery) force and any primary bonds formed during the compression period plus any flow which occurred during the compression period. Primary bond formation may be minimized as indicated above. The flow will be proportional to the sol fraction initially present and that formed (even momentarily) during the test as a result of breaking bonds, and inversely proportional to internal viscosity.

Several experimental conditions are generally recognized as influencing the compression set of polyether-urethane foams. The preceding discussion appears to explain these observations (57):

Factors favoring bad set are known to include:

Large excess of water in foam formulation.

High amine catalyst concentration.

Very active catalysts for the NCO/H_2O reaction.

Slow curing (e.g., room temperature, with many prepolymer systems).

Measurement of set at the surface of the foam.

High relative humidity during compressed state, combined with recovery in the dry state.

Factors favoring good set include:

Mild catalyst for the NCO/H_2O reaction.

Theoretical or slight excess of water in the foam recipe.

Low catalyst concentration.

Fast cure (e.g., oven cure).

Plasticizers (effective in only some cases).

Permitting recovery of foam at 70°C. after compression period.

A consideration of the isocyanate-water reaction (eqs. 21, 22) will show the relation between most of the above observations on compression set. A very fast catalyst for reaction (21), a high catalyst con-

$$\sim\!NCO + H_2O \rightarrow \sim\!NH_2 + CO_2 \quad (21)$$

$$\sim\!NH_2 + \sim\!NCO \rightarrow \sim\!NHCONH\!\sim \quad (22)$$

centration, or a large excess of water (in the activator or from the atmosphere, as at the foam surface or during a long cure time) would promote reaction (21) at the expense of (22), i.e., stop chain growth, giving linear or branched molecules and many free ends in the cross-linked molecules, all with free —NH_2 end groups. The linear and branched molecules would flow during the compression period, thus contributing to poor set. The amine end groups would be capable of reacting with any biuret and allophanate groups in the polymer, and even with urea and urethane groups (though only slowly), to form primary bonds in equilibrium with the compressed state.

The indicated effect of plasticizers, relative humidity during testing, and recovery at 70°C. can all be explained by increased mobility of the linear and branched molecules and free ends. Thus, high relative humidity during the compression period would permit absorption of water by the foam, with the water acting as a plasticizer in the hot foam, permitting increased creep and flow during the compression period, hence high set. Occasionally a plasticizer is found which improves the set of a foam, probably by increasing the rate of movement of polymer segments during the recovery period. Permitting foam to recover at 70°C., the same temperature as the compression period, nearly always gives good set, apparently due to increased rate of movement of polymer segments during the recovery period.

In practical terms, these reactions leading to creep, stress relaxation, and flow apparently are not important in properly formulated urethane foams at temperatures at least as high at 70°C. (158°F.). Foams having excellent compression set at 70°C. are readily produced. These reactions may become progressively more important as the temperature is raised above 100°C., however. These considerations may be a guide to the development of urethane foams having even better compression set at high temperatures than is now available.

The same considerations may apply to urethane elastomers, with the added feature that urethane elastomers produced to date often have a higher sol content than commercial urethane foams. Thus, flow is usually more pronounced in urethane elastomers than in urethane foams.

4. *Softening of Urethane Polymers during Flexing*

The softening of urethane foams and elastomers as a result of flexing, rolling, dead loading, and repeated extension is well recognized in the industry. A typical series of flex fatigue curves for a polyether-urethane foam is shown in Figure 28 (58). The sample was flexed at

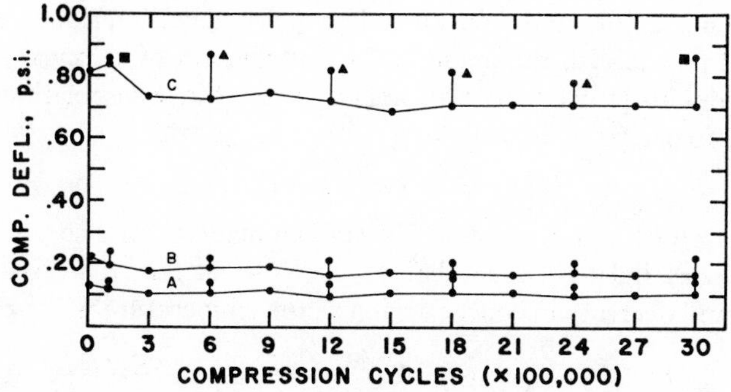

Fig. 28. Flex fatigue resistance of poly(oxypropylene) glycol-urethane flexible foam, 2 lb./cu. ft. density. A, 25% deflection, B, 50% deflection, C, 75% deflection, ▲, measured after 18 hr. recovery for each curve; ■, measured after 64 hr. recovery for each curve. (Taken from ref. 58.)

30 cycles per second, cycling from 30 to 80% deflection, a modification of ASTM D-623-52T, method A. The compression-deflection was measured with an Instron testing machine, with 1 minute rest. Compression-deflection was also measured after 18 hours' or 64 hours' recovery time, as shown. It is readily seen that permitting the foam sample to recover for a sufficient time was accompanied by a regain of all or nearly all of the original compressive strength.

The extent of softening of the urethane polymer may be a direct function of the extent of the interchain attractions of the hydrogen bond and van der Waals types: the greater the attractions, the greater the potential softening. In line with this expectation, certain polyester-urethane flexible foams were shown to soften more than certain polyether-urethane flexible foams (58). It appears likely that softening could also be proportional to the sol content of the polymer. In this case some permanent loss of strength might be expected, perhaps proportional to the sol content. Loss of strength may also be proportional to the free end content, particularly if the ends are quite long. Both the sol content and the free ends might contribute to the original strength, in part via chain entanglements which might be disrupted during flexing. The principal effect, however, is believed to be due to the disruption of interchain forces.

The extent of softening will also be influenced by the severity of the test conditions, of course. Conditions may be so extreme, e.g., due to heat build-up in the sample, that primary bonds are broken, as well as secondary bonds.

Weisfeld, Little, and Wolstenholme (67) have described research designed to establish the quantitative contribution of secondary bonding to modulus in urethane elastomers. From the basic relationship of modulus to degree of cross linking:

$$G = (\nu_e/V)\, RT$$

it was assumed that a correction should be made for the concentration of secondary links between chains, (ν_s/V), and that these secondary links would decrease in concentration as the temperature is increased:

$$(\nu_s/V) = (\nu_s/V)_o(1\text{-}e^{-E_a/RT}) \cong Ae^{-E_a/RT}$$

E_a is the Arrhenius-type activation energy. The experimental modulus should then be given by the equation:

$$G = (\nu_s/V + \nu_e/V)\, RT \cong ARTe^{-E_a/RT} + (\nu_e/V)\, RT$$

The contribution of secondary bonds to the modulus was established by measuring the modulus at various temperatures and using some correction factors.

The data indicated that in a peroxide-cured urethane elastomer of undisclosed structure the per cent contribution of secondary bonds to the room temperature modulus varied from 19 to 48.5% as the primary cross link concentration (ν_e/V) was changed from 3.20 to 1.65 $\times 10^{-4}$ mole per milliliter. The value for E_a was about 2.86–2.05 kcal./mole for these elastomers.

Diamine-cured MDI-polyester elastomers showed 20–57% contribution of secondary bonds to the room temperature modulus with E_a being 4.2–3.4 kcal./mole. Several linear urethanes were prepared from MDI and various polyols. These gave E_a values of 2.0–2.7 kcal./mole at 0–350% elongation, whereas those most likely to give good orientation showed E_a values of 6.8–10.3 kcal./mole at 650% elongation.

These results serve to add a degree of quantitative interpretation to the role of interchain forces in urethane elastomers. In agreement with results noted earlier this approach also showed that interchain forces became less effective as cross linking was increased. The obvious temperature dependence of these interchain forces also accounts for typical loss of mechanical properties by many cross-linked urethanes at temperatures above about 80–100°C.

IX. Summary of Structure-Property Relations in Urethanes

Just as with other polymers, the properties of the various forms of urethane polymers are influenced primarily by molecular weight, effective intermolecular forces, stiffness of chain segments, crystallinity, and degree of cross linking. The general trends of influence of each of these features are illustrated and then the role of specific structural groups in the urethane polymers is discussed (56).

The effect of molecular weight on urethane properties may be assumed to be the same as for other polymers, as indicated in Figure 29. Not all the properties will show exactly the same relation to the molecular weight, of course. The limiting molecular weights for the various forms of urethane polymers are not known accurately. For highly crystalline urethane polymers, e.g., from hexamethylene diisocyanate and 1,4-butanediol, the limiting value may be somewhat less than 10,000, the reported molecular weight of fibers from this polymer (4).

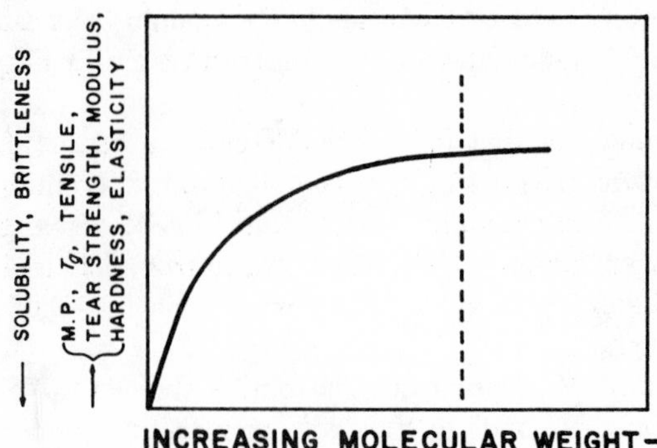

Fig. 29. Relation between molecular weight and polymer properties. (Taken from ref. 56.)

The value is doubtless very much higher for noncrystalline urethanes.

The shape of the molecular weight vs. property curve is very much like the reverse of the curve relating properties to time of exposure to hydrolytic conditions (58). It may be assumed that hydrolysis breaks chains, thus increasing the sol fraction of a urethane and moving the average molecular weight toward lower values. Little change in properties would be expected until the average molecular weight reaches the range in which properties begin to fall off with further decreases in molecular weight.

Changes in effective intermolecular forces may be expected to show the trends illustrated in Figure 30. The term "effective intermolecular force" is used to indicate a combination of the intermolecular attractive forces that are possible for the structural groups present, combined with the geometric structure or "fit" that regulates the extent to which these forces can operate. Property contributions due to the intermolecular attractions will often be reduced relatively easily as the temperature is raised; e.g., above about 80–100°C.

Modulus (tensile, shear, and compression), tear strength, hardness, melting point, and glass transition temperature have been shown to increase with increasing effective intermolecular forces. For example, the effect on modulus, tear, and hardness was demonstrated with polyester elastomers, where the effectiveness of intermolecular forces was controlled by controlling the degree of cross linking (Table XII) and by increasing the aromatic and urethane contents (Table XIII and Fig. 7). Similar effects on polyether elastomers were shown in Table

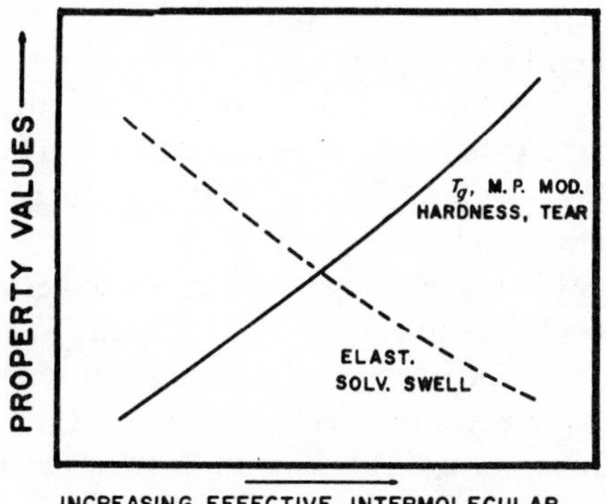

Fig. 30. Relation between urethane properties and effective intermolecular attraction, stiffness of chain segments, and degree of crystallization for polymers with no or only slight crystallization. (Taken from ref. 56.)

XXIII and Figure 19. The effect on melting point was shown in Figures 1 and 2. The elasticity and solvent swelling will be reduced as the effective intermolecular forces increase. The effects on solvent swelling and glass transition temperature were illustrated nicely in a polyether elastomer series (Table XX) and Figure 11. The reduction of elasticity was shown in the comparison of glycol- and diamine-extended elastomers (Table VII).

The role of reinforcing fillers is normally that of increasing intermolecular attractions (filler-to-polymer). Thus relatively little advantage is realized by adding fillers to certain polyester-urethane and polyether-urea-urethane elastomers with strong intermolecular attractions, but much more to other elastomers with weak intermolecular attractions.

An increase in stiffness of chain segments may be expected to have the same effect as would increases in effective intermolecular attractions (Fig. 30). Property contributions from chain stiffness would often be less temperature-sensitive than those from intermolecular attractions. The effect on T_g is illustrated by a comparison of polyether elastomers prepared from tolylene diisocyanate and from hexamethylene diisocyanate (Tables XX and XXI and Fig. 11). The effect on modulus, tear, and hardness is shown for a polyester elastomer series in Table XI, comparing aliphatic glycol chain extenders with an aromatic glycol extender, and in Table IX, comparing elastomers from 3,3′-dimethyl-4,4′-diphenylmethane diisocyanate and 3,3′-dimethyl-4,4′-diphenyl diisocyanate. The effect of increasing the aromatic contents of elastomers was shown in Table XIII and XXIII and Figures 7 and 19. The influence on melting point was shown in the comparison of linear urethanes (Tables II and III). The effect on elasticity was shown in the comparison of elastomers extended with thiodiethylene glycol, 1,4-butanediol, and a diamine (Table VII).

An increase in the degree of crystallization would also have the same influence as increases in effective intermolecular attractions and stiffness of chain segments (Fig. 30). Effects of this type would naturally be lost at temperatures above the melting points of the crystallites involved.

Changes in the degree of cross linking do not affect properties in all urethane polymers in the same way. In those noncrystalline polymers having a high degree of effective intermolecular forces, e.g., the polyester-urethane elastomers, increases in cross linking first serve to reduce the effective intermolecular forces by reducing the fit. As M_c values decrease, those forces eventually become relatively weak so that further changes in M_c values result in changes which might be predicted for hydrocarbon elastomers. This effect of small increases in cross linking at high M_c values in polyester-urethane elastomers is analogous to the effect of introducing cross linking into crystalline polymers.

In noncrystalline urethane polymers having relatively lower degrees of effective intermolecular forces, e.g., polyether elastomers and foams, the effects of changes in the degree of cross linking are generally analogous to those in most other polymers. As cross linking increases the polymer changes progressively from a linear, thermoplastic, soluble form to an elastomer with moderate cross linking, and finally with further increases to a thermoset, rigid structure. General trends are illustrated in Figure 31.

The effect of M_c changes on solvent swelling, elongation, tear, and modulus was illustrated for polyether foams in Table XXVI. The influence on glass transition values for polyether foams was illustrated in Figure 20 and Table XXVII. The effect on modulus for elastomers of high effective intermolecular attractions was shown in Figure 5, and on tear strength, elasticity (elongation set), and compression set in Table XII. Compression set may be considered one form of creep, thus justifying the curve for creep.

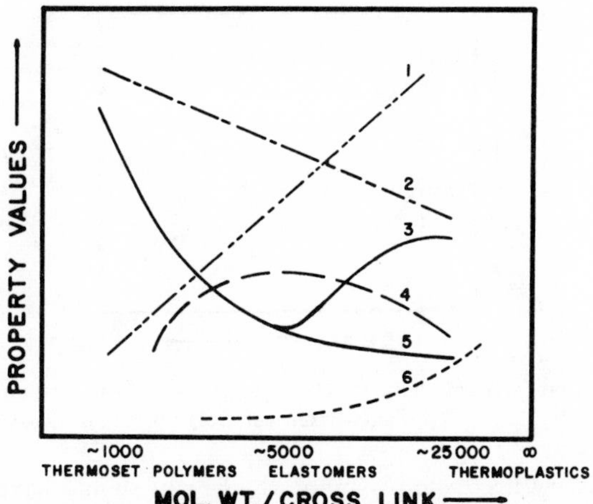

Fig. 31. Properties of urethanes related to molecular weight per cross link for amorphous polymers. Curve 1: solvent swelling, elongation, and tear strength, Curve 2: glass transition temperature and melting point, Curve 3: modulus and hardness for polymers with high intermolecular attractions, Curve 4: elasticity, Curve 5 modulus and hardness for polymers with relatively low intermolecular attractions, Curve 6: creep and compression set. (Taken from ref. 56.)

Property contributions arising from primary cross linking will be relatively independent of temperature up to that temperature at which the weakest primary bond begins to break at a significant rate.

A second useful approach to the effect of structural changes on properties is a consideration of modulus-temperature curves for a series of polymers. Every polymer has a typical curve, as illustrated in Figure 32, in which a modulus such as a dynamic modulus is plotted against temperature. At temperatures below A′ the polymer is in a glassy state, where rotation of chain segments has been frozen out, and the polymer is stiff and brittle. Temperature A′ is approximately the "glass transition" temperature.

At temperatures somewhat above A′ the chain segments begin to rotate, with the result that the polymer modulus is greatly reduced and the polymer becomes elastomeric in nature. As the temperature is increased still further the modulus eventually falls off, indicating flow of the molecules. For linear, noncrystalline polymers this flow will occur at moderate temperatures; for cross linked polymers it will occur at the temperatures at which the cross links begin to break.

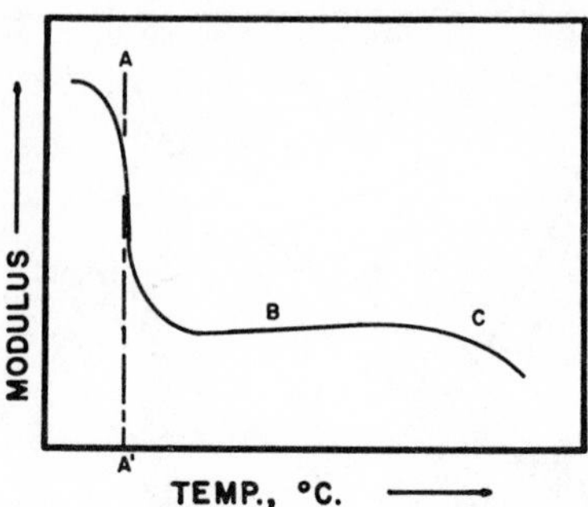

Fig. 32. Relation between temperature and modulus for a typical polymer. (Taken from ref. 56.)

A satisfactory urethane plastic or rigid foam should have T_g values well above room temperature, whereas elastomers and flexible foams should have T_g values well below room temperature.

The effect of each structural unit in urethane polymers upon the A (glass transition), B (room temperature for elastomers), and C (high temperature) portions of the modulus curve may be predicted with reasonable assurance in the manner shown in Table XXXI. For added usefulness, additional property features are included in Table XXXI. A ↑ symbol means that the indicated property is favored; ↓ indicates that the property is not favored; (—) indicates little or no effect. The magnitude of the effect is suggested by the weight of the arrow.

As is apparent from Table XXXI, several structural features may function in opposition to each other when the design of polymers for specific applications is considered. Thus, if one desires the best chemical resistance, highest modulus, and best temperature resistance in a coating or rigid foam he may achieve this through the use of highly functional components with a maximum aromatic content, but flexibility and elongation will suffer.

Similarly, if one wishes the best high temperature properties in an elastomer, some strong chemical cross links, such as may be derived from triols, should be present in the polymer. In most polymers, increases in these cross links will raise the glass transition temperature somewhat, and will reduce the tear strength and modulus in the elastomers with high intermolecular attractions.

At the present time one cannot predict with confidence the exact

TABLE XXXI[a]
Effect of Urethane Structural Features on Property-Temperature Curves

Structural features	A: Low temp. Flexibility	B: Room temp. Modulus	B: Room temp. Tear	B: Room temp. Elasticity	C: High temp. Modulus	C: High temp. Creep
1. Cross linking						
a. Strong (triol, isocyanate trimer)	↓	↑(↓)[b]	↓	↑[c]	↑	↑
b. Weak (biuret, allophanate)	↓	↑(↓)[b]	↓	↑[c]	↑	↑
2. Intermolecular forces						
a. "Fit"	↓	↑	↑	↓	↑	—
b. Urea	↓	↑	↑	↓	↑	—
c. Urethane	↓	↑	↑	↓	↑	—
d. Ester	↓	↑	↑	↓	↑	—
e. Aromatic	↓	↑	↑	↓	↑	—
f. Fillers	↓	↑(−)[b]	↑	↓	↑	—
3. Stiffness of segments						
a. Stiff (aromatic)	↓	↑	↑	↓	↑	—
b. Flexible (ether, hydrocarbon)	↑	↓	↓	↑	↓	—

[a] Taken from ref. 56.
[b] The special case of the effect on polyester-urethane elastomers of high intermolecular attractions is shown in parenthesis.
[c] Elasticity may be reduced with very large increases in cross linking.

contribution of each structural feature. Rather, in each specific polymer series one must experiment extensively to find exactly the optimum balance of properties for his own use.

X. Conclusions

Sufficient data are available from studies of urethane foams, elastomers, and coatings to draw semiquantitative conclusions regarding the effect of any gross structural change on most polymer properties. These relationships apply to other areas of application as well; e.g., adhesives and sealants.

Future research may be expected to provide more reliable control of the reactions involved in preparing urethanes, thus better control over structure. Similarly, a more quantitative and extensive knowledge of polymer properties may be expected. The result of these combined efforts will be a more precise knowledge of structure-property relationships and an improved ability to produce polymers having the properties desired for a wide range of applications.

References

1. Arnold, R. G., paper presented at the American Chemical Society meeting, Division of Rubber Chemistry, Cleveland, May, 1956.
2. Athey, R. J., *Rubber Age* **85,** No. 1, 77 (1959).
3. Athey, R. J., *Ind. Eng. Chem.* **52,** 611 (1960).
4. Axelrood, S. L., and K. C. Frisch, *Rubber Age* **88,** 465 (1960).
5. Axelrood, S. L., C. W. Hamilton, and K. C. Frisch, *Ind. Eng. Chem.* **53,** 899 (1961).
6. Bailey, M. E., G. C. Toone, G. S. Wooster and E. G. Bobalek, *Offi. Digest* **32,** 984 (1960).
7. Bayer, O., *Angew. Chem.* **A59,** 257 (1947).
8. Bayer, O., E. Müller, S. Petersen, H. Piepenbrink, and E. Windemuth, *Angew. Chem.* **62,** 57 (1950); *Rubber Chem. and Technol.* **23,** 812 (1950).
9. Bayer, O. and E. Müller, *Angew. Chem.* **72,** 934 (1960).
10. Blaich, C. F., Jr., and A. J. Sampson, paper presented at the American Chemical Society meeting, Division of Rubber Chemistry, Sept., 1960.
11. Boivin, J. L., *Can. J. Chem.* **36,** 1405 (1958).
12. Bolin, R. E., J. F. Szabat, R. J. Coté, E. Peters, P. G. Gemeinhardt, A. S. Morecroft, E. E. Hardy, and J. H. Saunders, *J. Chem. and Eng. Data* **4,** 261 (1959).
13. Bulletin, "Adiprene L, A Liquid Polyurethane Elastomer," E. I. du Pont de Nemours and Company, Inc., March 15, 1958.
14. Bunn, C. W., *J. Polymer Sci.* **16,** 323 (1955).
15. Catlin, W. E., U. S. Patent 2,284,637 (to Du Pont), June 2, 1942.
16. Cluff, E. F., and E. K. Gladding, *Proc. Intern. Rubber Conf.,* Washington, D. C., Nov., 1959, p. 543; *J. Appl. Polymer Sci.* **3,** 290 (1960).
17. Cluff, E. F., E. K. Gladding, and R. Pariser, *J. Polymer Sci.* **45,** 341 (1960).
18. Cluff, E. F., E. K. Gladding, and J. B. Rogan, *J. Appl. Polymer Sci.* **5,** 80 (1961).
19. Colodny, P. C., and A. V. Tobolsky, *J. Am. Chem. Soc.* **79,** 4320 (1957).
20. Conway, B. E., *J. Polymer Sci.* **46,** 129 (1960).
21. Conway, B. E., and S. C. Tong, *J. Polymer Sci.* **46,** 113 (1960).
22. D'Alelio, G. F., *Fundamental Principles of Polymerization,* J. Wiley and Sons, Inc., New York, 1952.
23. Damusis, A., J. M. McClellan, Jr., and K. C. Frisch, *Ind. Eng. Chem.* **51,** 1386 (1959); *Offi. Digest* **32,** 251 (1960).
24. Dickinson, L. A., *Rubber Age* **82,** No. 1, 96 (1957).
25. Flory, P. J., *Principles of Polymer Chemistry,* Cornell Univ. Press, Ithaca, N. Y., 1953, Chapters 11, 13, and p. 580.
26. Flory, P. J., N. Rabjohn, and M. C. Shaffer, *J. Polymer Sci.* **4,** 225 (1949).
27. Gee, G., *Trans. Faraday Soc.* **42,** 585 (1946).
28. Gruber, E. E., and O. Keplinger, *Ind. Eng. Chem.* **51,** 151 (1959).
29. Heiss, H. L., *Rubber Age* **88,** 89 (1960).

30. Heiss, H. L., J. H. Saunders, M. R. Morris, B. R. Davis, and E. E. Hardy, *Ind. Eng. Chem.* **46**, 1498 (1954).
31. Hill, R., and E. E. Walker, *J. Polymer Sci.* **3**, 609 (1948).
32. Houwink, R., *Elastomers and Plastomers, Their Chemistry, Physics and Technology, Vol. I, General Theory,* Elsevier Publishing Co., Inc., New York, 1950.
33. Houwink, R., *Elastomers and Plastomers, Their Chemistry, Physics and Technology, Vol. I, General Theory,* Elsevier Publishing Co., Inc., New York, 1950, p. 237.
34. Houwink, R., *Rubber Chem. and Technol.* **29**, 888 (1956).
35. Hudson, G. A., H. L. Heiss, and J. H. Saunders, paper presented at the American Chemical Society meeting, Atlantic City, Sept., 1956.
36. Iwakura, Y., Y. Taneda, and S. Uchida, *J. Appl. Polymer Sci.* **5**, 108 (1961).
37. Kogon, I. C., *J. Org. Chem.* **23**, 1594 (1958).
38. Kogon, I. C., *J. Org. Chem.* **24**, 83 (1959).
39. Landel, R. F., *J. Colloid Sci.* **12**, 308 (1957).
40. Moacanin, J., *J. Appl. Polymer Sci.* **1**, 272 (1959).
41. Müller, E., O. Bayer, S. Peterson, H. Piepenbrink, W. Schmidt, and E. Weinbrenner, *Angew. Chem.* **64**, 523 (1952); *Rubber Chem. and Technol.* **26**, 493 (1953).
42. Müller, E., *Kunststoffe* **50**, 437 (1960).
43. Mullins, L., and N. R. Tobin, *Proc. Rubber Technol. Conf., 3rd Conf., London,* 1954; p. 397.
44. Offenbach, J. A., and A. V. Tobolsky, *J. Colloid Sci.* **11**, 39 (1956).
45. Patton, T. C., A. Ehrlich, and M. K. Smith, *Rubber Age* **86**, 639 (1960).
46. Pflueger, E., *F.A.T.I.P.E.C., Compt. rend. 4th Congr., Lucerne,* 141 (1957); *Chem. Abstracts* **54**, 17908*b* (1960).
47. Pigott, K. A., B. F. Frye, K. R. Allen, S. Steingiser, W. C. Darr, J. H. Saunders, and E. E. Hardy, *J. Chem. Eng. Data* **5**, 391 (1960).
48. Pigott, K. A., R. J. Coté, K. Ellegast, B. F. Frye, E. Müller, W. Archer, K. R. Allen, and J. H. Saunders, *Rubber Age,* in press.
49. Quant, A. J., *SPE Journal* **15**, 298 (1959).
50. Rehberg, C. E., and C. H. Fisher, *J. Am. Chem. Soc.* **66**, 1203 (1944).
51. Reilly, C. B., and M. Orchin, paper presented at the American Chemical Society meeting, Atlantic City, Sept., 1956.
52. Remington, W. J., and R. J. Athey, Federation of Paint, Varnish and Production Clubs, *Off. Digest* **31**, 612 (1959).
53. Sampson, A. J., and C. F. Blaich, Jr., *Rubber Age* **89**, 263 (1961).
54. Sandridge, R. L., A. S. Morecroft, E. E. Hardy, and J. H. Saunders, *J. Chem. and Eng. Data* **5**, 495 (1960).
55. Saunders, J. H., *Rubber Chem. and Technol.* **32**, 337 (1959).
56. Saunders, J. H., *Rubber Chem. and Technol.* **33**, 1259 (1960).
57. Saunders, J. H., *Rubber Chem. and Technol.* **33**, 1293 (1960).
58. Saunders, J. H., S. Steingiser, P. G. Gemeinhardt, A. S. Morecroft, and E. E. Hardy, *Ind. Eng. Chem., Chem. and Eng. Data Series* **3**, 153 (1958).
59. Schollenberger, C. S., H. Scott, and G. R. Moore, *Rubber World* **137** (4) 549 (1958).

60. Seizinger, R. K., S. Davis, J. M. McClellan, and K. C. Frisch, *Rubber Age* **85**, 977 (1959).
61. Smith, C. H., and C. A. Peterson, *Modern Plastics* **38** No. 11, 125 (1961).
62. Smith, T. L., and A. B. Magnusson, *J. Polymer Sci.* **42**, 391 (1960).
63. Smith, T. L., and A. B. Magnusson, *J. Appl. Polymer Sci.* **5**, 218 (1961).
64. Treloar, L. R. G., *The Physics of Rubber Elasticity*, 2nd ed., Clarendon Press, Oxford, 1958, pp. 70, 86.
65. Trick, G. S., *J. Appl. Polymer Sci.* **3**, 252 (1960).
66. Trifan, D. S., and J. F. Terenzi, Jr., *J. Polymer Sci.* **28**, 443 (1958).
67. Weisfeld, L. B., J. R. Little and W. E. Wolstenholme, paper presented at the American Chemical Society Meeting, Division of Polymer Chemistry, St. Louis, March, 1961.

APPENDIX A. COMMERCIALLY AVAILABLE ISOCYANATES

Tolylene diisocyanate is the isocyanate normally used for flexible foam; therefore, it is the type produced in greatest quantity and is the best characterized. Tentative specifications have been established by the American Society for Testing Materials, as shown in Table I. The various isomer mixtures are produced by Mobay Chemical Co., E. I. du Pont de Nemours and Co., and the National Aniline Division of Allied Chemical and Dye Corp., and the mixtures are sold under the trade names Mondur, Hylene, and Nacconate, respectively.

TABLE I
Tentative ASTM Specifications for Commercial Tolylene Diisocyanates (ASTM D-1786-60T)

Specifications	80/20 Isomers	65/35 Isomers	2,4 Isomer
2,4-Isomer, %	80 ± 2	65 ± 2	97.5 min.
2,6-Isomer, %	20 ± 2	35 ± 2	
Purity, min., %	99.5	99.5	99.5
Hydrolyzable chloride, max., %	0.01	0.01	0.01
APHA color, max.	50	50	50
Total chlorine, max., %	0.2	0.2	0.2

The ASTM has also established analytical procedures (D-1638-60T) for the following methods for TDI: isomer content, total chlorine, assay, hydrolyzable chlorine, acidity, freezing point, specific gravity, and color.

Other isocyanates available in developmental or commercial quantities are listed in Table II. Producers' data for physical properties are also given.

TABLE II

Typical Properties of Commercial and Developmental Isocyanates

Compound	Melting point, °C.	Boiling point, °C.	Sp. gr.	n_D^t	Mole wt.	Flash pt., open cup, °C.
2,4-Tolylene diisocyanate[a–c]	19.5–21.5	120/10 mm.	$1.22^{25}_{15.5}$	1.5654^{25}	174	132
65/35-Tolylene diisocyanate[a–c]	3.5–5.5	120/10 mm.	$1.22^{25}_{15.5}$	1.5666^{25}	174	132
80/20 Tolylene diisocyanate[a–c]	11.5–13.5	120/10 mm.	$1.22^{25}_{15.5}$	1.5663^{25}	174	132
4,4′-Diphenylmethane diisocyanate[a–c]	37–38	194–199/5 mm.	1.19^{50}	—	250	202
Dianisidine diisocyanate[d]	119–122	200–210/0.5 mm.	—	—	296	—
Tolidine diisocyanate[d]	69–71.5	—	—	—	264	—
Hexamethylene diisocyanate[a]	—	140–142/21 mm.	$1.04^{25}_{15.5}$	1.4516^{25}	168	140
m-Xylylene diisocyanate[d]	—	150–152/3.5 mm.	1.16^{20}	—	188	—
Phenyl isocyanate[a,d]	∽−30	165	1.09^{20}_{4}	$1.5367^{19.6}$	119	—
p-Chlorophenyl isocyanate[a,e]	28	87.5/10 mm.	—	—	154	110
o-Chlorophenyl isocyanate[e]		86/10 mm.	—	—	154	—
m-Chlorophenyl isocyanate[e]	−4	72/10 mm.	—	—	154	—
3,4-Dichlorophenyl isocyanate[a,e]	42	113/10 mm.	—	—	188	—
2,5-Dichlorophenyl isocyanate[e]	27	108/10 mm.	—	—	188	—
Methyl isocyanate[e]	—	38	—	—	57	—
Ethyl isocyanate[d,e]	—	59–60	0.90^{20}_{4}	1.3801^{20}	71	<−7
n-Butyl isocyanate[d]	—	115	0.88^{20}_{4}	1.4043^{25}	99	<27
n-Propyl isocyanate[d]	—	83–84	0.90^{20}_{20}	—	85	<27
Octadecyl isocyanate[a,d]	10–20	170/2 mm.	$0.86^{25}_{15.5}$	1.450^{25}	∽295	185

[a] Mobay Chemical Co.
[b] E. I. du Pont de Nemours and Co.
[c] National Aniline Division, Allied Chemical Corp.
[d] Carwin Chemical Co.
[e] Ott Chemical Co.

APPENDIX B. COMMERCIALLY AVAILABLE POLYETHERS

Polyether polyols derived from propylene oxide are the most widely used resins for polyurethanes. One of the first of these compounds produced in volume in a purity grade suitable for polyurethane production ("urethane grade") was poly(oxypropylene)glycol of molecular weight 2000. Specifications and some additional typical properties established by the ASTM are shown in Table I.

TABLE I

Specifications and Properties of Poly(oxypropylene) Glycol Molecular Weight 2000 (ASTM D-1786-60T)

Specifications:	
Hydroxyl no.	54.5–57.5
Acid no., max.	0.1
Modified APHA color, max.	50
Unsaturation, meq./g., max.	0.04
Water, %, max.	0.1
Sodium and potassium, p.p.m., max.	10
Properties:	
Sp. gr., 25/25°C.	1.003–1.006
Index of refraction, n_D^{23}	1.448–1.449
Copper, %	<0.002
Manganese, %	<0.001
Flash pt., Cleveland open cup, °C.	232

In addition to the poly(oxypropylene)glycol, a variety of glycols, triols, and polyols of higher functionality have been offered by a number of suppliers. The polyols that have been identified chemically are listed in Table II. Several other polyols have been offered commercially, but these are not included in Table II because their chemical identity has not been disclosed.

Analytical methods for poly(oxypropylene)glycol of molecular weight 2000 have been reported by the ASTM (D-1638-60T) for the following properties: sodium and potassium, acid number, alkalinity number, hydroxyl number, unsaturation, water, suspended matter specific gravity, viscosity, and color.

TABLE II. Major Suppliers of Polyethers

Chemical identification	Type of polyol	Trade name	Mol. wt. range	Supplier
Poly(oxypropylene) glycols	Diols	Niax Diol	400–4000	1
		Pluracol P	400–4000	2
		Voranol P	2000	3
		Poly-G	400–2000	4
		PPG	400–2000	5
		Actol 21-56	2000	7
		Fomrez ED	2000	8
Poly(oxypropylene)-poly(oxyethylene) glycols (block copolymers)	Diols	Pluronic	1000–2800	2
Poly(oxypropylene) adducts of glycerin	Triols	Niax Triol LG	1000–3000	1
		Pluracol GP	3000	2
		Voranol CP	2700–5000	3
		Poly G	1000–4000	4
		Triol G	400–3000	5
		Actol 31-56	3000	7
		Fomrez ET	1500–3000	8
Poly(oxypropylene) adducts of trimethylolpropane	Triols	Pluracol TP	300–4000	2
Poly(oxypropylene)-poly(oxyethylene) adduct of trimethylolpropane	Triols	Pluracol TPE	4500	2
Poly(oxypropylene) adducts of 1,2,6-hexanetriol	Triols	Niax Triol LHT	700–4400	1
Poly(oxypropylene) adducts of pentaerythritol	Tetrols	Pluracol PeP	400–600	2
Poly(oxypropylene)-poly(oxyethylene) adducts of ethylenediamine (block copolymers)	Tetrols	Tetronic	1000–5000	2
Poly(oxypropylene) adducts of sorbitol	Hexols	Niax Hexol LS	700	1
		Pluracol SP	500–700	2
		Atlas G	500–5000	6

1. Union Carbide Chemicals.
2. Wyandotte Chemicals.
3. Dow Chemical.
4. Olin-Mathieson.
5. Jefferson Chemical.
6. Atlas Chemical.
7. Allied Chemical.
8. Witco Chemical.

APPENDIX C. COMMERCIALLY AVAILABLE POLYESTERS

The polyesters most suitable for the production of polyurethanes have been essentially saturated, of low acid number, and of very low water content. However, within the last year the increased use of polyesters of low cost, particularly for coatings, has been noteworthy. The exact chemical compositions of very few of the polyesters sold foı urethane production have been identified. Nevertheless, some commercial polyesters designed especially for urethane production are listed in Table I.

TABLE I

Commercial Polyesters for Urethane Production

Trade name	Hydroxyl no.	Acid no.	Viscosity, cps.[a]	Typical use
Multron R-68[b]	45–52	1.2 max.	800–900$^{73°}$	Flexible foams
Multron R-70[b]	50–57	1.2 max.	850–1000$^{73°}$	Flexible foams
Multron R-18[b]	57–63	1.2 max.	1000–1100$^{73°}$	Flexible foams, soft elastomers
Foamrez 50[c]	49–55	2 max.	17–22,000$^{25°}$	Flexible foams
Foamrez 112R[c]	61	1.9	15,000$^{25°}$	Soft elastomers
Multrathane R-14[b]	52–58	1.5 max.	475–650$^{73°}$	Elastomers
Multron R-12[b]	158–175	4 max.	400$^{73°}$	General purpose coatings
Multron R-4[b]	270–290	4 max.	2000–3000$^{73°}$	Rigid foams, chemically resistant coatings
Multron R-2[b]	390–420	6.8–9	14,000$^{73°}$	Wire coatings
Foamrez 131[c]	412	1.5	165,000$^{25°}$	Casting
Selectrofoam 6002[d]	440	1.5 max.	270–350,000$^{25°}$	Rigid foam
Multron R-38[b]	120–150	—	Solid	High temp. resistant wire coatings

[a] Temperature of viscosity measurement is given in °C.
[b] Mobay Chemical Company.
[c] Witco Chemical Company.
[d] Pittsburgh Plate Glass Company.

APPENDIX D. TRADE NAMES AND GENERIC NAMES

Name	*Generic name*	*Manufacturer*
Actol	Poly(oxypropylene) polyols	Allied Chemical Corp.
Adiprene	Polyether-urethane elastomers	E. I. du Pont de Nemours and Co.
Castor Wax	Glycerides of 12-hydroxystearic acid	Baker Castor Oil Co.
Chemigum SL	Polyester-urethane elastomers	Goodyear Tire and Rubber Co.
Dabco	1,4-Diaza[2.2.2]bicyclooctane, "triethylene diamine"	Houdry Process Co.
DB Castor Oil	Refined castor oil	Baker Castor Oil Co.
Desmodur	Isocyanates	Farbenfabriken Bayer, A.G.
Desmophens	Polyesters	Farbenfabriken Bayer, A.G.
Dimer Acid	Dimerized linoleic acid	Emery Industries, Inc.
Foamrez	Poly(oxypropylene) polyols, and polyesters	Witco Chemical Co.
Hylenes	Isocyanates	E. I. du Pont de Nemours and Co.
Igamid U	Linear polyurethane from hexamethylene diisocyanate and 1,4-butanediol	I. G. Farbenindustries
Lockfoam	Polyester-urethane foams	Lockheed Aircraft Corp.
MOCA	3,3′-Dichloro-4,4′-diaminodiphenylmethane	E. I. du Pont de Nemours and Co.
Mondurs	Isocyanates and isocyanate-terminated prepolymers	Mobay Chemical Co.
Moltopren	Polyester-urethane foams	Farbenfabriken Bayer, A.G.
Multrathane	Chemical intermediates for polyester-urethane elastomers	Mobay Chemical Co.
Multrons	Polyesters	Mobay Chemical Co.
Nacconates	Isocyanates	National Aniline Division, Allied Chemical Corp.
Niax	Poly(oxypropylene) polyols	Union Carbide Chemicals Co.
Perlon U	Linear polyurethane from hexamethylene diisocyanate and 1,4-butanediol	I. G. Farbenindustries

Pluracol	Poly(oxypropylene) polyols	Wyandotte Chemicals Corp.
Pluronic	Poly(oxyethylene)-poly(oxypropylene) glycol block copolymers	Wyandotte Chemicals Corp.
Polystal	Polyester-polyisocyanate adhesives	I. G. Farbenindustries
Selectrofoam	Polyesters, polyethers, and prepolymers	Pittsburg Plate Glass Co.
T-9	A stabilized stannous catalyst	Metal and Thermit Co.
Teracol	Polyether derived from tetrahydrofuran	E. I. du Pont de Nemours and Co.
Tetronic	Polyols derived from ethylenediamine and alkylene oxides	Wyandotte Chemicals Corp.
Turkey Red Oil	Sulfonated castor oil	Nopco Chemical Co.
Voranol	Poly(oxypropylene) polyols	Dow Chemical Co.
Vulcollan	Polyester-urethane elastomers	Farbenfabriken Bayer, A.G.
Vulcaprene	Polyester elastomers, and polyester-amide-urethane elastomers	Imperial Chemical Industries, Ltd.

INDEX

A

Abrasion resistance, effect of chain stiffness on, 311
  effect of cross linking on, 325-326
  effect of intermolecular forces on, 311
Absorption spectra of isocyanates, 29
Acid chlorides, retarders for isocyanate reactions, 163, 213
Acids, catalysts for, isocyanate: alcohol reaction, 161–162, 212–214
    isocyanate: amine reaction, 176, 212
    isocyanate: carboxylic acid reaction, 187
    isocyanate: phenol reaction, 189, 212
    isocyanate reactions, 213–215, 228
Active hydrogen compounds, effect of structure on reactivity of, 131–132, 174, 204–208
  relative rates of reactions of with isocyanates, 204–208
Acyl isocyanates, preparation of, 22, 24
Adhesives, history of development of, 5, 7
Adiprene, elastomer, history of, 12
Aliphatic diisocyanates, melting points of linear polyurethanes from, 272
Alkylene carbonates, polyethers from, 41
Allophanate group, as cross link, in foam, 315–316, 321, 329
    temperature sensitivity of, 286, 292, 315–316, 321–322, 329, 342–343
  reaction with amines, 221, 321–322, 329
Allophanates, dissociation of, 198
Amide group, effect of on melting points of polymers, 270
  molar cohesive energy of, 269
Amine equivalent analysis, 29
Amino acids, reaction with phosgene, 81
3-Amino-2,4,6-tribromophenyl isocyanate, reaction of with alcohols, 156
Analytical methods, for isocyanates, 29–30
  for polyethers, 349
Anhydrides, of isocyanate and carbamic acid, decomposition of, 180, 182–183
  of isocyanate and carboxylic acids, decomposition of, 186–188
Aromatic group, effect of, on elastomer properties, 276, 280–281, 287–289, 291, 295
    on melting points of polymers, 272
  molar cohesive energy of, 269

B

Bases, as catalyst, for isocyanate: alcohol reaction, 165, 167, 212–214, 221
    for isocyanate: carboxylic acid reaction, 187, 212
    for isocyanate: phenol reaction, 189, 212
    for isocyanate trimerization, 212–214
    for isocyanate: urea reaction, 221
    for isocyanate: urethane reaction, 221
    for isocyanate: water reaction, 221
    for prepolymer gelation, 213–214
Benzyl isocyanate, reaction with alcohols, 160

4,4′-Biphenylene diisocyanate, reaction of with alcohols, 159
p-Biphenyl isocyanate, reaction with alcohols, 142–144
Bitolylene diisocyanate, preparation of, 21
Biuret group, as cross link, in foams, 225, 226, 315–316, 329
temperature sensitivity of, 292, 315–316, 321–322, 329, 342–343
reaction of with amines, 221, 321–322, 329
Biurets, dissociation of, 194
Blocked isocyanates, 118–121
use in coatings, history of, 8
Branched polymer, definition of, 265
Bristles, preparation of, 4
Brittleness of polymers, effect of chain stiffness on, 287–289, 311–312, 339
effect of intermolecular forces on, 287–289, 311–312, 338–339
effect of molecular weight on, 262, 338
m-Bromophenyl isocyanate, reaction of with alcohols, 142–144
Bubble stability. *See* Foam formation
Butylene oxide, polymerization of, 38–39
n-Butyl isocyanate, properties of, 348
t-Butyl isocyanate, isobutylene from, 98
1-*t*-Butyl-2,4-phenylene diisocyanate, reaction of with alcohols, 160
p-*n*-Butylphenyl isocyanate, reaction of with alcohols, 142–144
5-*t*-Butyl-1,3-xylene diisocyanate, reaction of with alcohols, 160

C

Carbamoyl chloride, preparation of, 18, 20, 22
Carbamoyl halides, reaction of with active hydrogen compounds, 87
Carbodiimide, formation from isocyanates, 93, 97
as product of polyurethane pyrolysis, 96–97
reactions of, 116–118
Carwin Chemical Company, role of in polyurethane development, 13
Castor oil, addition of sulfur compounds to, 53–54
alcoholysis of, 52–53
alkaline cleavage of, 52
coatings from, 325
composition of, 50
elastomers from, 314
history of use of, 6, 9
hydrogenation of, 53
oxidation of, 52-53
properties of, 49
reactions of, 51–54
source of, 48–49
thermal decomposition of, 51–52
uses of, 54
Catalysis in control of polymer formation, 211–215
Catalysts, neutralization of, 213–215
Chemical resistance of coatings, effect of cross-linking on, 323–326
Chemigum SL elastomers, history of, 12
m-Chlorophenyl isocyanate, properties of, 348
reaction of with alcohols, 142–144
o-Chlorophenyl isocyanate, properties of, 348
p-Chlorophenyl isocyanate, properties of, 348
reaction of with alcohols, 141–144
1-Chloro-2,4-phenylene diisocyanate, reaction of with alcohols, 143, 151, 156
2-Chloro-1,4-phenylene diisocyanate, reaction of with alcohols, 206
with amines, 206
with ureas, 206
with water, 206
2-Chloro-*p*-tolyl isocyanate, reaction of with alcohols, 143

Coatings, history of development of, 5, 7–9
Colloid chemistry of foam formation, 235–249. *See also* Foam formation
Compression set, degree of recovery in, 332–333
effect of cross linking on, 284, 292, 294, 298, 301, 317–324, 331–335, 340–341
effect of intermolecular forces on, 332–333
in foam, factors affecting, 333–335
measurement of, 331–332
rate of recovery in, 332–333
Creep, effect of cross linking on, 284–285, 327–329, 331–335, 340–341, 343
Cross-linked polymer, definition of, 265
Cross linking, control of, in elastomers, 292, 308
in foams, 274, 284, 292, 296–300, 308
effect of on intermolecular attractions, 263, 285, 340
on polymer properties, 264–268, 284–285, 292–294, 296–300, 302–309, 317–326, 340–341, 343
Crystalline polymers, effect of cross linking on, 264, 340
Crystallization, effect of on polymer properties, 263, 340
in elastomers, 277, 290
effect of polyester molecular weight on, 277
favored by intermolecular attractions, 263
similarity to cross linking, 263
Curtius rearrangement, 22–24
p-Cyclohexylphenyl isocyanate, reaction with alcohols, 140

D

Dabco, catalyst for foam formation, 229–230
Degree of cross linking, definition of, 266–267
Density of polymers, effect of intermolecular forces on, 263
Desmodur isocyanates, use of in coatings, 7
in foams, 9
Desmophen polyesters, use of in coatings, 7
in foams, 9
Diamines, as curing agents for elastomers, 273–274, 290–291, 294–295, 311–312, 337
3,3′-Dichloro-4,4′-diphenylene diisocyanate, reaction with alcohols, 159
2,6-Dichloro-1,4-phenylene diisocyanate, reaction with alcohols, 160
4,6-Dichloro-1,3-phenylene diisocyanate, reaction with alcohols, 156
2,5-Dichlorophenyl isocyanate, properties of, 348
3,4-Dichlorophenyl isocyanate, properties of, 348
reaction with alcohols, 143
Dimer acid, polyesters from, 45
Dimerization of isocyanates, 91–94, 95
Dimers of isocyanates, dissociation of, 93, 113
reactions of, 113–116
with alcohols, 113–114
with allophanates, 96
with amines, 114–115
with ammonia, 114
with phenol, 114
3,3′-Dimethoxy-4,4′-biphenyl diisocyanate, elastomers from, 291, 296
properties of (dianisidine diisocyanate), 348
reaction of with alcohols, 151, 159
Dimethylacetamide, solvent for polymer swelling studies, 285, 317, 319–322

3,3′-Dimethyl-4,4′-biphenyl diisocyanate, elastomers from, 280–281, 291
properties of (tolidine diisocyanate), 348
reaction of with alcohols, 151, 154, 158–159
with polyesters, 154
3,3′-Dimethyl-4,4′-diphenylmethane diisocyanate, elastomers from, 280–281, 291
preparation of, 21
reaction of with alcohols, 151, 157
3,4-Dimethylphenyl isocyanate, reaction with alcohols, 143
2,4-Dinitrophenyl isocyanate, reaction with amines, 174
reaction with water, 181
3,5-Dinitrophenyl isocyanate, reaction with amines, 174
3,3′-Diphenyl-4,4′-biphenyl diisocyanate, reaction with alcohols, 159
4,4′-Diphenyl isopropylidine diisocyanate, elastomers from, 280
4,4′-Diphenylmethane diisocyanate, elastomers from, 280–289, 291, 337
preparation of, 21
properties of, 348
reaction with alcohols, 143, 151, 153–155, 158, 160
reaction with polyester, 153
use of in adhesives, history of, 7
Dipole moments of isocyanates, 28
Dow Chemical Company, role in polyurethane development, 6
Durene diisocyanate, reaction with alcohols, 157
Du Pont de Nemours, E.I., role of in polyurethane development, 4–13

E

Elasticity of polymers, effect on, of chain stiffness, 263, 278, 311–313, 340, 343
cross-linking, 284–285, 317, 340–341, 343
crystallization, 262, 340
intermolecular forces, 311–313, 338, 343
molecular weight, 262, 337–338
See also Resilience
Elasticity, theory of, 267–269
Elastomers, control of cross-linking in, 274, 284, 296–300
history of development of, 5, 11–13
preparation of, 273–275
relations between properties and structure, 276–316
structure of, 273–275
Electronegativity of isocyanate group, 29
Elongation of polymers, effect on, of chain stiffness, 278, 280, 302–303, 313
cross-linking, 264, 284, 293–294, 302–303, 317–319, 323–324, 340–341
crystallization, 262, 340
intermolecular forces, 288–289, 302–303, 313
molecular weight, 262
Elongation set, effect of cross-linking on, 284, 340–341
Emulsifiers, use of as foam stabilizers, 244
Entanglements of polymer chains, contribution to properties, 275, 332–333
Epichlorohydrin, polymerization of, 41
Epoxycyclohexane, polymerization of, 41
Ester group, effect of on melting points of polymers, 270
flexibility of, 270
molar cohesive energy of, 269
participation of, in hydrogen bonding, 270
Ether group, effect on melting points of polymers, 270–271
flexibility of, 263, 270, 343
molar cohesive energy of, 269

Ethyl carbamate, distinction from urethane polymers, 1
Ethylene diisocyanate, preparation of, 23
Ethylene oxide, polymerization of, 33, 36
Ethyl isocyanate, preparation of, 24, 26
  properties of, 348
  reaction of, with alcohols, 149
    with thiols, 204
N-Ethylmorpholine, catalyst for foam formation, 229, 233

F

Farbenfabriken Bayer, role of, in polyurethane development, 5–13
Fibers, preparation of, 4, 5
Fillers, role of reinforcing polymers, 330, 339, 343
Flexible foams. *See* Foams
Flexibility of polymers, effect of crystallization on, 263, 340
  See also Elasticity
Flex resistance, effect of cross-linking on, 292
  effect of intermolecular forces on, 330, 335–337
Flow of polymers, 327–337
2,7-Fluorene diisocyanate, elastomers from, 276
Foams, cross links in, 224–225, 234
  density control in, 315
  elasticity of, 250–254
  end groups in, 226–227, 234, 315, 334
  flexible, history of development of, 5–10
  formation, "boiling" in, 245–246
    bubble growth in, 237–241
    bubble stability in, 237, 241–249
    catalysis of, 227–235, 239–241, 252, 256–259
    cell size control in 240, 245
    cell structure in, 236–238, 247–248
    chemical reactions in, 220–235
    closed cells in, 251–259
    coalescence in, 239, 245
    collapse in, 244, 246, 251
    colloid chemistry of, 235–249
    compression set in, 232–235, 259
    curing process in, 232–235
    development of gel strength in, 228, 249–259
    dissolved gases as nucleating agents in, 240
    drainage in, 242
    effect of surface tension on, 241–249
    effect of viscosity on, 229, 243–247
    film rupture in, 242–244, 251–252
    free energy of bubble formation, 241–244
    growth of molecular weight in, 250
    hole formation in, 244
    importance of relative rate of gas evolution, 228–230, 232, 251
    "index number" in, 226
    nucleation in, 237–241
    one-shot process for, 224–227
    opening of cells in, 250
    prepolymer process for, 224-227
    selective control of reactions in, 230, 232, 252
    semi-prepolymer process for, 225
    stoichiometry in, 225-226
    viscoelastic changes, 249–259
    voids in, 251
  molecular structure of, 224–225
  oxidation resistance of, 231
  preparation of, 314
  relation of properties to cell structure, 255–259
  rigid, history of development of, 5–10
  shrinkage of, 253–254
  sol content in, 227, 234
  solvent swelling of 227, 233–234
  viscosity of, 250–254
Formamides, conversion of to isocyanates, 28

G

Gel, definition of, 266
Glass transition temperature, definition of, 264

effect on of chain stiffness, 262, 264, 280–281, 302–310, 317–320, 339
chain substituents, 264, 289
cross linking, 264, 286–287, 302–304, 317–320, 340–341, 343
intermolecular forces, 263–264, 282, 302–310, 317–320, 338–339, 343
molecular weight, 262, 264, 338
plasticizers, 264, 306–307
Glycols, curing agents for elastomers, 273–274, 278–283, 293, 302–311
Goodyear Aircraft Corp., role in polyurethane development, 5, 10
Goodyear Tire and Rubber Company, role in polyurethane development, 12

H

Hammet linear free energy relationship, in isocyanate: alcohol reaction, 141–144
in isocyanate-carboxylic acid reaction, 187
Hardness of polymers, effect on of chain stiffness, 263, 278, 280, 283, 311–312, 339
cross linking, 284–285, 293–294, 297, 323–326, 340–341
crystallization, 263–264,
intermolecular forces, 263, 281–282, 284, 287–289, 311–312, 338
molecular weight, 338
1,6-Hexamethylene diisocyanate, elastomers from, 276, 279, 290, 302-308
preparation of, 19
properties of, 348
reaction of, with amines, 205–206
with alcohols, 157, 169–171, 205–206
with ureas, 205–206
with urethanes. 205–206
with water, 205–206
1-Hexylvinyl isocyanate, reaction of with alcohols, 148–150
Hofmann rearrangement, 22–23
Hydrogen bonding, effect of "fit" on, 272
in elastomers, 275
in linear polyamides, 273
in linear polyurethanes, 271–273
See also Intermolecular forces
Hydrolysis of polyurethanes, relation to properties, 338

I

I. G. Farbenindustrie, role in polyurethane development, 3–5
Impact resistance of coatings, effect of cross linking on, 325–326
Imperial Chemical Industries, Ltd., role in polyurethane development, 12
Inorganic isocyanates, preparation of, 25
reactions of, 100–103
Inorganic isothiocyanates, preparation of, 25
Intermolecular forces, effect of on polymer properties, 263, 270–272, 282, 285, 287–288, 329–337, 338–339, 343
factors affecting effectiveness of, 263, 271–272, 285, 338, 340
temperature coefficient of, 273, 337
Isocyanate group, bond lengths, 28
Isocyanates, abbreviations for, xv
analytical methods for, 347
charts of reaction equations, 104–106
commercially available, properties of, 348
dimerization with isothiocyanate, 93
effect of structure on reactivity, 131–132, 139–144, 174, 180–181, 187
as Friedel-Crafts reagents, 85
generalized mechanism of reactions, 129–130
halogenation of, 99

homopolymerization of, 99
lachrymatory character of, 30
photolysis of, 100
preparation of, 2, 18–28
from carbamates, 25–26
by Curtius rearrangement of acid azides, 22–24
from diazonium salts, 27
by double decomposition reactions, 24–25
from formamides, 28
by Hofmann rearrangement of amides, 22–23
from isocyanides, 27
from isothiocyanates, 27
Lossen rearrangement of hydroxamic acids, 22, 24
from olefins and iodoisocyanate, 28
by phosgenation of amine carbamates, 19
by phosgenation of amine hydrochlorides, 18
by phosgenation of amines, 18–22
by phosgenation of SO_2 salts amines, 19
from substituted ureas, 26–27, 111
from urethanes, 25–26, 107–109
rates of reaction with active hydrogen compounds, approximate activation energies for, 208
effect of temperature on, 207
reactions of, 63–121
with acetoacetic esters, 84
acetylacetone, 84
acid anhydrides, 81
acyl ureas, 73
alcohols, 73–75, 95–96, 134–173, 204–208, 220, 222
catalysis of, 136–150, 161–173, 209–214, 221, 222
mechanism of, 130, 172
olefins from, 73–74
aldehydes, 88–89
alkylene oxides, 98–99
aluminum azide, 91
amides, 67–69, 204–208
amidines, 73
amines, 65–66, 76, 173–179, 205–208, 220, 222, 234
catalysis of, 176–179, 222
mechanism of, 176, 178
amino acids, 65–66
amino acid ester, 66
amino oximes, 73
amino sulfonic acids, 66
ammonia, 173
benzalethylamine, 89
benzoic acid in dimethyl sulfoxide, 133
bisulfites, 87–88
boric acid, 84
boronic acids, 84
carbamic acids, 180
carbodiimides, 90
carbon dioxide, 91
carboxylic acids, 79–81, 186–188, 204–208
catalysis of, 187, 212
mechanism of, 186
cyanamide, 73
derivatives of phosphorus acids, 83–84, 87
diazoamino compounds, 73
diazomethane, 90–91
diketones, 82
dimethyl ketene, 90
dimethyl sulfoxide and benzoic acid, 133
dinitrogen tetroxide, 100
dioximes, 82
enolizable compounds, 82
Grignard reagent, 98
halogen acids, 86
hydrazoic acid, 73
hydrazines, 65
hydrogen cyanide, 85-86
hydrogen peroxide, 83
hydrogen sulfide, 86
hydroperoxides, 82
hydroxamic acids, 82
hydroxy acids, 80–81
hydroxy esters, 74
hydroxylamine, 66, 82

hydroxysilanes, 84
imides, 67, 73
isothioureas, 73
malonic esters, 84
methylene aniline, 90
methyl sulfonic acid, 83
nitramines, 73
nitroalkanes, 84
nitrosobenzene, 88
olefins, 88
organo metallic compounds, 98
oximes, 82
phenols, 75–76, 189–190, 208
catalysis of, 189–190, 212
mechanism of, 190
phenyl hydrazones, 73
phosphines, 87
phosphorus pentachloride, 100
phosphorus pentasulfide, 100
polyesters, 222, 224–232, 253–254
polyethers, 213, 222, 224–232
pyrole, 84–85
sulfimides, 73
sulfonamides, 69
sulfoxides, 89
sulfuric acid, 83
thioketones, 89
thiols, 86, 198–204, 208
catalysis of, 198–204
mechanism of, 199–200
thiophenols, 86
thioureas, 73
unsaturated compounds, 88–91
ureas, 69–70, 190–194, 204–208, 220
catalysis of, 191–194, 209–214, 221
urethanes, 71–72, 194–198, 204–208, 220
catalysis of, 195–197, 210–214, 221
water, 76–79, 180–186, 204–208, 220–222, 224–235, 252
catalysis of, 182–186, 209–214, 221, 224–235, 252
mechanism of, 180, 182
general catalysis of, 130, 135, 208–214
reduction of, 100
resonance forms of, 63, 129, 131, 139
trade names of, 347, 352
transjointing reactions of, 100
Isocyanatobenzyl chloride, polymerization of, 85
Isocyanides, 2
Isocyanurates. *See* Trimerization
Isopropenyl isocyanate, preparation of, 23
reaction of with alcohols, 149
Isothiocyanates, preparation of, 22

K

Kinetics of isocyanate reactions, factors affecting, 132–134, 150–151

L

Linear polymer, definition of, 265
Lockfoam, history of, 10
Lockheed Aircraft Corporation, role in polyurethane development, 5,10
Lossen rearrangement, 22, 24

M

Melting point of polymers, effect on, of chain stiffness, 271–272, 313, 339
crystallization, 263, 340
intermolecular forces, 270, 272, 313, 338
molar cohesive energy, 270
molecular weight, 262, 338
1,8-Menthane diisocyanate, reaction of with alcohols, 163
Metal compounds, as catalyst, for isocyanate: alcohol reaction, 163–173, 209–212
amine reaction, 179, 210, 212
phenol reaction, 189–212
trimerization, 197–198, 212
urea reaction 193, 209–212
urethane reaction 196–197, 210–212
water reaction, 184–186, 209–212

1-Methoxy-2-methylphenyl isocyanate, reaction with alcohols, 143
1-Methoxy-2,4-phenylene diisocyanate, reaction with alcohols, 143
m-Methoxyphenyl isocyanate reaction,
with alcohols, 142–144
with amines, 174
with water, 181
o-Methoxyphenyl isocyanate, reaction with alcohols, 142
p-Methoxyphenyl isocyanate reaction,
with alcohols, 140–144
with amines, 174
with water, 181
Methylene diisocyanate, preparation of, 23
Methyl isocyanate, preparation of, 18, 24, 26
properties of, 348
structure of, 28
β-Methyl-β-(*p*-phenyl isocyanato) propyl isocyanate, reaction with alcohols, 160
Mobay Chemical Company, role in polyurethane development, 5–13
Modulus of polymers, effect on, of chain stiffness, 263, 278, 281–283, 287–289, 295, 302–312, 317, 323, 339, 343
cross linking, 264, 268, 284–285, 293–294, 297, 301–304, 309, 317–320, 324, 340–341, 343
intermolecular forces, 263, 278, 281–285, 287–289, 302–312, 317, 323, 338–339, 343
molecular weight, 338
plasticizer, 306–307
Molar cohesive energy, effect of on melting points of fibers, 270
of organic groups, 269
Molecular weight, effect of on polymer properties, 262, 338
Moltoprene foam, history of, 9
Monsanto Chemical Company, role in polyurethane development, 5–10
Mullins effect, 330

N

1,5-Naphthalene diisocyanate, elastomers from, 11, 276–281, 306–308
history of use in elastomers, 11
reaction of with alcohols, 160, 205–206
amines, 205–206
ureas, 205–206
urethanes, 205–206
water, 205–206
α-Naphthyl isocyanate, reaction with alcohols, 160
phenols, 189
National Aniline Division, role in polyurethane development, 6
2-Nitro-1,4-phenylene diisocyanate, reaction of with alcohols, 160
m-Nitrophenyl isocyanate, reaction with alcohols, 142–144
amines, 174
o-Nitrophenyl isocyanate, reaction with amines, 174
water, 181
p-Nitrophenyl isocyanate, reaction with alcohols, 139–144
amines, 174
preparation, 19
Nopco Chemical Company, role in polyurethane development, 13
Nucleation. *See* Foams, formation of
1-Nylons, by homopolymerization of isocyanates, 99

O

Octadecyl isocyanate, properties of, 348
Octamethylene diisocyanate, melting points of linear polyurethanes from, 271–272
preparation of, 24
t-Octyl isocyanate, reaction with alcohols, 146
Ott Chemical Company, role in polyurethane development, 13

P

Peroxides, curing agents for elastomers, 292, 337
1-Phenoxy-2,4-phenylene diisocyanate, reaction with alcohols, 160
Phenyl isocyanate, preparation of, 22, 25, 26
  properties of, 348
  reaction of with alcohols, 136–150, 156, 157, 160, 161–166, 204–208
    amines, 173–179, 208
    ammonia, 173
    carboxylic acids, 187–188, 204–208
    phenol, 190
    poly(oxypropylene) glycol, 172, 179
    thiols, 198–204, 208
    thiophenol, 204
    ureas, 191–193, 204–205, 208
    urethanes, 194–198, 204–208
    water, 181–184, 204–205, 208
  trimerization of, catalyzed, 198
β-(*p*-Phenyl isocyanato)butyl isocyanate, reaction of with alcohols, 160
β-(*p*-Phenyl isocyanato)ethyl isocyanate, reaction of with alcohols, 160
m-Phenylene diisocyanate, elastomers from, 291, 307–308
  melting point of linear polyurethane from, 272
  reaction of with: alcohols, 141–144, 151, 154, 155, 157–158
    polyester, 152
p-Phenylene diisocyanate, elastomers from, 280, 291
  reaction with alcohols, 141–144, 151, 157, 161, 205–206
    amines, 205–206
    ureas, 205–206
    urethanes, 196, 205–206
    water, 205–206
Phosphines, as catalysts for dimerization, 212
Plasticity, effect of intermolecular forces on, 299–300
Plasticizers, effect of on glass transition temperature, 264, 305–307
  effect of on modulus, 305–306
Polyamide, preparation of from anhydride of carbamic-carboxylic acids, 81
Polyesters, coatings from, 6–9, 323
  commercially available, properties of, 351
  decarboxylation of, 47
  effect of molecular weight on elastomer properties of, 277
  effect of structure on elastomer properties, 276–277, 281–282
  elastomers from, 6, 11–13, 275–293, 309–312, 337
  foams from, 6, 9–11, 323–324
  history of use of, 4–13
  hydrolysis of, 47–48
  oxidation of, 48
  preparation of, 45–47
  properties of, 47, 351
  reactions of, 47–48
  thermal decomposition of, 48
  trade names for, 352–353
Polyethers, analytical methods for, 349
  coatings from, 9, 323–326
  commercially available, properties of, 350
  elastomers from 275, 293–314
  foams from, 6, 10–11, 316–323
  history of use of, 6–13
  oxidation of, 42
  preparation of, 32–42
  properties of, 43–44, 350
  reactions of, 42–43
  thermal stability of, 42
  trade names of, 350, 352–353
  unsaturation in, 35–36, 43
  "urethane grade," 6, 43
Polymer formation, catalysis in control of, 211–215
Polymer properties, effect on, of cross linking, 264, 340–341, 343
  crystallization, 263–264, 340

ease of rotation of chain segments, 264
intermolecular forces, 263, 338–339
molecular weight, 262, 338
stiffness of chain units, 263, 339–340
Polymer-solvent interaction parameters, 268, 304
Poly(oxypropylene) glycol 2000, specifications and properties of, 349
Polystal adhesives, history of development of, 7
Polythioethers, preparation of, 41–42
Polyureas, 3
Polyurethanes, definition of, 1
history of development of, 3
pyrolysis of, 96–97
Prepolymers, coatings from, 8, 9, 325
gelation, catalysis of, 221
intermediate, in preparation of elastomers, 11–12, 273, 287, 293–295
in preparation of foams, 11, 315, 316
polyether, surface tension of, 245
role of in polyurethane development, 9, 11–12
Propenyl isocyanate, reaction of with alcohols, 148–150
n-Propyl isocyanate, preparation of, 24
properties of, 348
Propylene oxide, polymerization of, 33–37, 39–41
β-Propylvinyl isocyanate, 149

R

Raman spectra of isocyanates, 29
Resilience of polymers, effect on of
chain stiffness, 311, 339–340
cross linking, 297, 317, 340–341, 343
free ends, 300
intermolecular forces, 311, 339
See also Elasticity
Rigid foams, chemistry of formation of, 223–225
viscoelastic changes in, 254
See also Foams
Rotation of chain segments, effect of on polymer properties, 264
structural factors affecting, 264
Rubber elasticity, theory of, 267–269

S

Secondary chemical bonds. *See* Intermolecular forces
Silicone oil, use of, as foam-nucleating agent, 240
as foam stabilizer, 240, 241, 245–249
Softening points of polymers, effect of cross linking on, 264, 286–287, 340–341
Sol, definition of, 266
relation to flow in polymers, 328, 333
Solubility of polymers, effect on of
chain stiffness, 263
crystallization, 263–364
molecular weight, 262, 338
Solution properties of polyether-urethanes, 301–302, 304
Solvent, effect on isocyanate: alcohol reaction, 140–141, 146–148
effect on isocyanate: thiol reaction, 202–203
Splitters, 118–121
Steric hindrance, effect of on reactivity, 132, 174–175, 200–201, 222, 229
Stiffness of chain units, effect of on polymer properties, 263, 278, 280–283, 291, 295, 339, 343
in elastomers, 275
Stress relaxation, 292, 327–337
Styrene oxide, polymerization of, 41
Sulfonyl isocyanates, preparation of by phosgenation, 22
Swelling of polymers by solvents, effect on of chain stiffness, 302–303, 339
cross linking, 264, 268, 285, 302–303, 317–319, 340–341
crystallization, 340

intermolecular forces on, 302–303, 339

T

Tear strength, effect on of chain stiffness, 276, 278, 281–283, 287–289, 295, 311–312, 339, 343
cross linking, 284–285, 293–294, 340–341, 343
intermolecular forces, 263, 278, 281–285, 287–289, 311–312, 388–339, 343
molecular weight, 338
test method, 294
Tensile strength, effect on of chain stiffness, 278, 287–288, 302–313, 339
cross linking, 268, 284–285, 302–310, 317–319, 324, 340–341
crystallization, 263, 340
intermolecular forces, 263, 278, 285, 287–288, 302–313, 338–339
molecular weight, 338
Teracol 30, history of use of, 6
Tertiary amines, as catalysts, for dimerization, 91–92, 212
for foam formation, 228–233, 252
for isocyanate: alcohol reaction, 138–142, 161–173, 209–212, 221, 222
for isocyanate: amine reaction, 176–179, 212, 222
for isocyanate: carboxylic acid reaction, 187, 212
for isocyanate: phenol reaction, 189–190, 212
for isocyanate: thiol reactions, 198–204
for isocyanate: urea reaction, 191–194, 209–212, 221
for isocyanate: urethane reaction, 195–196, 212, 221
for isocyanate: water reaction, 182–186, 209–212, 221
for trimerization, 94–96, 212
effect of on compression set in foams, 229
Tetrachloro-1,3-phenylene diisocyanate, reaction of with alcohols, 156
Tetrahydrofuran, polymerization of, 37–38
2,2′-5,5′-Tetramethyl-4,4′-biphenylene diisocyanate, reaction with alcohols, 151
Tetramethylene diisocyanate, melting point of polyurethane from, 272
Thioether group, effect of on elastomer properties, 278
on melting points of polymers, 271
Tin compounds, as catalysts, for foam formation, 228, 230–232, 252, 256–259
isocyanate: alcohol reaction, 165–172, 209–212, 221, 222
isocyanate: amine reaction, 179, 212, 222
isocyanate: urea reaction, 193, 209–212, 221
isocyanate: urethane reaction, 221
isocyanate: water reaction, 184–186, 209–212, 221
effect of on foam permanence, 230–231
Tolylene diisocyanate, air analysis, 29
color test for, 29
isomer ratio analysis, 30
preparation of, 21
safety in use, 30–32
2,4-Tolylene diisocyanate, analytical methods for, 347
elastomers from, 276, 279, 280, 289, 291, 293–295, 302–314
history of production of, 5
properties of, 348
reaction of, with alcohols, 133–134, 143, 151–160, 169–171, 205–206
with amines, 176, 205–206
with polyester, 153

with ureas, 205–206
with urethanes, 205–206
with water, 205–206
specifications for, 347
2,6-Tolylene diisocyanate, reaction of, with alcohols, 151, 157, 205–206
with amines, 205–206
with ureas, 205–206
with water, 205–206
60:40-Tolylene diisocyanate, reaction of with alcohols, 151, 222
65:35-Tolylene diisocyanate, analytical methods for, 347
properties of, 348
specifications for, 347
use of in foam production, 253–254
80:20-Tolylene diisocyanate, analytical methods for, 347
coatings from 323–326
properties of, 348
reaction of, with alcohols, 159, 167–171
with polyesters, 151, 222
with water, 185–186
specifications for, 347
use of, in foam formation, 223, 253–254, 314–324
m-Tolyl isocyanate, reaction of with alcohols, 142–144
o-Tolyl isocyanate, reaction of, with alcohols, 142, 157
with amines, 174–175
with ureas, 191–193
with urethanes, 195–196
with water, 182–183
p-Tolyl isocyanate, reaction of, with alcohols, 140–144, 157
with amines, 174–177
with water, 181
Toxicity of isocyanates, 30–31
Trade names, 352–353
2,4,6-Tribromo-1,3-phenylene diisocyanate, reaction of with alcohols, 156
Trichlorofluoromethane, as blowing agent for foams, 225
2,4,6-Trichloro-1,3-phenylene diisocyanate, reaction of with alcohols, 156
m-Trifluoromethylphenyl isocyanate, reaction of with alcohols, 142–144
Trimerization of isocyanates, 94–97, 98
Trimers of isocyanates, products of polyurethane decomposition, 96–97
reaction of, 116
Triols, curing agents for elastomers, 284–286, 293, 300, 302–311
Triphenylmethane triisocyanate, use in adhesives, history of, 7

U

Undecyl isocyanate, preparation of, 23
Union Carbide Chemicals Company, role in development of polyurethanes, 6
Urea group, effect of, on elastomer properties, 278, 294–295
on melting points of polymers, 270
molar cohesive energy of, 269
Ureas, catalysts for the isocyanate:-amine reaction, 176–178
hydrolysis of, 113
reactions of, 111–113
with alcohols, 112
with amines, 112
with carboxylic acids, 112–113
with other ureas ("dearrangement"), 112
thermal decomposition of, 111–112
Urethane, definition of, 1
Urethane group, as cross link, thermal stability of, 286–287, 297–298, 320–321, 342
effect on elastomer properties, 287–289
effect on melting points of polymers, 270
flexibility of, 270
molar cohesive energy of, 269
Urethane oils, use of in coatings, history of, 9

Urethanes, dissociation of, 106, 119
hydrolysis of, 111
reactions of, 103, 106–111
with active hydrogen compounds, 107–111, 118–121
with alcohols, 108–111, 119–120
with amines, 108–109, 119–120
with carboxylic acids, 109–110
thermal decomposition of, 106–108
m-Urethanophenyl isocyanate, reaction of with alcohols, 141–144
p-Urethanophenyl isocyanate, reaction of with alcohols, 141–144
Uretidine dione. *See* Dimers of isocyanates

V

van der Waals forces. *See* Intermolecular forces
Vinyl isocyanate, preparation of, 23
reaction of with alcohols, 149
Viscosity, bulk, effect of intermolecular forces on, 299–300
Vulcaprene A elastomer, history of development of, 12
Vulcollan elastomers, history of development of, 11

W

Water, as blowing agent in foams, 315
as curing agent, for coatings, 323
for elastomers, 274, 278, 312
effect of on compression set of foams, 334
Wyandotte Chemicals Corporation, role in polyurethane development, 6

X

1,3-Xylylene diisocyanate, elastomers from, 291
properties of, 348
reaction of with alcohols, 160, 169–171
1,4-Xylylene diisocyanate, reaction of with alcohols, 160